Volume I
The Foundations of Ethics
and Its Relationship
to Science

Science Ethics and Medicine

Edited by
H. Tristram Engelhardt, Jr.
and Daniel Callahan

THE HASTINGS CENTER
Institute of Society, Ethics and the Life Sciences

Institute of Society, Ethics and the Life Sciences
360 Broadway
Hastings-on-Hudson, New York 10706

Library of Congress Cataloging in Publication Data
Main entry under title:

Science, ethics, and medicine.

(The Foundations of ethics and its relationship to science ; v. 1)
Includes index.
1. Science and ethics—Addresses, essays, lectures. 2. Medical ethics—Addresses, essays, lectures. I. Engelhardt, Hugo Tristram, 1941- II. Callahan, Daniel, 1930- III. Series. [DNLM: 1. Ethics, medical. 2. Science. 3. Ethics, professional. W1 F0989 v. 1 / [W50 S416] BJ57.S3   174'.2
76-5438
ISBN 0-916558-01-0

Printed in the United States of America

Contents

Contributors

DANIEL CALLAHAN is Director of the Institute of Society, Ethics and the Life Sciences. He received his B.A. at Yale and his Ph.D. in Philosophy at Harvard. He is the author, most recently, of *The Tyranny of Survival* and *Abortion: Law, Choice and Morality*. He is a member of the Institute of Medicine, National Academy of Sciences.

ERIC J. CASSELL, M.D., is Clinical Professor of Public Health at Cornell University Medical College and a Diplomate of Internal Medicine in private practice. For the past several years Dr. Cassell has been doing research and writing on the underlying bases of medical practice and the relationship between doctors, patients, and disease. He is the author of *The Healer's Art*.

H. TRISTRAM ENGELHARDT, JR., Ph.D., M.D., is Associate Professor in the Institute for the Medical Humanities and the Department of Preventive Medicine and Community Health of the University of Texas Medical Branch at Galveston. He is the author of *Mind-Body: A Categorial Relation* and co-editor of *Evaluation and Explanation in the Biomedical Sciences*.

AMNON GOLDWORTH is Professor of Philosophy at San José State University. He is the editor of a forthcoming critical edition of Jeremy Bentham's *The Deontology, Including a Table of the Springs of Action and the Greatest Happiness Principle*.

SAMUEL GOROVITZ is Professor and Chairman of the Philosophy Department, University of Maryland at College Park. He is senior editor of *Moral Problems in Medicine*.

PATRICK A. HEELAN is Acting Vice President for Liberal Studies, and Professor of Philosophy at the State University of New York at Stony Brook. He has done research in physics and the philosophy of science and has lectured on the philosophy of medicine. He is the author of *Quantum Mechanics and Objectivity*.

LESTER S. KING, M.D., is Contributing Editor of the *Journal of the American Medical Association* and President of the American Association for the History of Medicine. He is editor of *Clio Medica* and author of *Medical World of the Eighteenth Century; The Growth of Medical Thought;* and *The Road to Medical Enlightenment, 1650-1695.*

JOHN LADD is Professor of Philosophy at Brown University. He is chairman of the Committee on Philosophy and Medicine of the American Philosophical Association. He is author of *The Structure of a Moral Code,* translator and editor of *Kant's Metaphysical Elements of Justice,* and editor of *Ethical Relativism.*

MARC LAPPÉ is Associate for the Biological Sciences at the Hastings Center, where he directs the Genetic Research Group of the Institute of Society, Ethics and the Life Sciences. He is also Adjunct Assistant Professor at SUNY, Purchase. He has done research in transplantation and tumor immunology and has taught widely in the natural sciences. He is the co-editor of *Ethical, Social and Legal Dimensions of Screening* and *Ethical Issues in the Human Uses of Molecular Genetics.*

ALASDAIR MACINTYRE is University Professor of Philosophy and Political Science at Boston University. He is the author of *A Short History of Ethics* and *Against the Self-Images of the Age: Essays in Ideology and Philosophy.*

EDMUND D. PELLEGRINO, M.D., is Professor of Medicine at the Yale University School of Medicine and Chairman of the Board of Directors of the Yale-New Haven Medical Center. He is Director of the Institute for Human Values in Medicine and editor of the *Journal of Medicine and Philosophy.*

GUENTER B. RISSE, M.D., Ph.D., is an Associate Professor and Chairman of the Department of the History of Medicine, University of Wisconsin Center for Health Sciences. He is interested in late eighteenth-century medical ideas and has recently translated Rothschuh's *History of Physiology.*

MICHAEL SCRIVEN is Professor of Philosophy, Professor of Education and Special Assistant for Program Evaluation to the Vice-Chancellor of the University of California at Berkeley. He was a founding member of the Board for Ethical and Social Responsibility of the American Psychological Association and is co-editor of *Evaluation News.* He is the author of *Primary Philosophy* and numerous articles in the philosophy of science.

STEPHEN TOULMIN is Professor of the Committee on Social Thought, University of Chicago. He is the author of *Human Understanding, Wittgenstein's Vienna* (with Allan Janik), and *Knowing and Acting.*

MARX W. WARTOFSKY is Professor of Philosophy at Boston University. He is the author of *Conceptual Foundations of Scientific Thought* and of a forthcoming book on Ludwig Feuerbach. He is editor of *The Philosophical Forum* and co-editor (with Robert S. Cohen) of the series *Boston Studies in the Philosophy of Science.* He serves on the editorial committee of *The Journal of Medicine & Philosophy.*

Preface

THE EMERGENCE OF BIOETHICS as a field has been a striking phenomenon in recent years. That the painful moral problems posed by advances in medicine and biology provide one reason for the intense interest is perhaps obvious enough. For what society, especially our own, can claim that it knows what to do about defining death, altering behavior, doing research on fetuses or genes or artificial organs, or screening for genetic and other diseases? And our anxiety shows. Yet lying behind those issues is a more pervasive mood in our culture—that of a fundamental uncertainty about values, moral rules, and ethical principles. The dilemmas of biomedicine are only one among a spectrum of moral issues evident in the sciences, the law, politics, and our educational institutions.

That is the larger cultural context of this book. But is also has an institutional history. For some seven years now, the Institute of Society, Ethics and the Life Sciences, The Hastings Center, has attempted to grapple with moral, legal, and social problems of biomedicine. Institute research programs have focused on death and dying, behavior control, health policy, genetic counseling and engineering, and population control. Our approach to the issues has been interdisciplinary, drawing on philosophy, medicine, biology, the social sciences, law, history, and theology. We have tried to examine the larger ethical questions as well as carrying through that examination to the legislative and social policy arena.

While ethical disagreement is as obvious a feature of our own Institute as that of the society at large, nonetheless it has often been remarkable to see how people with very different ethical premises and world-views can come to some agreement on practical matters of ethical decision making. But a key to that kind of agreement is, frequently enough, a tacit willingness not to take on in a direct confrontation the nature, origins, and validity of basic ethical assumptions and systems. If it is at all remotely possible to achieve some practical consensus on this issue or that, why ask for trouble by going still more deeply? Unfortunately, the root issues cannot forever be evaded, nor should they. Sometimes a consensus cannot be reached, and one is driven down to the depths. At other times, it is by no means evident that a social or legal consensus is well-founded—it may just represent a chance concurrence of taste, bias, or mutual lack of thought.

This book represents an initial attempt to do that which we at least can no longer avoid: to ask about the origin and validity of our moral assumptions, to see the way in which ethics and science have mutually influenced each other, to move away from practical problems of decision making to some of the larger theoretical issues which ultimately come to shape the way decisions are made. The title of the project from which this volume stems is "The Foundations of Ethics and Its Relationship to Science." It is, admittedly, an ambitious title and an impossible project. But that title captures well enough our perception of a problem and our aspiration to deal with it. We hold it out less as a standard by which the work should be judged (though that is appropriate enough) than as a goad to ourselves, if no one else, to get down to those basics which are all too easily put to one side.

That moral philosophy has been in disarray for some decades is a proposition with which few will argue. Nor will many contend that there is any greater clarity at present on the moral assumptions and goals of science and medicine. Perhaps it is too much to hope that progress can be made—perhaps we are, as a society and a culture, going to be forced to live with, and to live out, the present confusion. But both moral philosophy and the sciences do share a common premise, so far unchallenged: that it is always worth the effort to understand more, to attempt to think more deeply, to remain congenitally uneasy in the face of confusion, uncertainty, and unanswered questions.

The essays published here represent the first of four projected volumes on the general topic of the foundations of ethics and its relationship to science. Strictly speaking, the following essay, by Daniel Callahan on "The Emergence of Bioethics," was not part of the conference series from which this book resulted. However, a collateral part of the ongoing research project involves an annual survey of the field of bioethics. It is the emergence of that field which, in a broad and fundamental way, represents the cultural context of the present volume.

This volume was made possible by a grant from the National Endowment for the Humanities. We gratefully acknowledge that support, and in particular would like to thank Dr. Richard Hedrich of the Endowment for his most helpful substantive contributions. We would also like to thank Carol Levine, Managing Editor of the *Hastings Center Report*, for her able and effective editorial work on this book.

H. Tristram Engelhardt, Jr.
Daniel Callahan

The Emergence of Bioethics

Daniel Callahan

FOR ARISTOTLE, one recalls, ethics was a branch of politics, not the other way around. Whatever the merits of that view, recent events in the United States have pointed out the enormous extent to which ethical problems have quickly been transformed into political controversies. Simultaneously, it has become apparent how often issues taken to be primarily political turn out to conceal fundamental moral conflicts. If Watergate provided the most sensational demonstration of an intertwining of the ethical and the political, the development of the field of bioethics deserves at least a lengthy footnote in the cutural history of our times. The occasion of this volume, the first of a projected series on the foundations of ethics, provides an appropriate occasion to develop some thoughts for that note.

Allow me to begin on a personal note. When some colleagues and I began organizing the Institute of Society, Ethics and the Life Sciences in the late 1960s, there was no shortage of media attention to some new issues of ethics and the life sciences. The early spate of heart transplants, the ensuing debates over the definition of death and the procuring of organs, the futuristic speculations about genetic engineering, and the publicizing of José Delgado's electrically-controlled bulls were ripe fare for a public well-tuned to technological drama. Yet, curiously enough, one could find only a handful of scholars and researchers paying serious attention to the patent array of difficult moral dilemmas these technological events revealed. The idea of forming an institute devoted to exploring such problems seemed pertinent and timely (no less so, one might observe, than the idea of forming special institutes to tackle issues which, in an earlier day, would have been left to the traditional workings of the university).

The initial reaction within those agencies which were the most likely source of money to support the venture was, however, anything but ecstatic. Was it not well-known that ethics is a notoriously "soft" subject, primarily expressive of personal taste, cultural relativism, and the absence of any accepted methodology? Did not the history of philosophical ethics indicate how little progress, if any, had been made since the time of Plato and Aristotle, and did not the history of theological ethics show how quickly religious morality became a cover for sectarian strife and oppression? Most important, was it not well-recognized how great the gap is between public policy, legislative struggles and court decisions, at one pole, and the precious hair-splitting or muddy, grandiose speculating about the good life and the nature of human nature that are the stock-in-trade of academic ethics, at the other pole? Who would possibly care to listen, and what difference would it make, anyway?

Compare that situation with 1975, the time I am now writing. This has been the year of the trial of Dr. Kenneth Edelin, convicted of manslaughter in Boston for allowing the death of a fetus allegedly born alive during an abortion; the court hearing on the fate of Karen Ann Quinlan, comatose and wasting; the lifting of a ban on research involving fetuses by the Secretary of DHEW on the recommendation of the National Commission for the Protection of Human Subjects; the cessation of a research project on the XYY syndrome by a Boston researcher subjected to merciless public and private criticism (though his project had passed all the pertinent review committees); and the calling of the Asilomar Conference, which saw those scientists present lift a voluntary scientific moratorium on research on recombinant DNA, a moratorium originally established because of concern over the unknown potential hazards of such research. This same year has also seen a sharp increase, as a result of congressional pressure, in the budget of the National Science Foundation's program on science and human values, the establishment of a special unit in the National Institutes of Health to coordinate research on ethical topics, and an increasing spate of congressional and state hearings on one or another issue of bioethics and public policy. Add to this the rapid proliferation of university courses, workshops, conferences and publications in bioethics and, clearly enough, much has happened in the past five or six years.

For the social scientist, all this might serve as ample evidence for a study of the way in which a new field, bioethics, and a new class of professional practitioners, those called "bioethicists," have become legitimized. For the political scientist, it would provide rich pickings for a study of the way in which issues, at one time apparently remote and abstract, enter the political stream, and not only enter it, but once having done so, rapidly become highly politicized. My own concern here will be the meaning of those developments (and others to be mentioned) for the field of bioethics itself. What have those in the field themselves learned? What are the leading present issues, and what are likely to become the issues of the future? And since there are some, what is the meaning of the various strains and tensions which have emerged as the field has developed?

The research program which represents the genesis of this volume and those which will subsequently appear provides a useful point of departure. The program as a whole has the broad title of "the foundations of ethics and its relationship to science." Why should there be such a research program? In one sense, the answer is obvious: if one is going to explore issues of biomedical ethics, then it makes eminent good sense to spend some time asking just what ethics is and how, if at all, ethical codes, propositions, prescriptions, and systems can be grounded. It makes no less sense to take a look at the way in which the scientific enterprise has influenced conceptions of ethics, and vice versa. But a question may occur to the perceptive observer of the field. Why is it that only *now*, some six years after the founding of the Institute and a number of years after the field of bioethics gained momentum, that a sustained attempt will be made to explore the nature of ethics. Is that not where everyone, including ourselves, should have started?

Not necessarily. Three problems, rarely addressed directly, have lurked just below the surface for some time now. Are the new dilemmas posed by medical and biological advances really all that "new" or do they reduce, in the end, to variants on some of the oldest human questions? Does the value of research in bioethics lie in its potential ability to resolve issues at their deepest level, or, more modestly, in its potential to assist in the development of workable public policies? What kinds of ethical analysis, strategy, and theory are most valid for coping with the specificities of biomedical decision-making? In sum, it was simply not clear just where one ought to begin.

Perhaps the strongest initial impetus for the field came from what appeared to be very concrete problems requiring the making of very specific decisions. Under what circumstances should death be pronounced? Should psychosurgery be carried out if it promised to reduce the aggressiveness of a disturbed patient? Should pregnant women at risk for bearing a defective child be urged (or even forced) to undergo prenatal diagnostic procedures? That these questions were often posed by physicians, or biomedical researchers, and posed because of their practical importance rather than their theoretical interest, served to press the field to look to what seemed historically novel in the dilemmas, to the devising of practical solutions, and to a notion of ethics which laid its greatest stress on its ability to serve biomedical practitioners. That the field developed as professedly interdisciplinary served in many respects to strengthen a general thrust toward the practical—it counted among its practitioners not only philosophers, but also clinicians, biological researchers, legal scholars, social scientists and those concerned with public policy. Among them were many who would happily settle for the development of a practical consensus on the issues, even if there was considerable disagreement on its theoretical basis. That those drawn to the field, and especially those who needed money to work on the problems in a sustained way, were under considerable pressure to prove the "relevance" of ethics, only served to confirm those tendencies.

But there has always been a cross-current as well, often enough co-existing in the same people struggling with the concrete issues. This current has been prone to move beyond the specific contemporary biomedical dilemmas to the broader and deeper issues underlying modern life and technology, of which medicine is only one example. Here the leading questions are different. What is the nature of the covenantal relationship that ought to exist between the physician and the patient? (Paul Ramsey) What is the "normatively human"? (James M. Gustafson) What are the ends of man and what is the relationship of human health to those ends? (Leon R. Kass) What has been the effect of the Baconian axiom that "knowledge is power" on the development of modern medical technology? (Hans Jonas) That those asking such questions have been more prone to see the present biomedical dilemmas as instances of the reemergence of old, enduring human questions (save Jonas on this point), to favor looking toward solutions at the theoretical rather than the practical level, and to believe that the role of ethics was to move beyond immediate demands for decisions back to a longer, slower search for some enduring truth is hardly surprising.

While the existence of these different currents in the field is by no means undesirable, their different emphases have probably contributed to a fair degree of confusion concerning the ends and means of bioethics. Three latent consequences of this confusion are worth exploration: first, the emergence of a distinct "backlash" in many scientific quarters against the field of bioethics; second, a tension within the field itself concerning the pertinent roles of the different disciplines; third, considerable division about the role of those called "ethicists" in public policy debate.

1. *The "backlash" against ethics.* As I mentioned above, the initial problem of those attempting to establish the field of bioethics was the considerable skepticism that anything called "ethical analysis" could have any public impact whatever. By 1975, however, a remarkable shift had become apparent. Ethics, its critics now allege, can cause both mischief and confusion. It

can cause mischief if only because those drawn to it are as capable of acting and speaking irresponsibly as any other segment of the community. It can cause confusion because ethics seems far better at asking questions than providing answers; old values are threatened or dissolved without anything better being put in their place. Those, at least, are some of the broad charges. More concretely, there is a strong suspicion among many in the biomedical community that much of the new concern for ethics represents a disguised or latent form of antiscientific or antitechnological feeling; that the label of ethical analysis is nothing but a cover for attacks on the personal morality of researchers or physicians; that those in ethics display a consistent ideological bias in favor of the protection of individual rights at the expense of that general welfare which medical research and progress can bring; and that most of those drawn to ethics are classic "armchair philosophers," with little knowledge of or experience with the actualities of research or practice.

There is no need to deny that some evidence can be found to support charges of that kind. The rapid growth of the field in recent years has meant that it has drawn representatives of just about all schools of thought (and non-thought), all types of personalities, and a full spectrum of political and social views. But that is also to say that one can just as easily find evidence to show that, as generalizations, none of the charges can stand very close scrutiny.

The evidence of strain between those concerned with ethical issues and those concerned with the advancement of scientific knowledge and clinical application needs to be examined more carefully. It is impossible, for example, to posit any simple dichotomy between "ethicists," on the one hand, and researchers and clinicians, on the other. The bioethics movement is well-represented by scientists and medical practitioners; it is by no means peopled entirely by philosophers, theologians, and legal scholars. A major early impetus to the field, in fact, was provided by the work in the late '60s of the eminent Harvard anesthesiologist, Henry K. Beecher, M.D., on the ethics of human experimentation. More recently, it was not those from the humanities or the social sciences who raised the ethical issues posed by research on recombinant DNA, but the researchers themselves. Some of the nastier struggles over ethical issues have been among scientists themselves rather than between scientists and nonscientists. The pressures to break off the Boston XYY studies originated with a group of scientists, and the criticisms of E. O. Wilson's book *Sociobiology,* on the grounds of its alleged support of a socially dangerous genetic determinism, came almost exclusively from scientific quarters.

If it is possible, then, to reject any strict interpretation of the "ethics backlash" as a simple struggle between those within and those outside of science and medicine, there may nonetheless be a looser sense in which that interpretation has some meaning. For it is of course true that a prominent feature of bioethics has been the influx of a large number of people outside science who have concentrated their attention, and critical faculties, on the goals, methods, and practices of medicine and the scientists. And this has on many occasions fostered an apparent tension between ethics and science.

Put in one way, there need be no tension whatever—ethics seeks to discover the nature of a good life, to examine moral principles and to analyze the relationship of those principles to moral dilemmas; science seeks to understand the natural universe and to develop empirical truth. There is nothing in principle incompatible about these two quests.

But there is another way of looking at the matter. Working scientists are normally committed to the advancement of science and, these days, also to the furthering of an economic and social climate necessary to give science the kind of support it would like to have. That is perfectly natural and acceptable. In their *professional* roles, however, there neither is nor need be any similar commitment to the promotion of science on the part of nonscientists, whether philosophers, lawyers, or historians; their duties and interests lie elsewhere. It should, therefore, be perfectly acceptable for them to raise any kind of question they like about the scientific enterprise, whether about its ends or its means. Some do just that. Put another way, nonscientists have no special moral duty toward science, just as the scientist has no special moral duty toward philosophy or the legal professions. All of the professions of course can make a legitimate claim that they contribute to human welfare, but none can claim that theirs has such a uniquely valuable status as to require special tribute and support from all the others.

At a 1975 meeting of Institute Fellows, H. Tristram Engel-hardt, Jr., M.D., made a similar but even broader point: ". . . there is a dialectic of interests that can set the community of scientists at odds with that of the general community. The community of scientists is explicitly focused on empirical truth, while the community generally has other concerns that may take precedence." Frequently, philosophers, theologians, lawyers, and others try to speak to or (more hazardously) for those "other concerns." Often scientists share those other con-cerns and no conflict arises; but sometimes they do not, and the stage is set for a struggle.

2. *Interdisciplinary strains.* Interest in bioethics has involved a broad coalition of specialists from the sciences, the humanities, and the social sciences. As an example of the possibilities of interdisciplinary work, it has shown some remarkable successes. This is all the more noteworthy consider-ing the generally dismal record of interdisciplinary programs in universities and other places. The reasons for the successes of bioethics are probably not difficult to locate. Most of the organizations which gave the strongest impetus to the field were, and remain, committed to interdisciplinary work—the Center for Bioethics of the Kennedy Institute, the Society for Health and Human Values, and the Institute of Society, Ethics and the Life Sciences. The nature of the issues, and their novelty, made it evident that, if they were to be dealt with at all, they could not remain the province of any one discipline. Psychosurgery is not just a medical issue, or a philosophical issue, or a legal or policy issue—it is all these at once; and a movement in any one of those fields has immediate implications for all of the others. Finally, the relative rapidity with which the problems appeared caught most of the traditional disciplines off guard—none of them appeared particularly well-equipped to take them on. It was only natural to look toward a cooperative effort with other disciplines.

As the field has developed, however, some signs of strain have begun to appear. While it is too early to judge what they will do to the field as a whole, they are worth noting and watching. First, many of those from traditional disciplines have had to struggle to get bioethics accepted as a legitimate area of inquiry among their colleagues and within their profession. Short of that, their advancement within their professional field may be seriously jeopardized. If not to themselves, they have to prove to their colleagues that one can be a "good" philosopher while working on, say, euthanasia, a "good" legal scholar while working, for instance, on behavior control in prisons, or a "good" English scholar while spending time on clinical rounds in a medical school. One way that many increasingly seem to be employing to gain that legitimacy is by talking of the problems of bioethics in the jargon of their profession, and with all the narrow rigor and standard methodologies accepted in their field. In the process, it may also be more profitable professionally to direct one's efforts toward one's disciplinary colleagues, and toward the publication of articles in the accepted trade journals of an established field. An evident outcome of this tendency could be a diminishment of bioethics as an interdisciplinary field.

Second, all of that is closely tied with the pressures in our society toward professionalism. It is that pressure, in both large and small ways, which has so often in the past meant the demise of interdisciplinary programs and fields. Academic rewards, at least, go to those who can prove they are solid professionals in one field. Bioethics is a hybrid where one might, if lucky or particularly skilled, impress people generally in a variety of fields—but not necessarily impress anyone spectacularly in any one field. That can be professionally fatal. As a practical matter, it is terribly difficult to keep up with one's own traditional field while, simultaneously, trying to familiarize oneself broadly with other fields. This is particularly acute for those from the sciences, who rarely feel they can take a significant portion of their time away from the laboratory or divert attention from the difficult task of keeping up with the never-ending deluge of new scientific findings.

Third, while there have always been questions about the methodology appropriate to bioethics, they were voiced in a relatively mild way a few years ago. Now, with the maturing of the field, they are being pressed more insistently. The term "bioethics" itself, or the phrases "ethics and the life sciences," or "medical ethics," may seem to imply that the basic subject matter is ethics, and ethics has traditionally been a subject branch of philosophy or theology. It is thus only a short step to saying that, while bioethics is and must be interdisciplinary, the dominant position should be held by those with a training in ethics. That claim can be disputed. From the physician's perspective, the context of any ethical decision is that of the concreteness of particular cases. Without a direct exposure to that contextual setting, as well as a constant immersion in it, ethical theorizing will lack any footing in reality. It may be interesting to philosophers, but it will not have much helpful to say to clinicians.

A variant on that struggle goes on between the social scientist and the philosopher. Characteristically, the impetus of the social sciences is to gather empirical data about the realities of moral problems (sociologically, economically, or psychologically), about the way in which decisions are actually made within specific cultural and political institutions, and about the range of variables that seem to influence decision making, whether individual or general. A commonly-stated conviction is that, in the absence of such data, any attempt to pass on to normative analysis will be irrelevant. It will certainly be of little use for policy makers, who must work for the most part with things as they are and not what they ought to be in some ideal world. An equally characteristic response by philosophers is that, while empirical data may be interesting to have, it is not all that imperative. One can always ask "what if . . .?" That is, "what if prisoners were given the option of psychosurgery or life sentences in prison?" "What if the state legislated mandatory genetic screening laws?" Once having asked a question in that form, it is then possible to go on to an examination of the possible moral consequences, the possible moral principles which might be brought to bear to judge such an eventuality, and the possibly appropriate means of ethical analysis which ought to be used. One does not, in that mode of reasoning, need to know if, for instance, there actually are states contemplating such laws, much less delay until a full survey has been taken of existing practices.

These are by no means new struggles. They represent some long-standing arguments between and among disciplines. But as bioethics develops, these struggles for turf, dominance, or sway are on the increase. One important outcome, evident to those soliciting money for research, is more pressure to display an acceptable methodology. What will, however, count as an acceptable methodology in one agency may not so count in another. Much will depend upon the comparative dominance of the disciplines of those who manage (and review) for such agencies. If bioethics is conceived of primarily as a part of the humanities, with methodologies which do not lay emphasis on data-collection, then there will be great reluctance to support that kind of research by scientific agencies, even if the subject matter of the ethical inquiry is medical or scientific. Those of course who can shape their mode of ethical inquiry in the direction of data-gathering are likely to fare better at the latter agencies. That all of the agencies may support "interdisciplinary" work does not obviate the possibility, even the likelihood, that they will judge the quality of the proposed work in terms of one dominant methodology.

3. *Ethics and public policy.* As long as ethics appeared "soft," oriented toward "abstract" and "theoretical" issues (or, alternatively, toward personal decision-making) there was little about it to threaten anyone. But as suggested above, the impact of bioethics is now being felt in public policy. The establishment by Congress of the National Commission for the Protection of Human Subjects of Biomedical and Behavioral Research symbolizes as well as anything else just how far and fast things have come. Regardless of the outcome of the work of that Commission, its very existence guarantees that a public spotlight will be put on problems which have mainly been saved from a fully critical exposure. That some of its work, together with the gradual emergence of a wide range of regulations based on ethical considerations, will create more and not fewer obstacles for a fully unfettered science and medicine now seems inevitable. In short, public policy is now and will even more in the future be influenced by bioethics. That bioethics in the long run may serve to reduce problems, or contribute to their resolution, seems quite conceivable, even likely. But in the

meantime, for a society long accustomed *not* to scrutinize care-fully scientific research or medical practice, it will probably be felt by those doing that work as more a hindrance than a help. Even the process of pausing, asking questions, establishing commissions and devising regulations can cause a perceptible slowdown and unwonted hesitation. Taken together with budget cuts (having nothing to do with bioethics), a slight cooling in the public ardor for science and medicine, and a slight reduction in the esteem felt for scientists and physicians, the entry of bioethics into the policy arena can easily be per-ceived as threatening, and so it is.

That seems to me the way matters now stand. Yet if bio-ethics is having an impact, it is not necessarily because those working in the field know exactly what kind of impact they think they should have. As a movement, bioethics has not been reformist in the usual sense. It did not emerge as a protest against moral abuse, as a movement to get laws changed or new legislation enacted, or as a very direct part of the mood of antitechnology which began sweeping the country by the late '60s (that it may have been an *indirect* result of that mood is certainly plausible). Its primary goal was to get some ethical problems of biomedicine put on the public agenda, to gain increased social and financial support for those who wanted to do scholarly work on those problems and, in general, to see if the emerging moral dilemmas could be handled in a thoughtful, reflective way. Direct evidence for that thesis can be found by examining the stated purposes of the major groups working within the field. Further corroboration can perhaps be found in the fact that some of the explicitly reformist groups in medicine (e.g., Health/Pac and Science for the People) have sometimes voiced the suspicion that those concerned primarily with ethical investigation are really card-carrying members of the liberal establishment, who, by the evasion of limiting themselves to respectable, fundable research, are actually obstacles to change and reform. The reform/radical groups in science and medicine are action-oriented, classically activist; the bioethics groups are not.

In the early years of bioethics it was probably enough to stand for the general and uncontroversial goals of better thought and research, more reflection, and interdisciplinary camaraderie in coping with tough questions. Now, as the power of bioethics genuinely to influence policy becomes apparent, and as strain appears within the movement itself, a more precise specification of its proper public policy possibilities and capacities (and suitable limits thereto) becomes urgent. It is by now axiomatic that scientific research can have unintended consequences. But an equally reasonable axiom is that bioethics can have unforeseen consequences also, not necessarily good. That is a moral reason to better specify goals and methods.

Bioethics, in its stance toward policy matters, has moved uneasily between social ethics, public ethics, and normative ethics. The distinction between these forms of ethics has been perceptively illuminated by Albert R. Jonsen and Lewis H. Butler in "Public Ethics and Policy Making."* "Social ethics," they write, ". . . may review critically the more general princi- ples of society. It may project longer time schemes for conserva- tion or change. It may envision more profound changes in the social or economic order." But public ethics, by contrast, "might be considered a subset of social ethics, and might be distinguished from it in general by three features. First, it would deal with a more precise problem, the problem of making particular public decisions about a particular matter of public concern. Second, it deals with an issue which is pressing and about which some determinations must soon be made. Third, it does not usually expect to work profound changes in the social order. . . . The style and content of public ethics remain somewhat vague. They may begin to emerge in the attempt to perform several distinctive tasks. . . . The three tasks may be described as: (1) articulation of relevant moral principles in the policy problem; (2) elucidation of proposed policy options in light of relevant moral principles; and (3) displaying ranked order of moral options for policy choice." And finally, "normative ethics is concerned with setting forth, for the whole of life or one of its spheres, a critically satisfying set of obligations and values. The policy-making process is located in one of those spheres, the political. But, as a process, it is less interested in the 'critical satisfactoriness' of the set of obligations and values and more

*Hastings Center Report 5 (August 1975), 19-31.

interested in actual decisions, actions, and resulting social arrangements."

In stating above that bioethics has "moved uneasily" among these three forms of ethics I mean only to point out the uncertainty which exists about the proper role and goals of bioethics. If that role is conceived of primarily as developing a normative ethic, then the emphasis will fall on comparatively more theoretical work, less engagement with immediate issues, and a bias toward traditional modes of philosophical or theological investigation. If the role is conceived of essentially as social ethics, then the bias may be in the direction of social science work, political theory, and cultural critique. If public ethics is seen as the suitable role, the greatest emphasis may then fall upon a close involvement with legislative and court struggles, immediate clinical experience, and a rapid development of workable rules-of-thumb. There is no reason why these three forms of ethics cannot coexist and mutually enrich each other, nor any reason why the same person might not, at different times, try to work with all three forms. But, given the increasing professionalization of the field, that kind of ecumenical spirit may not fare so well. Sooner or later, those who work professionally in a field will be tempted to come to some decisions about what counts as "serious" work. That is a genetic trait of professionalism.

I have concentrated my attention on some of the strains and tensions now apparent in bioethics. I believe they can provide some important insights into the present and likely future ways the ethical issues are and will be conceived. At present, it is possible to see movement in two directions, not necessarily compatible. First, the increasing penetration of bioethics into university curricula, especially in philosophy, religion, and biology departments, means that the issues should receive more careful, slower, more reflective consideration. At the same time, because of that very process, the issues will undoubtedly be subjected to the methodologies of the established disciplines, with a corresponding demand that they meet traditional tests for quality. That can only be accomplished by the disciplines selecting out those aspects with which their methodologies can most easily cope. It is in this respect not surprising that philosophers have gravitated toward working on some of the major conceptual puzzles that cut across much bioethical discussion—toward examining the concept of "person" or "personhood" (critical in the abortion debate), of "freedom" and "autonomy" (pertinent to problems of behavior control); or that both philosophers and legal scholars have been attracted to the concepts of "rights," given the ubiquity of proposed or putative rights in the field of bioethics—the right to health care, to terminate treatment, to death with dignity, to be born with a healthy genetic constitution, to treatment while institutionalized, to confidentiality of medical records, and so on; or that social scientists have been drawn to empirical studies on the extent to which human experimentation codes are actually implemented, the way in which different groups of practitioners tend to come to different ethical judgments, and the process by which public policy is actually devised and implemented. We can assume, then, that as established disciplines take on bioethical issues in established ways, they will adapt the issues to their own methodologies—not necessarily vice versa.

A second direction in which there is strong movement is, as mentioned, toward the increased politicization of the issues. In its harshest sense, this puts pressure on those working in the field to choose sides, to adapt their work in ways which will enhance its utility for polemical purposes, and to "take stands" even when the issues themselves do not lend themselves to strong, clean black-and-white resolution. For the philosopher or moral theologian this means pressure to become an outright moralist, vigorously prescribing rather than analytically describing. For the social scientist it can mean the seduction of collecting data to help support previously and independently determined moral positions. For the legal scholar the pressure is toward finding a way to make a legal case in support of one or another side in an ethical dispute.

In a milder sense, the politicization means increasing pressure on the field to address itself directly to immediately pressing juridical and legislative matters. In the nature of the case, they rarely lend themselves to the methodical care and slowness characteristic of the best forms of scholarship; problems must be dealt with *now,* well before all the pertinent evidence is in, all arguments carefully sifted, all contending principles methodically examined, and all consequences carefully explored. A characteristic dilemma, reported by many, is this. One has made a name, either nationally or locally, as an "expert" on a bioethical issue. A call comes from a legislative assistant or a legislator on some legislative aspect of that issue. Will one please testify next week on a bill, just entered, to make this or that change in the law? *"Next week!"* one responds. "Yes, we're sorry to give you so little warning, but we have to move rapidly." The choice, then is clear: either refuse to testify, on the grounds that one will not have enough time to think the particular issue through (which will invariably seem precious to a legislator who *must* act now, for good or ill); or go and testify, being quite certain that, at least in one's own eyes, one cannot do full, or even decent, partial justice to the issues. One can also of course be fairly certain that, if one does not testify, others— with fewer intellectual scruples or with an axe to grind—will be only too happy to respond. That legislative debates do not readily lend themselves to the niceties of academic disciplines and methodologies need not be underlined.

To those who struggled long and hard to get bioethics accepted both in the academy and in legislative discussion, one might say that these countervailing pressures represent an embarrassment of riches. One is, if not necessarily loved, at least wanted. But the very existence of the pressures should force the field to ask what it can best do and what its relative priorities should be. Perhaps there is some splendid way to reconcile all of these pressures into a coherent vision of the work and potential contributions of bioethics. Or perhaps, more modestly, one should not seek some grand vision but, instead, seek only to avoid the pitfalls inherent in any of the directions. These would include the trivialization of the serious which is often endemic to high professionalism, the lure of public power which more than once in our generation led the intellectual and expert classes to arrogantly think they could solve society's problems, and the opposite temptation—to keep serious matters within the academy on the grounds that they are too serious for mass public consumption. Bioethics is now subject to all of these hazards. How and if they will be avoided is a story yet to be unfolded.

Introduction

Science, Ethics and Medicine
H. Tristram Engelhardt, Jr.

THE ESSAYS IN THIS VOLUME are the product of a series of meetings in 1975 in which the authors—philosophers, physicians, historians of medicine, one scientist and one theologian—engaged in intense debate concerning the interrelationship of ideas in ethics, medicine, the history of medicine, and the philosophy of science. As the commentaries show, the discussions were spirited and interdisciplinary. Under the force of these debates, each paper was rewritten twice. In addition to the authors, the discussions included members and associates of the Institute who influenced the character of the debate, among them Daniel Callahan, Stanley Hauerwas, Hans Jonas, Stuart Spicker, and Robert M. Veatch.

The essays in this volume represent not merely the fruits of an interchange of ideas between individuals from diverse backgrounds, but an attempt to come to terms with ideas linking the humanities and the sciences. These works were commissioned out of the conviction that value-judgments of diverse sorts are presupposed by the sciences in general, and by medicine in particular; and that, moreover, science and ethics bear on each other in many ways. That conviction is sustained by these essays, for they exhibit the fundamental interdependencies of ideas in science and ethics. The values treated, in

1

fact, transcend the bounds of ethics itself, and include value-judgments in aesthetics as well as those peculiar sorts of evaluative judgments that fashion the structure of the sciences. Consider, for example, the values appealed to in Richard Feynman's almost teasing account of the structure of the protons:

> If experiments continue to confirm the need for quarks in protons, this is the way the theory will apparently develop: quarks of three colors, so nine in all, and eight kinds of gluons. This part sounds elaborate but is mathematically simple. And a long range force— which sounds simple but appears mathematically a bit unnatural. Suggestions to explain this long range force, such as Kauffmann's, all seem a little awkward and without an inner beauty we usually expect from truth. But sometimes the truth is discovered first and the beauty or "necessity" of that truth seen only later.(1)

Feynman mentions such evaluative criteria as simplicity, being mathematically unnatural, being awkward, the inner beauty of truth, and the necessity of truth. When framing our pictures of reality we appeal to such concepts. In terms of them we decide what will count as properly scientific explanations of reality. Science is not like taking a picture of the world around us. Rather, the nature of scientific accounts and their acceptability depend on concepts such as measurability, heuristic force, objectivity, and verifiability, not to mention choices concerning what will be measured and what will be verified.

As Lester King argues in this volume, similar "scientific values" have played a role in the development of medical theories. That is, medicine shares with science in general commitments to particular notions of reality, and it not only shares in such concepts (such as "The notion of value-free science is simply a sort of tool to help in choosing between opposing systems" [p. 230]), but is itself especially rich in the interplays among facts, ideas, and values. Medicine is, after all, not simply a science. It is a constellation of sciences and technologies bearing on the human condition with respect to physiological and psychological well-being, as well as social well-being, insofar as that social well-being is dependent upon physiological and psychological constraints (an example of medical treatment of social well-being in the case of an infertile couple would be using artificial insemination by a donor). It is for this reason that the science most often discussed in this volume is medicine. Medicine raises issues of the roles of value-judgments, prior expectations, and theories of science upon our views of reality. In addition it raises immediate ethical issues concerning the use of science (including human experimentation), the morality of particular biomedical technologies, and even the probity of exploring particular scientific hypotheses.

Even before one comes to the consideration of the relationship between ethics and the sciences, numerous varieties of value-judgments have played a role in structuring the sciences. On the other hand, judgments in the sciences play an important role in influencing our judgment of the social world about us. For example, in this volume Stephen Toulmin outlines the ways in which ideas in the sciences have influenced our appreciation of society, political theory, and questions in ethics. His thesis is: *"All changes in the biological concept of an 'organism' also entail corresponding changes in the 'organic' theory of society"* (p. 196). Science, in short, is not only fashioned by value-judgments, but plays a role in the fashioning of those very judgments which influence the character of the society in which science develops.

> Instead of considering ethics as basic to—that is, as being a source of ideas, ideals, and canons of practice for—medical practice and biological theory, we shall here, conversely, regard medical practice and biological theory primarily as basic to—that is, a source of ideas, ideals, and canons of practice for—ethical, social, and political thought. In point of historical fact, our ways of thinking about the social relationships between individual human beings influenced the development of fundamental patterns of thought in biology, medicine, and natural history; these biomedical ideas subsequently reacted back onto thought about human relations; and there has been a continual interplay between theories of *society* and theories of *organism*, which continues today. It is that reciprocal influence between biology and ethics that forms our central topic (pp. 196-97).

The relationship between the sciences and ethics is circular; each influences the other.

An adequate understanding of science and ethics will, then, require their mutual examination. A full account of either in isolation will not be possible. This should not be unexpected. An account of ethics turns at least in part on a theory of reality, including an account of society and human nature. For example, one will assign blame for injury to the extent to which one will hold that culpable ignorance or negligence is to blame. But, accounts of the scope of culpable ignorance turn on issues in the theory of knowledge. Samuel Gorovitz and Alasdair MacIntyre offer a helpful examination of this genre of reciprocal action between the sciences and ethics.

To begin with, they argue that one can distinguish between internal and external norms in science. They characterize internal norms as "those which derive from the essential character of scientific activity as a cognitive pursuit" (p. 250). In contrast, external norms "are those which govern motives either for participating in or for making use of the results of scientific activity. Internal norms are concerned with such factors as verifiability, truth, and reason; external norms are concerned with such factors as curiosity, ambition, and social utility." This division between the internal and external norms of science is the one usually presupposed in judging the action of natural science. It leads to conclusions that "those S.S. doctors who performed experiments on living prisoners in Auschwitz did not violate any of the internal norms concerning truth-seeking and problem-solving. Indeed, it might even have been the case with at least some of them that they were quite exceptionally devoted to these norms . . ." (p. 260). Given this picture of the nature of internal and external laws, science, is, from the viewpoint of internal norms, free of the general constraints of morals.

Moreover, within the prevailing contemporary view of science, "All scientific error will arise *either* from the limitations of the present state of natural science—from ignorance or from the willingness or negligence of the natural scientist, from ineptitude" (p. 252). This view of scientific error presupposes that one can, indeed, have exact knowledge concerning the deportment of individual objects. As Gorovitz and MacIntyre argue:

> Natural science did not in the seventeenth century discard quite as much of Aristotelianism as its philosophical protagonists supposed.

What it retained included an inability to give a plausible account of our knowledge of particulars, of individuals—an inability for which Aristotelianism is notorious. For natural science, on a modern physicist's view just as much as on Plato's or Aristotle's, the objects of knowledge are universals, that is, the properties of objects classified by *kinds*, and the generalizations that link those properties (p. 254).

This theory of knowledge thus led to a view of reality with implications for the assignment of blame and praise. Scientific error with respect to knowledge of particulars is due either to ignorance or ineptitude because particulars are knowable, on this account, as universals are—through generalizations. Concepts in science structure the understanding of ethical conduct. To fail to know a particular (that is, make successful predictions concerning the treatment of particular patients) is due to possibly culpable ignorance or due to blameworthy ineptitude.

Against this traditional view of science, Gorovitz and MacIntyre argue for a science of particulars. "Many particulars—salt marshes, hurricanes, and the higher primates, for example—cannot be understood solely as the sum-total of the physical and chemical mechanisms that operate on them. What effects such mechanisms have is affected by the unique history of that specific particular with all its contingent circumstances, contingent that is, and even accidental relative to the operation of the mechanisms" (p. 255). It is in terms of this notion of the science of particulars that Gorovitz and MacIntyre argue that "the S.S. doctors were indeed violating a relationship to men and to nature which is an essential part of the project of understanding men and nature; they thus failed as scientists and not only as men and citizens" (p. 261). Gorovitz and MacIntyre wish to sustain this point on the basis of the proposition that "unless one understands what it is for a tree, dolphin or gorilla to flourish, one simply fails to understand them." Science, in short, cannot be conceived of as value-free; in order to engage successfully in the scientific study of particulars, one must understand the goods and values important for the particulars under study. Science becomes intrinsically and properly concerned with values.

One's theory of science, or, even more generally, one's theory of knowledge, can thus have broad and important implications for human conduct. It is not as if one could isolate questions raised in science from those in ethics, or the converse. Each bears importantly on the other. To draw out this point again by means of an argument in the Gorovitz-MacIntyre paper: "Hundreds of years of understanding nature as the mere instantiation of universals, where particulars are nothing more than specimens for study in the quest for general truths have contributed strongly to the ecological violence which we have done to nature. That is, it is not merely the forms of our economy or of our technology, but also—perhaps surprisingly— those of our science which have contributed to our estrangement from nature and from other species." Views of science determine our patterns of conduct.

Interdisciplinary examinations of the interplay of science and ethics can offer us new ways to reformulate our questions about values, as well as about obligations. For example, Gorovitz and MacIntyre argue that endeavors such as medicine can, as sciences of particulars, be viewed as basic sciences in contrast to enterprises such as physics, which become derivative or second-order sciences in being further removed from particulars. They propose a way of radically realigning our ordering of the sciences.

> For in this stronger version the thesis would insist that nature consists of nothing but more or less complex particulars, that theoretical physics is the most abstract kind of knowledge, and that it therefore always has to be based on our knowledge of particulars gained by means of sciences of the concrete. The most fundamental sciences on this view, would be the disciplines concerned with our practical transactions with particulars: medicine, veterinary medicine, engineering, military and political sciences, and so on (p. 259).

A new view of the nature of knowledge leads to a reordering of our evaluations of various human enterprises.

Even on the "weaker version" of the Gorovitz-MacIntyre thesis, it still follows that "the dominant interpretation of natural science must be revised so as to allow a place for our knowledge of particulars alongside our knowledge of generalizations—it is clear that those sciences which do deal with particulars require a view of error quite different from that which is derived from the dominant interpretation." This view of knowledge and the sources of error has implications with respect to the ways in which one can speak of malpractice, and the assignment of blame and error in medicine. In fact, error becomes something to be expected in medical practice. Indeed, the study of medical injury and error becomes recognized as part of understanding the limits of our knowledge with regard to the particulars that medicine studies: human patients. In terms of this, one is offered a way of developing policies to meet the inevitable error and injury attendant to medical practice, without necessarily lodging blame against the physician. As Gorovitz and MacIntyre stress, this should have important implications for the development of social policies bearing on medical malpractice.

Marx Wartofsky develops a similar line of argument in order to stress the interplay between science and values, reiterating a point made by King, Toulmin, and Gorovitz-MacIntyre:

> What we see is seen not by the eye, but by the mind's eye: that is, through the mediation of the imagination, or by way of the theoretical constructs which are the products of the activity of the imagination (p. 170).

He adds, though, an evolutionary accent, that theories of science are themselves instruments of human adaptation and that the truth-value of cognitive claims is to be assessed in terms of their utility, their satisfaction of our needs. Knowledge, construed in these terms, has a fundamentally normative character.

In developing this thesis, Wartofsky argues for a proposition not dissimilar to the thesis of Gorovitz and MacIntyre, namely, that medicine is not a derivative science. As Wartofsky puts it, medicine is one of the fundamental ways in which one comes to terms with reality. Moreover, coming to terms with reality is never a purely theoretical enterprise; it is also always an endeavor of doing and making, of praxis.

> My claim here is that our species has developed its *general* cognitive capacities (both in its biological evolution as a species, and in its

post-biological or cultural evolution through various historical forms of social life), out of the specific demands made on cognition by different modes of praxis. Further, that medicine is such a primary or fundamental mode of cognitive praxis, with its distinctive structures and aims, and that therefore medicine is not a branch of human knowledge growing from some common tree which we can call "cognition in general," but is rather a root of this tree, and is therefore a *constituting* rather than a *derived* form of knowledge. What I want to claim, is that the general forms of human cognition have been shaped by medical theory and practice; that our general cognitive culture bears the imprint of the distinctive modes of medicine; and that an epistemology of medicine is therefore an approach to general epistemological reflection, rather than something to be derived from it (p. 168).

In knowing the world, one engages in acting in it and making it; conversely, in acting in the world and making it, one comes to know it. Moreover, in that interplay of knowing, doing, and making, the knower and the known fashion each other. Again, evaluation and explanation are not separable (albeit distinguishable) endeavors.

The essays by King, Toulmin, Gorovitz-MacIntyre, and Wartofsky thus offer a series of arguments concerning our understanding of the ways in which the core ideas of science and ethics bear on each other. Knowing and valuing are activities requiring an interdisciplinary account; their nature cannot be adequately construed within the confines of either science or ethics treated in isolation. Facts and values, theories of knowledge and theories of value mutually presuppose each other. The confluence of description, explanation and evaluation is particularly salient in the languages of health and disease. For example, in holding that an individual is ill or healthy, one does more than simply describe the world. One gives an evaluation as well. As I suggest in my treatment of health and disease in this volume, the evaluative norms invoked are complex and varied. There are multiple senses in which one can be ill, ranging from a physical or psychological inability to perform functions held to be essential to the human condition, to gross failures to realize a physical form pleasing to general human aesthetic taste. Again, the interplay of values and facts includes values far beyond the scope of ethics, though the role of ethical issues is often more obvious.

The role that issues of ethics play in the practice of the science or art of clinical medicine, it should be stressed, is not an external one. It is ingredient in the very ways questions are framed and answers sought. In fact, any careful treatment of the role of ethics in medicine will require, as Dr. Eric Cassell emphasizes, attending to the language of those engaged in the sciences and technologies involved.

> It seems reasonable in searching for the shape of an applied moral philosophy and, in particular, for a systematic or disciplined manner by which the moral particulars of the person are to be found by the applied practitioner, to start with the analysis of medical conversation (p. 157).

Cassell argues in this regard a thesis not unlike that of Gorovitz and MacIntyre, that attention to the language of physicians and patients will show that the facts of illness and disease are bound closely to "the particulars of the patient's person." Unlike Gorovitz and MacIntyre, Cassell sees this as an application of the pure sciences, rather than an approach to a science of particulars as the basic form of knowing.

John Ladd, in contrast, raises the question whether science and ethics are themselves compatible. Ladd has in mind what he terms the ideology of science or the scientific imperative: "Do everything in your power to maximize scientific knowledge!" (p. 152). He is arguing against a view of science as a moral activity in the sense that there would be a duty to advance science in preference to all other moral considerations. He holds that science is, *per se*, value-neutral: science can be good or bad, depending on its conduct and its context; the interest in pursuing knowledge through science should not be used in order to justify "deception, abridgment of liberty, or privacy."

In arguing that there can be immoral consequences from acting upon a supposed duty to advance science in preference to all other considerations, John Ladd does not present a radical critique of science. He wishes rather to place science within and under general ethical concerns. In contrast, Marc Lappé explicitly questions the value of truth seeking itself, not simply the fact that pursuit of truth can be used as an excuse to exploit the rights of others. In this sense, Lappé provides the most radical critique of science found in this volume; he holds that all new hypotheses in science deserve special moral analysis on the ground that they may dislodge our attention from morally pressing issues.

> At any time, a novel hypothesis poses a risk of dislocating human attention from one set of problems to another. Whether the later appropriation of its verified predictions leads to social decay or flourishing is rarely, if ever, in the hands or mind of the scientist who first formulates his idea (p. 97).

Lappé argues that scientists should consider the moral consequences of their hypotheses turning out to be true. Should those expected consequences be on the whole damaging to society, his suggestion is that such hypotheses not be verified.

Lappé has in mind hypotheses such as those bearing on the presumptive genetic basis for criminality and for differential intelligence between racial groups. In his critique, he thus brings to a focus much of the recent public debate concerning research to determine the relationship between XYY chromosome patterns and criminal behavior, and the genetic endowment of racial groups with respect to intelligence, and even studies bearing on the relative weight of genetic and environmental factors in the development of diseases.

Lappé advances four ways to decide the probity of forming particular hypotheses: 1. Some hypotheses can be held to be immoral in the sense of involving intrinsic danger to humans. He has in mind here discussions concerning the intrinsic danger of particular experimental techniques such as those employing bacterial plasmids. 2. Some hypotheses are mischievous in the sense that any sequence of testing them generates equally unsatisfactory moral outcomes. He imagines here testing a hypothesis which proposes that heredity is the principal basis for success in business. "There is every possibility that the scientist will have conferred (given any outcome) a degree of respectability to a system he may never have intended to support" (p. 109). 3. He holds that hypotheses should not be explored which are socially invidious. Here he places studies bearing on variations in the genetic basis of intelligence among racial groups. 4. And finally he holds that hypotheses which are holistically threatening should not be explored. "This class is characterized by hypotheses which posit a world view which violates social and moral norms. Here, it is critical to distinguish hypotheses which are holistically threatening by virtue of their *moral* content from those which ostensibly pose the same threat because of their revolutionary constructs." Under this final rubric Lappé places theories of the causation of disease which would place a major accent on genetic rather than social variables; he makes this criticism because "Individuals who were susceptible to disease by virtue of their social and economic conditions would thus be heavily penalized."

Lappé moves us, then, from John Ladd's more traditional critique of a scientific arrogance that would hold that the obligation to pursue the truth overrides moral obligations to experimental subjects, to a critique of the very notion of pursuing the truth. The question which Lappé raises is whether at times it is better not to know the truth in order to preserve established social interests in particular moral goods. In this Lappé suggests a departure from an attitude toward science which has fashioned the modern view of the human condition: truth in the end is socially liberating and science insofar as it leads to knowledge of the truth is good. Lappé places himself against the Baconian scientific ethos which criticizes those who are "afraid lest a deeper search into nature should transgress the permitted limits of sober mindedness,"(2) and against the Baconian faith in the virtue of seeking the truth regardless of its implications for our view of the human condition (a faith in truth which has been reiterated by modern exponents of the Baconian ethos such as Jacques Monod and J. Bronowski).(3)

In the opening essay Michael Scriven argues that ethics itself is a science. Here, again, the interlocking of scientific and ethical concerns is manifest. Scriven argues for an Equality Axiom as the basis for ethics, drawing out implications for issues such as abortion (equality is between persons, "people" in Scriven's language, and fetuses are not persons). His argument concerning ethics as a science is in part *a priori* and in part empirical. "If ethics is essentially scientific, then it presumably follows that any rational person must accept the case for ethical conclusions, to the extent that the reasoning can be made comprehensible, and the facts exhibited" (p. 21). In presenting his case, Scriven recruits not only logical considerations, but argues as well from political, sociological and anthropological issues. Scriven's paper thus raises again the question of the distinction and interdependence of facts and values, of statements about the way the world is and the way the world should be.

In all these essays and the commentaries upon them, a theme is reiterated: the concerns of science and ethics can be separated only artificially. The conclusions, if only tentative, of these wide-ranging discussions are that:

1. The images and metaphors of ethics are often borrowed from and influenced by theories of science and knowledge.
2. The sciences, in particular those sciences bearing on the human condition, are structured by value-judgments concerning what humans should be like and should be able to do.
3. Science and ethics, though conceptually distinguishable, are in fact inseparable due to a web of interdependent concepts and ideas.
4. It is necessary to place the activities of science within the broader scope of human activities in general.
5. Ethics, in order to guide conduct successfully in this world, must be attentive to the deliverances of the empirical sciences.

To the question, "What is the relationship between ethics and the sciences?" the answer is that the two are related as siblings, each drawing upon an overlapping conceptual inheritance involving basic judgments concerning the nature of reality and the nature of values. These are issues best addressed in an interdisciplinary context where the concerns of both ethicists and scientists can be voiced.

This series of essays indicates that there is a realm of value-judgments and concepts concerning the nature of reality that underlie both ethics and the empirical sciences. The humanities in their richest and deepest sense are concerned to bring these judgments to the fore. It is in terms of those judgments that we can place and integrate the diverse elements of the human endeavor. This theme is an old one. The foundations of ethics and the sciences involve those fundamental issues which in the past were addressed under the rubric of ontology or even metaphysics.

The truly singular figures in our cultural heritage have often recurred to the question of placing the empirical sciences as well as ethics in terms of overarching human concerns with knowing and with valuing. One finds such concern voiced in Edmund Husserl's discussion of the crisis of the European sciences,(4) as well as in Hegel's attempt to secure a language which would afford an integrated view of the inquiring and valuing mind. As one of the figures who framed many of the central questions of the contemporary age, it is perhaps well to end with a reflection of Hegel's, that both the world of empirical science and that of morals is framed by ideas. This is surely a point reiterated throughout this volume. We find in reality and in our systems of ethics the reflection of our minds, our attempts to know and to value. One may conclude from this that we never break free from the human predicament. If that is the case, then the humanities afford our best chance to come to terms with the powers of science and the interests of ethics by attending to the general concerns of humans. On the other hand, when we come to know the bounds of the human predicament, we do not have simply a limited view of reality, but reality as it must live in and through the ideas of the inquiring and valuing mind. The result is that we do not find ourselves in a world that is alien to us, one beyond the jurisdiction of our ideas and evaluations. Rather, in viewing reality, we come to see "only the mirror of ourselves.(5)

NOTES

1. Richard P. Feynman, "Structure of the Proton," *Science*, 183 (February 15, 1974), 601-610.
2. Francis Bacon, *Novum Organum* (1620) Book I, Aphorism LXXXIX.

3. Jacques Monod, *Chance and Necessity* (New York: Alfred A. Knopf, 1971); J. Bronowski, *Science and Human Values* (New York: Harper and Row, 1965).
4. Edmund Husserl, *Die Krisis der europäischen Wissenschaften und die transzendentale Phänomenologie* (The Hague: Martinus Nijhoff, 1962).
5. G. W. F. Hegel, *Philosophy of Nature*, M. J. Petry, trans. (London: George Allen and Unwin, 1970), Vol. 3, p. 213, Zusatz § 376.

1

The Science of Ethics

Michael Scriven

ETHICS IS THE EMPRESS of the sciences—no more, no less. In their time, both mathematics and theology have been referred to as the "queen of the sciences." Neither is a science and though a German may be queen of England, the arrangement is likely to prove an uneasy one. Ethics, on the other hand, is not only of royal but of native blood. Mathematics and theology each suffer from an additional defect as aspirants to the throne. Mathematics is not an essential or even an ideal component of science or its application, though indeed where feasible it is potentially useful (as well as potentially disastrous, as in most nonstatistical applications to the social sciences); nor is it a science itself. The second aspirant—theology—suffers from the absolutely fatal defect of being founded on, or attempting to support, a claim that at the very least, is *scientifically* unsupportable. This suffices to make the suggestion that theology rule the sciences somewhat bizarre. Neither of these flaws cloud the claim of ethics, which affects every application of science, directly or indirectly, and which rests on no assumptions that transcend science; and which is indeed— properly understood—a science itself. Its imperial status derives from its control over all applications of science, but also from its subtlety and difficulty. It uses every tool that science has ever devised; but it requires additional skills beyond that huge repertoire.

The case for coronation is sketched out in what follows. Typically enough, it involves in part a presentation of credentials, in part a consideration of the claims of more notorious pretenders, and in part a refutation of the attacks of enemies. Some attention is also paid to the nature of the plot that has delayed public recognition of this most worthy candidate.

I. Which Member of the House of Ethics?

Not everything that has been or is called ethics has a right to be called a science. The claim is made here on behalf of only one such ethics; it is said only that there is a true member of the family that does meet scientific standards. (There could not be more than one significantly different entry since it would contradict another at some point if significantly different and hence it and the other could not both be scientifically acceptable.)

What I take to be defining (or quasi-defining) features of an ethical system include such considerations as subject matter (it must refer to interpersonal behavior and attitudes, at least in large part), logical characteristics of the assertions (many of them must be normative/recommendatory/prescriptive; they must be capable of truth and falsity, contradiction, verification, etc.) and differentiae (it must be distinguishable from conventions, manners, prudence, and sociological ruminations, inter alia). And there must be one "formal" requirement or basic axiom of the system, to which we turn in the first section.

If there is nothing that can meet these considerations and the standards of scientific evidence, there is no science of ethics. In the past, people have suggested that comparative ethics, as a branch of cultural anthropology, should be called the science of ethics. But, of course, it is not ethics on the above definition, since it abandons the distinction between conventions or customs, and moral truth—it endorses relativism in the one sense of that ambiguous term that is incompatible with a science of ethics. On this point, and on the distinction between ethics and prudence, we need to be quite explicit, since they are absolutely crucial.

It is also *plausible*, though not definitionally necessary, that there should be substantial overlap between the "theorems" of the science of ethics and the claims of major ethical systems—at least with respect to content. That is, one would expect scientific ethics to assert *something* about the moral status of lying, cheating, stealing, killing, and so on.

II. Ethics vs. Custom and Opinion

What's right for the Eskimos may well not be right for us—in one sense. If this were not so, ethics would be overrigid and nonadaptive. But in another sense, what's right (or wrong) must be right (or wrong) for all, or else ethics fails to be ethics, i.e., the notion of being right (as opposed to wrong) evaporates completely. The easy way to understand this is by clinging to the scientific "analogy." Let's use a medical example. The correct treatment for a certain skin condition, when it occurs in an Eskimo village, may well be different from the correct treatment for the same condition if it occurs in a Yucatan village (since, for example, the ambient conditions vary enormously with regard to temperature and humidity, making certain salves useless in one situation). In spite of this *appropriate* relativism—which is no more than relevance—there is also a supervening absolutism, a rejection of *inappropriate* circumstantial variations: for example, there are many treatments that will be *completely wrong in both situations*, even if the local doctor, witchdoctor, or populace thinks they are right. And the best treatment, in both cases, may have to contain (at least) one particular substance.

In the moral situation, similar considerations are present:

1. Suicide by the enfeebled aged in marginal subsistence Eskimo communities may well be justified (now or once);

2. Suicide by the enfeebled aged elsewhere may well not be justified.

3. Brutal slaughter of the enfeebled aged may be illicit in all communities, whether or not their members believe it to be justified.
4. Any treatment of the aged may have to regard them as having a moral "right to consideration."

As long as there are right and wrong moral claims, whose rightness or wrongness is not determined by local *beliefs*, there is the kind of "absolutism" required for the scientific status of the subject. It is no more threatening to that status that most moral prescriptions depend upon local or personal *circumstances* for their validity than is the corresponding fact about most medical prescriptions a threat to the scientific status of medicine. There are of course many moral and medical truths that are not situation-dependent, including causal, conditional, definitional, and empirical generalizations.

III. Ethics vs. Prudence

We have been talking about the epistemological status of ethics, the sense in which there has to be an ethical truth that transcends opinion if there is to be a subject of ethics that deserves our serious respect, whether it is a science or not. An ethics that aped or that was no more than local opinion could certainly not be scientific, for else the earth would have been flat in the tenth century (since that's what public opinion said then), and round now; and it could not have been *ethical* since it makes the enterprise of a moral reformer moronic (if what is right is what the people think to be right, the reformer is always morally wrong). Similarly, an ethics that did not go beyond simple prudence could not be ethics, for the calls to self-sacrifice, to martyrdom, to heroism, the very calls that *distinguish* the trumpets of morality would not be distinctive to all—indeed, they would not even be necessary. If it could be shown that the case for heroism is *just* like the case for a savings account or hospitalization insurance or watering the garden before it begins to shrivel up, there would be no need to have the concept of duty as supervening over self-interest, no need to talk of moral virtues—indeed, morality would be no more than a modest exercise in extracting the implications of self-interest. The very nature of morality, as it has always been conceived, requires more than this, involves the essential contrast of ethics with egoism.

IV. On Overdefining Ethics

A system which meets the constraints just discussed, which yields results that cover most of the areas of behavior covered by traditional ethical systems (the Ten Commandments, etc.) and which can be given a scientific foundation and methodology—such a system is entitled to be called a science of ethics. It may well have features that some eminent philosophers, theologians, and moralists have abjured as marks of nonethical systems; it may lack other features which some such writers have maintained were essential for ethics. Any claims to those effects must be examined with care, of course, to see whether a logically fatal error has been made. But it is conceded in advance that *some* features, positive or negative, for which *some prima facie* case can be made, will make the ethical system to be described here less than a perfect match to the ideal ethical system of many, perhaps most, writers on the subject. It must be noted that these features will differ considerably from one group of writers to another, however. There is, I believe, no unanimous support for a characterization of ethics which is crucially different from the one proposed here.

The situation, then, is not unlike that when the kinetic theory or the entropy definition of temperature was proposed. An analysis was put forward of a preexisting concept, an analysis that was not exactly coextensive with it, that was definitely not cointensive with it (i.e., did not have the same meaning in all contexts), but was so useful and comprehensible and so close to the analyzed notion that it became the accepted equivalent, the working substitute, as well as an enlightening analysis.

V. A Minimal Formal Definition of Ethics

Let us now consider one specific version of the general claim that ethics is a science. We will set up a system based on a particular axiom. So we define ethics as the system of recommendations (etc.) that follows from the single axiom asserting the *prima facie* equality of the rights of all people. For the moment, we will work with the intuitive notion of the concepts embodied in this formula. Later, we will tidy up some aspects of some of them—none prove particularly troublesome.

It is asserted first that this axiom generates—that is, in conjunction with empirical claims, it implies—an ethical system within the meaning of the term as previously discussed. That this is so is lent some plausibility by the similarity of the axiom to the Golden Rule and other single formulae which have been proposed as the basis for the moral life. More plausibility is provided by examining the legal reasoning that has used the (narrower) doctrine of equal legal rights (as in, for example, the Fourteenth Amendment) to support a wide variety of specific moral injunctions. Full plausibility requires a detailed proof of the dispensability of the very few other axioms that have been proposed as necessary. These *axioms* must of course be distinguished from *specifications* of moral (or legal) rights and obligations, in the particular circumstances of a particular person, state, and time; the society in general benefits from making the implications of its laws clear and hence the body of law is very great. (The axioms of arithmetic or geometry are almost trivial, and few in number, but the theorems they lead to are infinite in number.) But the (essentially) moral argument that proceeds in legislatures, moderated as it is by political and economic considerations, stems from this single axiom, not just in democracies which accept it as a political premise but whenever else an attempt at moral argument proceeds. What we call moral disagreements are nearly always disagreements about the implications, in a particular situation, of this axiom, not about its truth; and where they are of a different nature, they usually concern the question of the range of application of the axiom (Is a fetus a person?), not its truth.

More detailed support for this first claim—the "adequacy claim," as I shall call it—is one of several omissions from this paper resulting from constraints of time and space. But enough has surely been said to make the claim somewhat plausible. An examination of the Ten Commandments, for example, readily suggests how most of them can be derived from the "Equality Axiom" with the help of other factual assumptions, for example, about the practical utility of verbal and marriage contracts, property ownership, and so on. Some of these assumptions are debatable, but that is not the fault of ethics but of sociology.

The second assertion about the Equality Axiom is that it can be shown to be an *optimal* basis for interpersonal relationships. It is in fact *the* optimal basis, under certain constraints about the inflexibility of adult attitudes. (It is suboptimal with regard to the range of attitudes that one can reasonably regard as part of the human potential. The optimum for that situation will be described later.) This claim will be referred to as the "provability claim," since for this to be the correct axiom for ethics, it must be shown to provide the best (optimal) basis (cf. geometric axioms).

There are several reasons for the (sub)optimality argument, but they all capitalize on the systematic management of uncertainty, that is they are all game-theory-related. (The other side of this coin is that an omnipotent evil god has no reason to go straight.) But before we get into these details, let's stand back for a moment and look at the kind of enterprise we're embarking on.

VI. The Paradox of Making Ethics a Science

If ethics is essentially scientific, then it presumably follows that any rational person must accept the case for ethical conclusions, to the extent that the reasoning can be made comprehensible, and the facts exhibited. Since the reasoning is often not very complicated and the facts often simple, it appears we would have shown that ethics is no more than an extension of common-sense, which appears to violate the requirement that it be sharply distinguishable from prudence. The following distinctions must be borne in mind.

1. We shall first argue that ethics is an optimal strategy for a *society*. That does not entail that it defines the strategy of prudence for each member.

2. We shall also argue that ethics is the optimal strategy for a society to *teach its members*. It does not follow that untaught individuals will find it best for them, in a society which has not taught ethics to its members.

3. We shall then argue that, under a certain range of conditions, an individual will be right to *move* his or her life strategy toward the ethical position. It does not follow that the ethical act will be prudent for that individual prior to coalition.

4. Hence, from every point of view, except that of the perfectly ethical person or policy, there is a clear difference between prudence and ethics; and even in those two special cases, the difference still exists conceptually though the selfish, that is, the "prudent" decision, is no longer the rational one. (Prudence can be seen as—in one sense—an orthogonal dimension to egoism-altruism.)

VII. Ethics as Public Policy and Political Science

While people may plot in private for their own advantage, in public they seek to give their case the raiment of ethics, for the very good reason that only that format can have a truly general appeal. Even when we are haranguing the Anglos against the marauding Sioux—social group against social group—we still adopt a moral line, maintaining that the Sioux are ruthless ravagers who have *forfeited* their rights to trial or lands. The ultimate move—denying that the Sioux have any rights at all, perhaps because they are heathen or nonhuman—*still* retains the principle of equality of people as the axiom. The form and starting-point of moral argument is an invariant.

Doesn't this example just show how empty the whole approach is, how slippery, superficial, and close to mere rationalizing the rhetoric of ethics becomes? Under pressure, it seems that we simply shift our definition of person to suit our wishes. First, let us consider more closely the pragmatic reasons for the axiom: then it will be easier to see if the charges of vacuity are sound. The Axiom of Equality is invariant in moral discussion partly because it provides a basis for *public* policy-making, since *it alone* maximizes the consideration given to all who are affected by the policy, doing this by alloting all a *prima facie* equal stake. The superiority of this approach is simply that it oppresses none and hence provides the least possible reason for revolution; and that is an important consideration when the power of any individual, as an assassin, is increased by the Great Equalizers, the handgun or the long gun. *"Prima facie* equal" means, essentially, "actually equal, except to the extent that differences can be justified by applying principles of distribution which are themselves based on equal consideration." Thus, for example, the pay for a very risky but socially important public service job (such as the bomb squad on a police force) might be higher than that for others, because it can be shown that all will benefit from having the job done well and the higher pay is necessary to attract highly skilled applicants. Again, it might be possible to prove that allowing a "free market" to determine salaries is ultimately the best way to benefit all, which would show that there was nothing morally improper about very widespread *de facto* income differences.

Equality of rights—as we are using it, a simple conceptualization of the equality of consideration—is thus not very closely connected with equality of ability, strength, riches, and the like, and presupposes it no more in the real world than it does in card games, where all must be treated equally from the point of view of the rules, though the success of all will vary with luck, bankroll, and skill. The guarantee of equal treatment is the incentive to play, to support, and to enjoy the game, and any less than *that prima facie* equality simply creates an incentive for insurrection, disruption, perhaps chaos and violence—a poor return for all.

Now let us return to the charge that moral reasoning has no substantial content, being subject to evasion by redefining the term "person." *Who* is to get equal rights? The insane, the cretin, the fetus, the infant, the adolescent, the prisoner, the ape, the robot, the comatose, the alien, the senile, the crippled, the traitor, the terminal patient? Women, minorities, slaves, murderers, enemies, the vanquished? The list covers a formidable proportion of the most controversial moral problems, and none of them are settled by deriving theorems from the Axiom of Equality. They all require treatment of the membership problem, the problem of the extent of the moral franchise.

But, when we look back at the line of reasoning (it is only the first of several lines of reasoning) that we have used in arguing for the axiom, we can easily see a way to start on the problem of identifying a being with moral rights. We ask ourselves what assumptions are being made about the individuals in the community for which the argument given makes out a case for morality. The assumptions are minimal, but not trivial. They have nothing intrinsically to do with being a member of the biological species *Homo sapiens*. They are clearly connected with the capacity to act—for and against the interests of oneself and others; with *power*—the capacity to act in such a way as to substantially affect the interests of oneself and others; and with the capacity to control one's acts in the light of *reason*. Ethics does not depend for its force on universal rationality (in the evaluative sense of that word), but it does depend on a widespread *capacity* to reason (that is, on rationality as a dispositional property). It does not depend on the assumption that everyone has *equal* power; but it does depend on the assumption that those to whom it directly applies have (or *could* exercise) *significant* power, *either* individually or collectively. And, throughout the above, it obviously depends on the capacity to distinguish the self from others, and to distinguish benefits in terms of whom they benefit.

Although we shall not be in a position to flesh out this concept of a person fully until we have looked at the other lines of reasoning for ethics, we can immediately see that the *kind* of reasoning we're engaged in here demonstrates errors in both the jurors' and the defense's arguments in the Edelin abortion trial in Boston. Several of the jurors were much influenced by photos of the fetus, which impressed them, as they put it, "because it looked so human." Competent defense counsel would have explicitly met this point by exhibiting photos of chimpanzee fetuses, stillborn neonates, and other entities which also look very like humans but lack moral rights. The distinction between biological classification and moral categories must be exhibited and stressed at the very beginning of any serious discussion of the rights of entities whose moral status is in question. And of course one can hardly do that if one has no general theory of the origin and basis of moral rights.

The approach to ethics that we are discussing has other consequences for that trial and its misdefense. For example, it is clear that neurological development in the embryo is not at stake when we take a view of ethics as a social science. Viability is irrelevant, so is sentience—viability, because the terminal patient has rights; sentience, not that it hasn't a *secondary* moral relevance, because there *are* moral bars to wanton cruelty to sentient beings even if those things are not moral agents, that is, "first-class" moral citizens. The restrictions on vivisection make that clear. But the drowning of kittens that have no prospective home is not thought of as a grave moral crime and it is in exactly this category that second and third trimester abortion falls. There are other ways in which a fetus can acquire secondary moral rights, first through sponsorship by an individual with primary moral rights, notably the mother. Second, parties with a less immediate claim, such as a father, a prospective foster parent, or a community desperate for population growth may want to offer compensation to the mother for the suffering involved in completing the pregnancy; and *if* that offer of compensation is accepted, then a contractual interest is established. Third, the marriage contract, explicitly or implicitly, may give others than the mother a right that amounts to a property right in the survival of the embryo. But in the absence of these secondary considerations, the embryo has no claim to moral rights at all, because rights make sense, that is, can be justified, only for people, and only some human objects are people. (Notice the importance of having acquired a self-concept in the idea of a person, e.g., in distinguishing the fetus from the unconscious person).

It is almost time to turn to some of the bigger guns in the defensive armory of ethics. What we have been discussing so far is a political consideration, a kind of "negotiating" or "arbitrating" argument for the Equality Axiom. To the extent that political science *is* a science, it is certainly a matter for both conceptual and empirical investigation to determine an optimal premise or structure for establishing explicit and implicit social contracts between interested parties. I am arguing conceptually that a distribution of *prima facie* rights that is unequal automatically creates a group with a grievance, and *only* parity avoids this. That's only a *prima facie* argument for parity, but it is a start. On empirical grounds, if I read the relevant studies of dissent correctly (and there are very few of them), there is a strong native intuition of fairness even among the illiterate, and the presence of such a condition on negotiations is strongly felt as a desideratum, often as a necessitatum, a fact which provides additional support for the thesis.

To summarize: when public discussion of public policy occurs, the posture is almost always (in fact) and in almost all situations optimally, and in many situations necessarily, one of acceptance of the Equality Axiom.

VIII. The Specific vs. the General Claim

We have been discussing one specific and one general claim, and the latter is independent of the former in a way that it may now be important to point out. The *general* claim is that ethics is a science or a part of science or—more precisely—a social science that is largely a hybrid of other existing parts of social science. (Also, more precisely, we have distinguished between two components of the specific claim, *viz.*, the adequacy claim and the provability claim.) We have *also* been discussing the *specific* claim that the Axiom of Equality is the basic truth of ethics and is supported by various scientific considerations. *The general claim is immune to the defeat of the particular one, though it is established if the particular one can be established.* It may not be true that the evidence forces egalitarian ethics on us, but every line of argument I cover does show that the scientific approach must lead us to some conclusion as to the optimal principle(s) in question.

To some extent, ethics—as all science—simplifies a little in order to achieve comprehensibility. Just as scientific "laws" are typically only approximations, establishing a norm and not an exact universal, so the Axiom of Equality establishes a *prima facie* and not an exceptionless truth. Hence, minor deviations from it are not crucial counterexamples. Moreover, in common with all science, ethics creates its own theoretical concepts, "ideal concepts" as we appropriately call them, which insulate its generalizations from falsification. Thus the gas laws are often expressed in terms of the behavior of "ideal gases," and the deviations of real gases from ideal behavior are not taken to falsify the laws. Similarly, the Axiom of Equality is a normative axiom involving reference to the theoretical or ideal constructs of "equal rights," and "person" constructs which are partly defined by the axiom.

All this is not by way of showing that all possible criticisms of my theses are doomed to failure because of what might be called their unconstitutional vagueness, or, more honorifically, their ideal type incorrigibility. It is just that I want to make clear that the Axiom of Equality is not refuted *easily*, e.g., by one counterexample; and that the thesis that ethics is a science is not refuted by refuting the Axiom of Equality.

Refutation of the specific claim requires proving either that (1) there is a better-supported basic moral axiom or axioms (which of course concedes the truth of the general claim); or that (2) a logical error is involved in the claim that the axiom is supported by the considerations I propose as support; or that (3) a huge variety of different principles are appropriate in different situations, and principles like these do not coalesce into anything that looks or acts like moral principles. The claims that you cannot logically extract values from facts, recommendations from descriptions, "ought" from "is," are examples of the second kind of attack. That argument, associated with the use of the label "naturalistic fallacy," is itself fallacious; value conclusions *can* be derived by rational argument (not usually by simple deduction) from factual premises. Doing so has been demonstrated elsewhere, particularly in John Searle's essay, "How to Get 'Ought' from 'Is' " in *Speech Acts*,(1) and by myself, using a quite different approach, in "The Exact Place of Value Judgments in Science."(2) In general, one can say that there are several ways to do the trick, involving one or more of these elements; the use of *prima facie* reasoning (the "logic of considerations"); the use of definitionally true value judgments; the use of functional analysis plus definitional truths about the connection between performing functions and *prima facie* merit; the use of empirical-conceptual studies of real values (needs) as opposed to felt value (wants); the use of the definitional connections between felt wants and the *prima facie* (nonmoral) merit of instruments that promote those wants; and the notion of burden of proof.

The details of this will not be repeated here, but I would add that science is *not shown* to involve value judgments (one has not shown that there are scientifically-supported value judgments), by pointing out the huge social consequences of scientific research. All *that* shows is that the use and support and application of science is morally assessable—a fact which was never denied, is not the doctrine of value-free social science, and does not distinguish between science and food or architecture or maturation. The special problem about science is whether it *contains* value judgments, not whether it can *figure in* (be the subject term in) value judgments.

Now our theses in this paper concern extremely special cases of value judgments. Even if science does legitimately contain verifiable value judgments—and my assertion there would be that making value judgments is a *principal* aim rather than a *peripheral* activity of science—it is still possible that *moral* value judgments are not legitimate parts of science.

Conversely, however, if either the general or the particular thesis of this paper is correct, one has immediately demonstrated the falsity of the value-free claim about science.

IX. Ethics as Game Theory

A major problem in providing a scientific version of ethics is to convince one's audience that one is not committing the irrelevancies or the tired old fallacies of one's predecessors. The arguments here may not be free of fallacy; but their fallacies are—I hope—not the same or not obviously the same. I'll appeal to social evolution—but I'm not making the errors ascribed to Spencer and others, *viz.*, might is right. And in this section, though I found R. B. Braithwaite's book *The Theory of Games as a Tool for Moral Philosophy*(3) interesting, he does—indeed tries—nothing like what I'm doing. Let me give two arguments from the theory of games and decisions area, one general argument concerning decision-making under uncertainty and the other concerning the Prisoner's Dilemma.

Altruism (the internalization of the Axiom of Equality) is, it seems to me, the optimal strategy for a society in which external or natural or internal dangers (war, pestilence, fire, famine, and crime) are serious and may affect anyone.

The argument can be seen intuitively as an easy generalization from a simple case, so let me describe such a case. Suppose that we consider only threats to life, and only those such threats where the action of some members of the society could save the lives of others. Suppose that n lives are at hazard, and suppose that the actions of m others can save the n lives. Suppose, even more narrowly—and I stress that these assumptions typically do not affect the argument, only the ease of grasping it—that the m will lose their lives if they act so as to save the n who are at hazard. Ignoring for the moment differences in the social importance between individuals in the m and n group—something which we can easily handle using the procedure referred to when we explicated the concept of *prima facie* equality—we can now see the difference in expectations of survival between the altruistic and the egoistic society. We need only consider the cases where n is greater than m and the m know it. In the altruistic society, the m sacrifice themselves to save the n *since* they recognize the equal rights of all to life and see that net lives can be saved by this action. In the society of (equally rational) egoists, the n are lost since the m value their own lives more than those of others. (We can ignore the near zero number of cases where all m are completely convinced of getting completely recompensed in a next world.) So, in every such crisis, the egoists lose n minus m members. In a primitive society, at war with its neighbors in the jungle and with the elements, the frequency of occurrence of such "crunch" episodes will be much higher than in a stable socialist state. But even such states are usually at war at least once in every citizen's life and war produces many such situations. And, of course, the significance of such cases generalizes exponentially as we extend the argument to situations where something less than life itself is at stake for both parties; where, for example, it is a matter of contributing to a charity or voting for better schools or not smoking in conference rooms. It is clear that if a society can choose between having all its members altruistic or egoistic, then it is in the interest of each member to choose the former (since any given member is more likely to be in the n group than the m group, and it's the n group that gets saved). And this is the justification for a society to support moral education in its schools and provide moral support in its media—not that present versions of these are very effective.

But is it a justification for any *individual* to adopt altruism, in a *society* which hasn't? Only if taking that step will lead to others' taking it. Remember that even if one's altruistic behavior only affects a few other people with whom one interacts frequently, perhaps one's own family or business associates; and even if that influence is limited, *there are very substantial expectancy gains* (in terms of one's nonmoral values). Hence there is a pretty strong case for the individual to take that step.

The main argument for the individual to be moral is independent of the one just given. But there is a hybrid consideration which bears on the individual's concerns. The rational egoist Jones would presumably regard the ideal social strategy as one where everyone else valued Jones' welfare more than anything else, and where Jones shared this admirable but idiosyncratic commitment. The only problem with this master-ideal slave strategy is selling it. If omnipotent, one can implement it willy-nilly. But where dealing with people who can think and act, even in a very limited sphere, there is *no* way of putting it across, ever since the divine right of kings gave equal time to the barons. Hence it is appropriate for the egoist to consider some more feasible alternative strategies. And, I suggest, the best he can do *in general* is to join with the others in supporting institutions which are designed to, first, enforce; and, second, indoctrinate the moral system based on altruism. *Even though* this arrangement will impinge on the egoist himself, possibly partially converting him to altruism, that "cost" is much less than the expectancy gains, the social insurance policy achieved by having others around who will help him when he needs/deserve it. Exactly why the cost is less we will consider in the next section. What we're looking at is another example of the rationality of a selfish person *in certain circumstances* freely choosing to be made into an unselfish person.

The second theory-of-games argument arises from the Prisoner's Dilemma, a classic illustration of a two-person game in which agreements are not binding and one does not gain what the other loses.(4) The definition of that dilemma (whether to confess a crime when one's sentence depends on whether another prisoner also confesses) makes it impossible for either prisoner, in the usual situation, to achieve rationally the maximum payoff that is theoretically available. No "internal" solution of this problem can work. But there *is* a solution, as can be seen by asking oneself what each prisoner would have to be able to assume about the other prisoner in order to legitimate the choice of strategy tied to the maximum payoff. One answer, i.e., one sufficient condition, is that he could win if he could arrange that the other prisoner values payoffs to either prisoner equally, i.e., is an altruist himself, *and* believes that both prisoners are altruists. The details are not important enough to inflict on those who aren't familiar with the literature on this problem, and will be obvious (or obviously fallacious—in which case I pray for their comment)—to those who are familiar with it. Now I believe that a prior and known commitment to altruism (not "ostensible commitment to altruism") is the *only* workable solution. Whether it is or not, the fact that it is *a* solution is an argument for altruism, an argument whose interest depends on the extent to which the Prisoner's Dilemma is characteristic of an important class of social situations. I will not expand on this point, but merely state that I think a great many social situations in business, game-playing, and personal relations are models of the Prisoner's Dilemma.

X. The Relevance of the Preceding Arguments to the General Thesis (and to Practical Moral Problems)

Suppose that arguments like those just given are internally sound. Do they really provide scientific support for morality (perhaps indeed for the specific morality of altruism)? Given that most people want—for example—to survive (and those who don't aren't with us for long), they have an excellent reason for supporting, adopting, or constructing social institutions and personal attitudes that increase the expectation of survival. If the scientific facts and analysis, from economics or sociology or political science or theory of games, can demonstrate the superiority of having a moral system (defined along the above lines as something different from prudence) over not having one, then they have good scientific reasons for adopting an ethical system. And the subject which consists of all the arguments of this kind for morality, and all the arguments for particular moral conclusions based on this kind of morality, and the associated theories and taxonomies, has, it seems to me, a bulletproof claim to being a science.

But aren't we just assuming that survival (etc.) is morally good? Haven't we just built ethics on an ethical axiom, not on science? Not a bit. The interest in survival is pre- or nonmoral. On that interest, we build the ethical system. But the ethical system is perfectly capable—as are all the ethical beings it controls—of biting the hand that feeds it. The wish to survive may or may not turn out to be overridden by moral considerations. When morality has been created, a creature of desire indeed (perhaps even, in this sense, the "slave of the passions"), it may come back to haunt its creator; and it does, as in the cases of self-sacrifice to save the lives of others that we have discussed. That's no more a contradiction that the occasional rationality of adopting or letting oneself be brainwashed into adopting rationally unsupportable beliefs in order to save one's life.

Scientific theories, which we build on observations, often lead us to discoveries that show some of these same observations to be in error. Remember the splendid example of the discoverer of the true nature of paresis as tertiary syphilis, three of whose paretic subjects denied ever having had primary syphilis. The theory looked so good, although based only on just such data, that he was led to doubt the "inconsistent" data, and by simply infecting the aberrant patients with syphilis and discovering they *were* immune and hence *had* had syphilis, he was triumphantly confirmed.

Particular items in the data-base may be erroneous because of (1) incorrect observation or measurement; (2) direct incompatibility with other data; (3) indirect incompatibility via some theory. (Number 2 corresponds to a special case of this where the theory is minimal.) The only incomprehensible suggestion—or perhaps the only case without scientific interest—is the suggestion that *all* the data in *all* data-bases might turn out to be wrong. That can't occur, since refutation of one item rests on the acceptance of others.

Consider the area of prudential (nonmoral) value judgments. Part of the data-base is the felt wants of the individual. In evaluating any one of these, we appeal to (a) the known sources (theories) of error in subjective estimates of wants; (b) other, apparently contradictory, desires in the same data-base; (c) facts about the world which make the "raw values" incompatible. Thus the doctor tells the patient that the patient would be well-advised to change his attitude toward rich food, to give up a value. He *could* just suggest giving up the food—but he's already tried that and it's clear that more is needed. He may recommend books, hypnosis, or clinics, which will help achieve this value-change. Now, how can he support this recommendation; is it a case of imposing his own values on the patient? No; his justification comes from appealing to first, the patient's other values, and second, medical knowledge. Notice that the doctor may also or instead recommend the *addition* of a new value, such as that illustrated by enjoying exercise, for similar reasons. It is simply a limited case of this line of argument for the ethicist to argue for the addition of valuing others, that is, of altruism.

Exactly this same scientific or pragmatic model of attacking the data-base carries over to moral theory. The survival of the individual is at hazard in moral reasoning, even though it is that survival which gave birth to the system of moral reasoning. The only absurdity arises when someone says that perhaps the survival of *everyone* that does or might exist might be amoral. Then we would have to ask what the moral gains would be. Since moral gains must—on the view here—be gains *to* someone, this would have to be absurd, just as the precondition of all knowledge, namely, the existence of some knower, must be met for science to exist. Of course, *neither* of these are *moral* presuppositions. These comments partially elaborate on the claim that one can get values from facts, though the achievement is less controversially expressed as getting full-fledged value judgments out of some data on performances and preferences.

Hence it seems clear to me that no fallacy is involved in proposing these considerations from game theory, etc., as support for ethics. Whether they also support the egalitarian system of ethics needs independent consideration—in particular, consideration of the particular arguments I have proposed as actually providing that connection.

At this point, it may be worth recalling the earlier discussion of the abortion problem. It will be noted that our theory of games arguments once more revolve around the concept of a moral being as a decider, a planner, a collaborator, someone with preferences and open life-options. Clearly the fetus is not covered by such conditions—nor indeed is the neonate, and the problems of imprinting and adoptability aside, we cannot—on this view—condemn the practice of infanticide. With every passing day, of course, the infant moves toward first-class citizenship in the moral community, which is marginally relevant (until attained), and acquires increasing status as a second-class citizen, which is highly relevant. Nevertheless, monsters should normally be killed at birth, and the father of an unadoptable child whose mother died in labor and who does not want to raise the child, should let it die or kill it. In frontier days, one might argue for his obligations to the community; but the counterargument is that the community should provide foster care, and the argument itself has no bearing on the situation where we do not need to increase the population at the cost of heavy impositions on fathers and children.

XI. The Evidence from Psychology and History

The evidence that is important here bears on the issue of the lability or substitutability of values. It is far from being bulletproof evidence, but it strongly suggests that altruism is feasible, or at least that a substantial degree of altruism is possible for at least most, and I think all, *children*. (It's clear that some adults are hard to salvage and perhaps those bordering on senility are impossible.) This, of course, bears on the implementation of morality rather than on its justification; it remains an ideal for humans just as good health—whatever it may mean—is an ideal for humans, even if many humans are genetically or by trauma precluded from it.

What is most striking in the clinical, anecdotal, and historical data is the simple fact that the "life of service" (to others) is no less satisfying than the egoist's life. I have no need to argue, with Plato and other optimists, that the egoist's life is intrinsically unsatisfying. I have many other arguments for morality that will carry the day as long as the cost to the individual is not enormous. On the evidence available, one would have to bet that there is rarely any such cost, but I would settle for even odds.

An important fact that emerges from examination of the circumstances in which most people live provides a positive argument for altruism as an additional value (for those of us who lack it, prior to such discussions as these). In selecting a set of values from amongst those which are equally satisfying subjectively *if* attained, it is important to ask about the differential chances that they *will* be satisfied. And here we have to face the very considerable difference between the probability that the altruist will find opportunities to further the welfare of others in greater need than himself or herself, and the probability that the egoist will win everything (s)he wants. The latter must, typically, compete for scarce resources and will often lose. We may compensate for this up to a point by imbuing him with a love of competition itself. But that can't mean a love of fairness, of *fair* play, or else he loses his virgin egoism: his real love is *winning* competitions—since only that provides payoff for him in his currency. The game may add spice but seeing another win cannot provide joy. The risk of moral martyrdom exists, but is surely less likely than the gains just described.

Notice that free-enterprise capitalism, unless handicapped by a pejorative *definition*, is equally possible for the egoist and the altruist; only particular empirical evidence could show it to be immoral. Competition *per se* is not immoral, and I think the evidence is that it isn't automatically *conducive to* immorality. But the *way* it's taught in a particular society may easily (and often is such as to) put winning above fairness, in which case it becomes immoral.

So the argument for the individual is that there *are* gains in expectancy of satisfaction to be realized from conversion to altruism. The older and richer and meaner the individual is, the more stable and inegalitarian his society, and longer and costlier the conversion process, etc., the less compelling these reasons are—in the absence of conversion by others. But for his *children*, whose future cannot be guaranteed, the argument here decisively caps that given before. That is, morality is something to accept on condition that others accept it too, because the intrinsic cost is zero or negative (ignoring the costs of the treatment) and the expectancy gains are extensive. And one is justified in imposing moral education on children just and only because the cost is (or appears to be) near-zero.

XII. The Argument from Social Evolution

What evolves in evolution is not thereby necessarily or even probably good. But the preceding considerations show that morality in a society is a survival characteristic, and on the usual assumptions *and given its power over social behavior*, we would expect to find the Axiom of Equality showing up, explicitly or implicitly, fairly often in social codes. The fact that we do find this provides some evidence of its value to a society. The mythology attached to it varies, the support may come from hellfire or inspiration, but one way or another societies develop it, not as a theorem following from necessary religion but as a necessity which may yield religion as a necessary rationalization. In short, the latent function of ethics is survival (etc.), even if its manifest function is doing the work of the Lord, avoiding the inferno, or following in the Buddha's steps.

In the animal kingdom, similar arguments bear on the so-called maternal instinct and transfamily extensions of it. Is a herd a group of moral beings? No, though it is a group of beings with behavior patterns that are moral analogues. The barrier to full citizenship lies in the lack of capacity for reasoning about action; some combination of limitations on their language and their intelligence is the trouble. But surely their rights as second-class citizens are partly based on the quasi-morality they exhibit, as well as on the love for them of some people, ecological considerations, and the probability of generalizing cruel behavior toward some sentient beings into carelessness about other people's rights.

XIII. The Economic Arguments

An extension of the division of labor argument provides a powerful argument for ethics. Division of labor itself proves the rationality of having a police force. The drawbacks of police are (1) direct cost, (2) indirect cost of loss of productive labor, (3) corruptibility, (4) incompleteness of coverage, (5) inadequacy of power for some situations. All these defects can be eliminated at a modest one-time cost by internalizing the value system that the police system is supposed to enforce. Conscience is the internalized police force, and it is thus (potentially) a tremendously valuable instrument for the society, in economic terms alone. Of course, as every despot knows, internalizing loyalty to the despot is attractive; hence every democrat should regard control of the police, security and "intelligence" forces as a matter for constant and meticulous supervision.

The second argument from economics comes from the present situation in welfare economics, which always founders on the problem of interpersonal comparison of utilities. As with the Prisoner's Dilemma, the Axiom of Equality provides a solution and enables the whole apparatus of welfare economics to be applied without this hitch. This is perhaps more a convenience than an argument for the Axiom of Equality; but I would prefer to rate it as a heuristic argument. The Axiom so obviously fills a gap that only a bad argument (for value-free science) has kept open, that the subject's integrity and utility demands its use.

XIV. The Argument from Political Theory or Political Philosophy

The arguments for the superiority of democracy as a form of government were excluded from the domain of political science by the empiricists, who have long dominated that field, in the name of the false god of value-free social science. Relieved of that constraint, we can turn back to these arguments again with some interest; for democracy is the political incorporation of the Axiom of Equality. And we find—though many of them bear on relatively specialized aspects of particular incorporations of democracy—a number of general arguments that have some appeal. I have not found any that are not covered by some combination of the arguments I have already provided, but the point has considerable intuitive force—the essence of democracy is egalitarianism, and the weight of our perfectly rational commitment to it carries over to ethics.

XV. The Argument from Jurisprudence

Adding to these powerful and relevant areas of argumentation from which we can call for support for ethics, the arguments for a system of law must be mentioned. The argument for law is overwhelming; and it is practical; and its truth or validity depends only on evidence that comes from the domain of the social sciences. Now what is the relationship between the law and morality? It is clear that they overlap enormously. The two most obvious areas that lie outside the overlap are these: the law goes further into details of conduct where particularity is convenient than ethics does—for example, in specifying the details of traffic rules—and ethics goes further in specifying attitudes ("Thou shalt not covet thy neighbor's wife") because it does not need to restrict itself to the enforceable in the way which is necessary for the law. But these areas of difference are very slight compared to the areas of overlap. And hence the arguments for having a law governing, e.g., contracts (promises), cruelty to children, freedom of speech, abortion, etc., are all arguments for having these matters covered by a moral code. For at the very least there is an empirical case for respecting the law as well as having it; and the moral code is a simplified version of the principles expressed in (lying behind) a great many laws. A system of law works better if it is internalized; an internalized system of law is (most of and mostly) a morality. It is stupefying to realize that a generation of philosophers was content to accept the idea that there could not be good reasons for morality, whereas they were not about to challenge the argument for law.

XVI. The Argument from Sociological and Anthropological Analysis

A crucial feature of sociological and anthropological explanations of cultural patterns is that a distinction has to be made between manifest and latent functions of social institutions, or between the explicit and implicit values they incorporate. This distinction—difficult though it is to define precisely, and implement with a high degree of agreement between social scientists—is inescapable once recognized in a single instance, as, e.g., in the case of religion, where so much has been made of it. Let us apply it to morality, to the code of ethics that a society, or a large part of a society, adopts. Then we see that it is possible to analyze, experiment, investigate, and in other ways determine the latent function of an ethical code, just as it is possible to do the same with respect to the latent function of a religion. Difficult it may be, but it *is* an empirical matter. Now I have been suggesting that a study of the latent function of an ethical code will reveal that it has a very substantial effect on the probability of survival of members of that group, and hence of the group itself. Suppose that what I say is true. Then we have excellent grounds, using this conceptual distinction from social anthropology, to assert that there is a strong practical reason for society to have an ethical code. Suppose that what I suggest is not correct, namely that there is no latent function served by a moral code; then we have good practical reasons for supposing that it is mere superstitition to adopt one. In either case, it is clear that the social sciences have a critical bearing on the justification of ethics, and in the first case it seems clear that they are in a perfectly good position, using tools they already have (i.e., types of argument with which they are entirely familiar) to actually support an ethical code. For, just as the argument works in the general ethical case, so it can be made to work with a particular ethical code. The latent function of one code may be to increase the chances for survival; of another code, it may be to decrease the chances for survival (or of achieving good health, or some other desideratum of the society). In the case of religion, where the matter has been so extensively discussed, it's often suggested that an important latent function of religion is social cohesiveness, and this function would occur even if the manifest function—in a particular case, this might be the pacification of or obedience to the gods—is wholly illusory. Here we have a *prima facie* case for a religion. If, however, it can be shown that this *prima facie* case revolves around one particular component of the religion, namely the moral code; and that other components of the religion aren't necessary to support the moral code and in fact have quite undesirable side effects, e.g., a tendency to rely on God to solve our problems, or to suppose that injustice on earth will be compensated for in a life hereafter; then one has the makings of a rather good case for an ethical system, regardless of whether it has some intrinsic truth that can be verified by comparison with some external order of reality, in the way that would be appropriate if it were merely a descriptive account of some aspect of the world around us. Morality is a descriptive account of one dimension of the world around us, but the dimension is one that it creates itself, just as every game, including many social games, create their own terminology and reality. The "rights of man" are not to be found by looking at man, or at God, but by reconstructing certain aspects of the relationship between people. Ethics is normative just because it is "designed to" (that is, has the latent function of) recommend(ing) an optimal solution. In this respect, it's no different from any other applied science.

XVII. The Optimal vs.
the Sub-optimal Solution

Just as we have argued that the internalization of law or the police represents a pragmatic gain over the situation where they have external reality only, so we must be open to an argument that some attitudinal shift that goes beyond the one we have discussed might prove to be more powerful than the one so far discussed. We have been talking about the internalization of the Axiom of Equality. The kind of moral attitude that this generates might be described as a morality of respect for others. Others must be considered, considering them is seen as a duty, an obligation, something that ought to be done, and something that one therefore (as an altruist) wants to see done and is willing to do. But one can move to what has often been regarded as a somewhat higher plane than this by moving to a morality of *love* for others. Love for others will, of course, generate respect for others, although the reverse is not the case. The advantage of a morality founded on love—and there have been no lack of prophets to extol its virtues—is that it, so to speak, achieves the benefits of a morality of respect by a form of overkill *and* it also greatly strengthens the case for the individual to adopt such a moral system, because it greatly increases the rewards for the individual when he or she sees other individuals achieving happiness, and especially in situations where that happiness results from the actions of the individual doing the contemplating. The egalitarian is pleased when s/he is able to bring justice about: the humanist in that wider class of cases where pleasure can be produced.

The disadvantage of this approach is that it may simply be impossible for some people to achieve, people who can achieve the morality of respect. However, this might turn out to be only an adult-child difference, and the case could be made that children should be "taught" (i.e., we should try to teach children) the morality of love, hoping that at least the fallback position of the morality of respect would be attained. It might be argued, then, that the optimal solution for mankind is the morality of love; the morality of respect may be somewhat easier to achieve given certain constraints on the lability of adult value systems. The latter then becomes a sub-optimal solution, optimal only given those constraints as fixed. Across several generations, the fixedness of those constraints is obviously reduced, and hence in the long run the morality of love is likely to be the optimal solution. It carries with it an increased vulnerability to the pain of others, but there is no reason to adopt an attitude that makes that pain incapacitating rather than motivating.

XVIII. Conclusion

Whether these arguments for the Axiom of Equality (the morality of respect) and the morality of love go through is of importance in determining whether to accept the particular thesis of this paper. But even if they do not work, the general thesis must still be considered. It seems very queer to suggest that none of the arguments provided in the preceding sections provide grounds for having *some* moral system in the full sense of that term. We would indeed be talking about only a travesty of morality if we were giving merely utilitarian arguments for forms of behavior that ape the actions of a moral being. But we have been giving arguments for the adoption of moral values themselves, i.e., the internal causes of overt behavior. What is distinctive about true morality is that the moral acts spring from moral values to which the individual is committed, values that transcend his or her merely selfish considerations. It is this full-bloodedness that the deontologist finds lacking in the utilitarian system, and it is my hope that the system described here bypasses that instinctive negative reaction, without by-passing the powerful practical considerations that the utilitarian approach commends to us.

NOTES

I appreciate the suggestions on this paper made by Samuel Gorovitz, and by several others, especially Stephen Toulmin, Hans Jonas, John Ladd, and Daniel Callahan. I have endeavored to clarify the paper through their suggestions (and also those of my research assistant Mike Barger).

A few minor comments may be useful. (i) A more extensive treatment of some of the simpler aspects of this approach will be found in the chapter on morality in *Primary Philosophy* (New York: McGraw Hill, 1966). (ii) The incorrigibility of the Axiom of Equality seems very similar to that of the Principle of Inertia (Newton's First Law of Motion). (iii) The other concepts in ethics—virtue, consideration, conscience, integrity, supererogation—can in my view be defined quite satisfactorily for the general purposes of this discussion in terms of equality of rights and the morality here based on it, which directly generates a concept of moral goodness. (iv) This work develops from discussions at Oxford in 1950-1952 with Kurt Baier, then working on a thesis (under Stephen Toulmin) which was to become *The Moral Point of View* (Ithaca, N. Y.: Cornell University Press, 1958). There are of course similarities to later work, such as Rawls, but I regard him as ultimately an intuitionist, while I go for an absolutely solid connection with science. (v) Computers are well on the way to acquiring moral rights and will certainly be capable of moral integrity (with respect to justice) that will put the rest of us to shame. (vi) *Purely* formal principles such as the categorical imperative and other generalizability requirements are partly covered by the Axiom of Equality and partly indefensible. (vii) The present status of ethics as a science is closely comparable to that of clinical psychology—not good as usually practiced, even by the full-timers, but capable of reasonable results already and capable of excellent results in the possible but not highly probable eventuality that rationality gains a better hold (see P. E. Meehl, *Pychodiagnosis*, Minneapolis: University of Minnesota Press, 1974, pp. 225-302). (viii) The appeals to various strands in science given here by no means exhaust the relevant areas. One can include results from the study of behavior genetics, reciprocal inhibition, the tragedy of the commons, intrinsic motivation, behavior self-modification.

1. John Searle, *Speech Acts* (New York: Oxford University Press, 1973).
2. Michael Scriven, "The Exact Place of Value Judgments in Science," in *PSA 1972*, K. F. Schaffer and R. S. Cohen, eds. (D. Reidel Holland, 1974), pp. 219-247.
3. R. B. Braithwaite, *The Theory of Games as a Tool for Moral Philosophy* (New York: Cambridge University Press, 1955).
4. See R. D. Luce and Howard Raiffa, *Games and Decisions* (New York: John Wiley & Sons, 1957), pp. 94-102.

Commentary

Utilitarianism and the Science of Ethics

Amnon Goldworth

THERE ARE SOME OBVIOUS DIFFERENCES between utilitarianism in its original Benthamite form and Michael Scriven's approach. Bentham stressed self-regarding rather than other-regarding interest, and called for the use of sanctions which would artificially harmonize private interest with public interest. Professor Scriven is correct in criticizing utilitarianism as a moral travesty if it constitutes an attempt to establish an optimal strategy for society on strictly prudential grounds. But it is not a travesty of morality if we shift from a self-regarding to other-regarding perspective; that is, if we identify the motives to moral action in terms of benevolence or altruism. Indeed, there are several important considerations introduced by Scriven that will not go through without arriving at a form of utilitarianism. Perhaps Scriven is prepared to accept this conclusion. But, I wish to raise a number of points that, if correct, put his views closer to utilitarianism in its original form than he appears to recognize or acknowledge. I will not discuss Scriven's claim that ethics is a science except to note that in this respect he is keeping company with Bentham who viewed himself as the Newton of morals. Instead, I will concentrate on the Axiom of Equality and the morality of respect.

44

Where Bentham and I part company with Scriven concerns the class of beings who, under the Axiom of Equality, would have equal rights. Bentham supported a form of this axiom by arguing that in the aggregating of individual happiness each should count as one. However, this aggregated class is to include sentient as well as rational creatures. The reason had to do with Bentham's belief that, whether sentient or rational, a creature's "capacity to act in such a way as to substantially affect the interests of oneself and others," as Scriven puts it, is based ultimately on its feelings of pleasure and pain.

It is not particularly important that Bentham's psychology was erroneous or that he was mistaken in his view of pleasure and pain as polar concepts. Indeed, it is not crucial for Bentham's procedure for deciding what is right that we speak of pleasure and pain at all. Preferences will do. But, whether we speak of creatures who have the capacity to behave rationally or creatures who behave instinctively, the actions of both are influenced and accompanied by feelings.

Having spoken, in part, for Bentham, I will now speak for myself. First, it strikes me as a falsehood that animals other than man do not have the capacity to act in the interests of themselves or others. Obviously, they do not have the ability, as man does, to act in the light of reason. But to exclude nonrational creatures on this ground suggests a circularity. On the one hand, rationality is employed to demonstrate a capacity to act in the interests of oneself or others. On the other hand, the capacity to act in the interests of oneself or others is employed to demonstrate that reason is operative.

Second, Scriven observes that, "Ethics is normative just because it is 'designed to' (has the latent function of) recommend(ing) an optimal solution." He also observes that the internalization of the Axiom of Equality generates a morality of respect for others. But it is not at all clear that this view rather than the view that sentient as well as rational creatures have moral rights, and therefore deserve respect, may not be the optimal solution; particularly given indications that our moral sensibilities, which, as Scriven observes, are dependent on an altruistic perspective, cannot flourish if they are not extended to sentient creatures as well.

But what, in specific terms, is the optimal solution? Scriven presents us with a plausible argument for the optimal strategy when society is faced with external or natural or internal .dangers which are serious and may affect anyone. But what is the optimal strategy, which presumably would lead to the optimal solution, under other conditions normally encountered by man and other sentient creatures? Just as altruism calls for optimizing aggregate survival when there is a threat of destruction to the group, so altruism calls for optimizing the aggregate satisfactions of needs and wants where this cannot be maximally achieved by all. Short of an environment in which everyone, quite literally, gets what he or she needs or wants, or everyone, as in the case of the creatures in Huxley's *Brave New World*, get what they want because they have been engineered to want what they get, optimization of satisfactions occurs at a cost of dissatisfaction or submaximal satisfaction for some. Change the word "satisfaction" to "pleasure" and speak of maximizing happiness and you have Bentham's utilitarianism. Change this back to optimizing satisfactions, and you have utilitarianism in more contemporary dress.

A different way of putting this point is the following. The altruist must want to optimize social good, however understood, since there are no boundary conditions which allow him to be concerned with the good of one to the exclusion of the good of others. The altruist must also want to eliminate gratuitous bad where this refers to more than the practical minimum of dissatisfactions. Sacrificing himself or herself for the optimization of the social good is a morally right move for the altruist. But such sacrifice cannot be the right move if it does not optimize the social good. Thus, the altruist is required to analyze the trade-offs between sacrifice and social benefit. And this requires the development of a decision procedure which maps individual goods and bads onto a social good function or indicator. Change the words "good" and "bad" to "pleasure" and "pain" and introduce a hedonic calculus which maps the subjective states referred to by the latter terms onto an aggregate happiness indicator, and you have utilitarianism in its original form. Change it back, and you again have utilitarianism in contemporary attire.

It is of some interest to observe that although the notion of conflicting interest seems inappropriate in an altruistic setting, altruism, in some instances, is like a mirror which reflects back the reverse image of egoistic conflicts. The following anecdote is illustrative. As a young graduate student at Stanford University, I was assigned the task of correcting the written English of a visiting professor from Japan. Unlike some other Japanese visitors, this old gentleman adhered strictly to Japanese manner. As a result, much leaping up and bowing ensued in our encounters. This generated discomfort in me since his actions appeared to put me on a footing of professional equality which I did not at all feel. Yet his behavior indicated a concern of some sort for me which, in turn, generated a strong desire in me to reciprocate. This resulted in a minor crisis each time our meetings were over. Leaping to our feet and bowing to one another, we would head for the narrow doorway where each, in turn, would stop, and gesture to the other to proceed through. Altruism, of a sort, created as much of an impasse as would have occurred had he and I been egoists. As it was, being bigger and stronger than my companion, I solved the problem, each time it occurred, by gently but firmly pushing him out of the doorway.

One last point before concluding. Scriven asserted that the Axiom of Equality provides a solution to the problem of interpersonal comparisons of utility. I interpret this to mean that the axiom eliminates the need to use cardinal measurements of utilities. What I have already said suggests that this view is incorrect. But, let me spell this out in greater detail. I make four assumptions which are based on Scriven's observations and my own.

1. Everyone is altruistic;
2. Everyone is concerned with optimizing social good, as the aggregate of individual satisfactions, against the backdrop of external, natural, and internal dangers;
3. There are scarcities in natural resources so that all cannot get what they want;
4. Some are physically or mentally or materially better off than others.

Under these assumptions there will be occasions when those that are better off will be interested in giving a fair share, however this is understood, to those who are worse off in order to optimize social good. And similarly, the worse off will be interested in fair rather than excessive compensation. To determine such redistributions will require interpersonal comparisons. Indeed, unless altruism automatically generates only *pareto optimal* choices, I cannot see how interpersonal comparisons can be avoided.

In conclusion, I would say that if Scriven has provided persuasive grounds for the claim that ethics is a science, further examination indicates that the ethics in question is an updated version of utilitarianism.

2

Are Science and Ethics Compatible?

John Ladd

THE TRADITION THAT SCIENCE is one of the highest, if not the highest, human enterprise goes back to the ancient Greeks and has continued virtually unchallenged to the present. At one time, perhaps, the exaltation of science was accepted only by a minority of insiders. But today it is obviously part of the public faith of the scientific establishment, if not of our society at large. As Philip Handler puts it, "The search for truth is man's noblest enterprise."(1) Further, scientists comprise "The world's greatest army devoted to good works... for the scientists attack falseness of every kind and accept no doctrine until the last doubt has been disposed of."(2) In this paper, I want to discuss some philosophical questions concerning the supposedly superior moral status of scientific activity.

The attitude I want to examine may be illustrated by an anecdote. Once I attended a course in genetics in which some of the moral issues raised by recent advances were examined. During a discussion of serious genetic defects, the question of what should be done with newborn infants suffering from such defects was raised. Should an infant born with Tay-Sachs or Lesch Nayan disease be kept alive at all costs as long as possible? Yes, said one student. Why? asked the instructor.

Answer: by keeping the infant alive, scientists would be able to make fruitful observations of the development of the disease, thereby advancing our understanding of the disease and of genetic diseases in general.(3)

I do not think that this attitude is atypical: prolonging a miserable existence is good for science and science is good. Our universities and medical schools constantly indoctrinate students with the idea that they have a moral duty to advance science and that this duty takes priority over other considerations in their professional conduct. Their role gives scientists special rights over others, such as experimental subjects, as well as a right to a substantial part of society's resources. The advancement of science is considered more important than almost anything else.

My aim in this paper is not to denigrate science as such, or scientists. Rather, it is to examine critically the lofty claims made on behalf of science, claims that might be subsumed under the title "Ideology of Science." The doctrine that the pursuit of science is a highly moral activity is used to justify many of the demands made on behalf of science, both on individuals and on society at large. Individuals with scientific talents and training are expected to dedicate their lives to the cause of science as a "vocation," for which they are honored and rewarded. Society, for its part, is expected to make huge expenditures for the advancement of science. A mark of the exalted status assigned to science is the common assumption that moral considerations of other sorts—honesty, integrity, compassion, social responsibility, and justice—must give way to the objectives of scientific research in case of conflict.

Can these claims to special and superior moral status be substantiated? And if they can, what follows? But if they cannot, what follows instead? Are ethics and science compatible or incompatible? In what sense might they be incompatible?

The first part of this paper will consist of an examination of the theoretical basis for the kind of claims just mentioned: for a proper evaluation of these claims is a necessary preliminary to any attempt to answer the question of the compatibility of science and ethics.

The approach I shall adopt toward these claims is skeptical. The claims for a moral status for science will be evaluated on their own terms rather than by reference to extrinsic considerations. For, as I shall try to show later, it is logically possible to refute a set of moral claims without having to deploy positive counterarguments against them. Hence it is not necessary, for example, .to show that science is evil in order to defeat the moral claims made for it. So, for purposes of this paper, I do not need to dwell on the particular sins of particular scientists or on particular evils that science has ostensibly perpetrated on society.

This general approach to moral claims, which might be called *methodological skepticism*, is in the final analysis logically more devastating to a claim than the deployment of positive counterarguments against it. The latter procedure is weaker for many reasons: it is more dogmatic, since it requires arguing from a preset position; and it ignores the ambiguous nature of the concept of incompatibility as it is used in ethics.

Having assessed the claims of science to be a moral activity, I shall then turn to an examination of the problem of the compatibility of science and ethics. This problem, again, raises many different questions relating to the nature, source, and consequences of ethical compatibility and incompatibility. As we shall see, one kind of incompatibility, which I call "contingent incompatibility," between certain specific requirements of science and certain specific requirements of morality is not inconsistent with the claims of science to be a moral activity. In contrast, another kind of incompatibility, which I call "logical incompatibility," if it can be shown to exist between the claims of science and the claims of morality, has very significant consequences for the relationship between science and ethics.

I do not pretend to offer any definitive answers to the questions I shall discuss. My principal aim is to call attention to some of the issues that need to be explored in answering the question of the compatibility of science and ethics. As a philosopher, I conceive my first task to be to disentangle the theoretical issues that are involved in this question.

We must begin by noting that science, like other institutionally defined activities, roles, and professions, is subject to abuse. There can be evils attendant on how science is pursued, how it is used, or what it is used for. As a social institution, science often leads to interpersonal animosities, jealousies, and deceptions, because of the excessive competitiveness in the contest to be the first to discover something, the race for the Nobel Prize, or the scramble to get into medical school. The institutionalization of science often makes it profitable, or at least tempting, to cut corners morally and legally in the pursuit of science, as in human experimentation. And science, as a source of power, has often been used for unjust political and military purposes, for instance, by the Nazis or by the military in Vietnam. In addition to such moral abuses, scientists sometimes violate the norms of their own professional ethics: they are often guilty of plagiarism, misrepresentation of results, fabrication of evidence, and so on.(4)

Against all these acknowledged evils, one can reply that *abusus non tollit usum* (an abuse does not derogate from the proper use). All these abuses arise out of the institutionalization of science and are not due to the nature of science itself, that is, science *qua* science. The "proper use" of science is for the discovery of scientific truth. In this sense, science must be considered the activity of scientists *qua* scientists, that is, activity in the pursuit of scientific knowledge rather than as a social institution. Although sociological considerations may be important for other reasons, our present concern is with scientific activity as it occurs in observation, experimentation, the construction and testing of hypotheses, and calculations, insofar as they pertain to obtaining scientific knowledge. When we ask about the moral status of science, we refer therefore to this kind of scientific activity, defined by its purpose. Let us call it "science *per se*."

At the risk of oversimplification we might then accept as the supreme practical principle of science *per se* something like the scientific imperative: "Do everything in your power to maximize scientific knowledge!" Insofar as we are concerned with the moral status of science *per se*, we are in effect asking about the moral status of the scientific imperative. Does it have a moral basis? If it does not, is it compatible or incompatible with morality?

I. Liberal Ethics: The Values Approach

Most current discussions of the relationship between science and ethics approach the moral issues involved through a theory of values. The issues are formulated in terms of values, in particular, possible conflicts of values. Science *per se* is assumed to be a value and all the moral problems relating to science are conceived of as essentially questions of the relationship between one kind of value (e.g., science) and other kinds of value.

Thus, for example, it is taken for granted throughout Katz's impressive collection of materials relating to human experimentation that every moral issue concerning experimentation arises out of a conflict of values (or interests) such as the conflict between the interests of the individual subject and the interests of society.(5) In general, the values approach typically construes moral problems as problems of how to reconcile, balance, or weigh multiple, ostensibly conflicting values or interests. Moral problems take the form: what is the optimal or fairest solution? This way of conceiving of moral problems, which might be called the "dogma of liberalism," is implied in Mill's classical utilitarianism, in welfare economics (Arrow's theory of social choice), in Rawls's contractarianism, and in most other liberal theories of value subscribed to by political theorists and social scientists. The job of ethics, according to the liberal theory, is to arbitrate between conflicting values (or interests). Thus, Rawls writes: "Perhaps the principal aim of ethics is the formulation of justifiable principles which may be used in cases wherein there are conflicting interests to determine which one of them should be given preference."(6) In Perry's words, the subject-matter of ethics is the "moral economy."(7)

Basic to this conception of ethics is a distinction between two sorts of questions: (1) what has value? (Perry calls this the question of "generic value"); and (2) how should values be ordered? (Perry calls this the question of "comparative value").

The value-theoretical approach in what I have called the liberal theory focuses on questions of the latter sort, which are often conceived of, for example, as questions of distributive justice.

However, the value-theoretical approach to ethics begs important philosophical questions at the outset and forces us to deal with the moral issues in the relation of science and ethics in a misleading way. Thus, it assumes as an unquestioned premise of the argument that science *per se* is a value and as such has a *prima facie* claim to moral status. But this premise is precisely the one at issue, the one that we need to examine critically. Not only is the premise questionable, but the value-theoretical framework forces us to view the relevant moral issues as simply issues of adjudicating between values (or interests), that is, as questions of comparative value. The net effect is to trivialize the important issues.

The appeal of the liberal model of ethics lies, of course, in its catholicity, its comprehensiveness and all-inclusiveness. Almost anything that people want can be counted as a value.(8) For Perry, for example, any object of any interest to any person is a value. In this inclusive sense, not only are science, art, health, honesty, self-esteem, and freedom values, but so also are money, drugs, fame, and cockfighting. The key point should not be missed: as values, every one of them must in principle be taken into account in the ethical decision process and, in this sense, every value has what might be called a *prima facie* moral status. Essentially, and in practice, the distinction between real and apparent values, or true and false values, is blurred if not repudiated outright. (In view of the variety of theories of value, some qualification of this last statement may be required. No liberal theoretician, however, is likely to maintain that science is an apparent or false value!)

The liberal approach to ethics achieves much of its plausibility from an equivocation on the term "value." Without going into theory of value in detail, it suffices to point out that the term "value" is used in two quite different senses. First, it is used to refer to things, or kinds of things, of value, e.g., material or immaterial goods such as health, knowledge, or friends. Perry's theory that value is any object of any interest to anyone and hedonism are general theories of value in this sense. Second, "value" is also used to refer to a person's (or group of persons') beliefs about what has value (in sense one). In the second sense, we speak of *someone's* values, meaning, for example, his aspirations or ideals; and when doing so we must always specify *whose* values we are referring to, e.g., Smith's or Jones's values, Mormon values, middle-class American values, or a scientist's values. For to be a value in this sense always means to be valued by someone, just as to be a belief means to be believed by someone. The situation is complicated by the fact that we also use the phrase "value for X" ambiguously, meaning that something *is* good for X, e.g., a particular medical treatment, or that X *believes* that something is good. The first proposition is objective in the sense that the value obtains regardless of who believes or asserts it, whereas the second proposition is subjective or relative in the sense that it depends on someone's believing it. By the same token, whenever we speak of values in the first sense, we *ipso facto* agree to the valuableness of what we are talking about; whereas, when we speak of values in the second sense, we can and often do mean to disown them; for example, we can talk about Mormon values without accepting them.

It should be clear that these two senses of value generate two entirely different kinds of conflict of values. A conflict of the first kind pertains only to elements that are in themselves truly and genuinely valuable (regardless of what anyone thinks). A resolution of the conflict does not require the denial of the valuableness *per se* of any of the conflicting elements; it simply requires an ordering of them, a harmonizing, balancing, or ranking. Although X and Y are both values, in situation S, X has *more* value than Y. It is important to note that the need to order values occurs only when an individual (or group) has to choose between two values or two good things—between life and freedom.

A conflict of values in the second sense is logically quite different; it is essentially a conflict of beliefs or attitudes. Here the resolution of the conflict entails the rejection of one of the conflicting values, just as in general the resolution of a conflict between two beliefs entails the rejection of one of them. An example of a conflict of value-beliefs would be a disagreement about the rightness of blood transfusions between, say, a Jehovah's Witness and a Unitarian. A conflict of this type cannot be resolved by "balancing"; it can only be resolved through persuasion, the use of force, or some other measure that results in the giving up of one value-belief and the adoption of the other.

As I have said, the liberal usually tries to reduce all conflicts to the first sort. He tries to take care of the second kind of value conflict by turning a conflict of opinions into a conflict of interests. In order to make this move plausible, however, he has to make an additional assumption, namely, that everyone's opinion about value, regardless of logical incompatibility, is *per se* something of value because, say, it is a reflection of interest. The reduction of beliefs, commitments, concerns, and ideological loyalties to interests is perhaps a politically expedient move in a democracy, where it is necessary to blunt the impact of ideological differences. For obvious reasons, that kind of move takes the impact out of radical criticisms of our society. But the interpretation of the issue of science and ethics along these lines, i.e., as an occasional conflict of value (*read* interest), as with many other basic ideological conflicts, solves the problem by sweeping it under the carpet.

There are also ethical objections to the reduction of conflicts of value-beliefs to conflicts of values or interests. The reduction trivializes important moral differences between people. Not only does it blind us to the seriousness with which people adhere to their ethical beliefs but, by assimilating deeply held ideological differences to differences of taste, it also represents a supercilious and disparaging attitude toward people with whom one has serious ideological disagreements. There are other ethical objections to the identification of value-beliefs with interests (values, sense 1.) For example, it leads to an entirely fallacious notion of moral evil. In the liberal view moral evil is, as it is for the Aristotelian-Thomist, simply the choice of a lesser good over a greater good. Thus, one could say of Southam's injection of patients with live cancer cells without their consent, that what he did was wrong, because he preferred the good he hoped to achieve through his scientific experiment, a lesser good, over the greater good of "self-determination" of his subjects: both things were good, but one was comparatively better than the other. His mistake was one of ordering.

But moral evil is often something more radical than this; when, for example, it involves denying the goodness of what is good and the evilness of what is evil. Like Aristotle's vicious man who does not know what is right, the Nazi doctors were vicious, not simply because they preferred a lesser good to a greater good, but because they saw nothing wrong in what they were doing. The student mentioned at the beginning of this paper saw nothing wrong in prolonging the life (and suffering) of an infant merely for scientific purposes. It is simply not enough to say that it was a mistake in ordering or in priorities.

The whole issue of science and ethics comes into a new light once it is recognized that the relationship might involve more than occasional conflicts of values that are resolvable by a proper ordering. A possible conflict between science and ethics, either in general or in particular situations, might be more basic than a conflict of values or interests. It might be a conflict between what is moral and what is immoral, or between different conceptions of morality, and so on. Underlying all these possible conflicts is the notion of incompatibility. Therefore, our next task will be to examine this notion as it applies in ethical discourse.

II. Two Kinds of Incompatibility of Value

The two conceptions of conflicts of values just mentioned arise out of two different kinds of incompatibility, which I shall call "contingent" and "logical" incompatibility, respectively. Generally, contingent incompatibility obtains when two states of affairs (or actions) that are desired or desirable cannot, for contingent reasons, coexist. Two values (or duties) conflict—are contingently incompatible—inasmuch as they cannot both be realized (or performed) because of particular, contingent circumstances.

Logical incompatibility, on the other hand, holds between the assertion of a value and the denial of that value. In this sense, logical incompatibility is like a straightforward contradiction. The position that, for example, extramarital intercourse is wrong, is logically incompatible with the position that it is not wrong. Note that we are speaking here of the *negations* of moral propositions, not of assertions of the opposite. The negation of "*X* is wrong" is "*X* is not wrong," and the negation of "*X* is good" is "*X* is not good." To assert to someone who says "*X* is wrong" that *X* is right, or to someone who says "*X* is good" that *X* is bad, is not, strictly speaking, a denial. It is a counterassertion. Assertions and counterassertions are not logically incompatible in the sense intended here.

Contingent incompatibility is the source of moral and practical dilemmas of one sort or another: not only conflicts of interest and of value, but also conflicts of obligations, conflicts of loyalties, and so on. The dilemma faced by Sartre's young man who had to choose between joining the Resistance movement and staying home and taking care of his mother was due to the contingent incompatibility of the two courses of action: he couldn't do both. In other circumstances the two courses of action might have been compatible, if, for example, the Resistance forces had been located in the vicinity in which his mother lived. Similarly, the troubling dilemma of whether to save the mother or the child arises out of contingent facts about a particular mother and a particular pregnancy; under other circumstances—where pregnancy is normal—there is no dilemma. Again, the need to choose between spending limited resources on treatment or on research arises out of the contingent fact that resources are limited. Indeed, all dilemmas that involve weighing costs and benefits are due to contingent incompatibilities of one sort or another.

Dilemmas like these have both a practical and a logical side.(9) Although many philosophers frequently admit that, as a matter of practical reality, such dilemmas do arise, they mistakenly believe that such dilemmas are also logically absurd, that it is logically impossible for two contingently incompatible courses of action both to be right. They argue that, if I cannot keep one promise without breaking another, then it is not wrong to break one of them. And, by the same token, if I cannot save one life without destroying another, then it is not wrong to destroy one of the lives. Or, returning to our subject, if I cannot pursue a scientific investigation without resorting to deception, and if I have a duty to pursue this investigation, then it is not wrong to deceive. This position is, in my opinion, quite mistaken.

The basic premise in this sort of argument is the principle that X is wrong implies that X is not right and that X is right implies that X is not wrong. This follows from the assumption that opposites like right and wrong, good and bad, have the logical properties of contraries in the traditional square of opposition. In terms of deontic logic: $O(\text{not-}A) \rightarrow \text{not } (OA)$. I have argued elsewhere that this is an unacceptable principle and two distinguished writers have recently joined me in rejecting it.(10) There is no reason for saying that a particular act ceases to be a duty because, for contingent reasons, I cannot perform it, because, say, the performance of some other duty is more pressing. To assert this principle, then, amounts to denying that what Ross calls *prima facie* duties are duties at all. In the case of values, the absurdity of this principle is even clearer: the fact that under particular circumstances I cannot have both freedom and life does not imply that one of them is not a value.

Once it is admitted that it is possible for something to be right or good, that, for contingent reasons, cannot be done or had, some other moral consequences of an act's being right or good can be accounted for, namely, consequences that obtain when the act in question cannot be performed. These might be called "secondary moral consequences." For example, if I have to break a promise because of a conflict of obligations, I should, if possible, try to explain my action to the promisee and make some kind of recompense to him; it would not be inappropriate to say: "I am sorry that I couldn't keep the promise!" Sorrow, remorse, and regret are always appropriate, even if the action in question was unavoidable. The fact that I could not do what I had a duty to do does not wipe the slate clean. Yet that is what the position under attack requires us to believe.(11)

The point of this discussion is that logical incompatibility cannot be derived from contingent incompatibility. The fact that for some contingent reason I cannot do my duty (or avoid doing something wrong), does not imply that it was *not* a duty (or *not* wrong).

Hence a contingent incompatibility cannot be used to prove a logical incompatibility. For example, it is incorrect to infer from the fact that sometimes one has a duty to lie, say, to save a life, that lying is not wrong *per se*. From the contingent incompatibility in this case of saving a life and telling the truth, it does not follow that one of them is not right. I argue that to conclude that it does is unwarranted and that such cases reflect only contingent incompatibilities. One still has a duty not to lie and a duty to save a life, although by the nature of things one cannot do both. Just as one cannot do everything one wants to do, so one cannot do everything that one ought to do. It follows that for contingent reasons sometimes one has a duty to do something that is *per se* wrong, such as to lie or kill. Thus, a contingent incompatibility is neither sufficient nor, as I shall presently show, is it necessary to prove a logical incompatibility. In other words, I do not have to show that an action is right in order to prove that it is not wrong or to show that it is wrong in order to prove that it is not right (not a duty).

The application of the argument presented here to the question of science and ethics should be obvious. From the fact that in particular instances there is a contingent incompatibility between the demands of science and (other?) demands of morality nothing follows whatsoever concerning the general relationship between science and ethics. Since moral requirements are sometimes contingently incompatible with each other, the demands of science might or might not be moral. Contingent incompatibilities prove nothing in that regard. We must therefore look beyond contingent incompatibilities as reflected in particular cases or particular areas for an understanding of the relationship or lack of relationship between science and ethics. In order to do so, we must examine in more detail the notions of logical incompatibility and logical negation.

III. Ethical Negation and Ethical Neutrality

Logical incompatibility, as I have defined it, is a logical relationship between moral beliefs and attitudes or moral propositions, in which one of them is the denial or negation of the other. A few remarks concerning ethical negation are necessary as a preliminary to a discussion of logical incompatibility in connection with the relationship of science and ethics.

The logic of ethical negation has received much less attention than it deserves. This neglect is attributable, in part at least, to the fact that the category of negation is so often mistakenly assimilated to the category of opposites, as I have just pointed out. The concept of ethical negation, on the other hand, is important for an understanding of ethical controversy and ethical differences in general: that is, situations in which one party asserts, for example, that X is wrong, and the other party denies it, asserts that X is not wrong, without making any counterassertion about its rightness.

What we need, therefore, is a theoretical analysis of what a person is doing when he denies the rightness or wrongness of something, that is, when he asserts an ethical negation. And then we need an analysis of how an ethical negation can be supported or established. An adequate treatment of these two questions goes far beyond the scope of this paper. I must therefore limit myself to a few observations.

Let us begin with the most important and interesting ethical negations, namely, those which negate both the rightness and the wrongness of an act or activity—assertions to the effect that something is neither right nor wrong. This category is sometimes referred to as "moral indifference." I prefer to call it "moral neutrality." Aquinas gives as an example picking up a piece of straw while taking a walk. A large proportion of our everyday activities obviously come under this category. There may even be acts or activities that are universally held to be morally neutral.

Many of the most vehement moral disagreements in our society are between those who believe that a certain kind of conduct is wrong (or right) and those who believe it to be morally neutral. One example is the abortion controversy, which is usually between antiabortionists, who hold abortion to be morally wrong, and their opponents, who regard it as morally neutral; the same sort of division exists with regard to extramarital intercourse, pornography, smoking pot, and even racism, torture, the denial of liberty, the refusal of self-determination, ripoffs, and so on. In each of these controversies, one of the parties denies the wrongness of the thing in question without making any counterassertion as to its rightness. It is held to be morally neutral. Indeed, as I have already argued at length, no moral counterassertion would be sufficient to establish the negation of the original moral proposition. The failure to see this point explains why one cannot convince an antiabortionist that abortion is not wrong (morally neutral) by getting him to admit that there might be situations in which, for some special reason, it might be right (for example, in order to save the mother's life).

There are various kinds of assertions of moral neutrality: some are uncontroversial and others are controversial. The uncontroversial cases are those acts or activities that are regarded by all parties as compatible with morality but not required by it (Aquinas's picking up straw). The controversial cases, on the other hand, arise when moral assertions concerning them are logically incompatible, or when one party holds that the act or activity in question comes under the mantle of morality while the other party denies it. The claim that science is a moral activity clearly involves a controversial kind of assertion.

The positions that scientific activity *per se* is morally neutral or, on the other hand, that it is in some sense a moral activity, say, that it is morally right, morally valuable, or morally worthy are, of course, logically incompatible.

One might ask: what difference does it make how we answer this question, especially since it is framed in such general terms? One consequence of accepting science as a moral activity is that it would then be possible to have a moral justification for doing some things for the advancement of science that require the violation of certain ordinary precepts of morality; for example, the duty to advance science might, in certain cases, override the duty of truthfulness in the same way that the duty to save a life might, in certain cases, override the duty of truthfulness. On the other hand, if science *per se* is morally neutral, then there could be no such justification for overriding ordinary moral requirements like the duty of truthfulness.

IV. How is Moral Neutrality Established?

Before turning to the question of whether science is morally neutral, a few further remarks are necessary concerning the logic of ethical negations. It is possible to give only a brief outline of the logical principles that I shall use: a full exposition and justification of these principles must be given elsewhere. Basically, the form of argumentation used to establish the moral neutrality of an act or activity is, like all ethical argumentation, dialectical. In this regard, my conception of ethical argumentation is quite similar to that of Perelman and Olbrechts-Tyteca in their book, *The New Rhetoric: A Treatise on Argumentation.*(12)

The basic rule for establishing moral neutrality is what I call the *onus probandi* rule. According to this rule, the *onus probandi* in ethical disputes always rests on the person who asserts something to be morally right or wrong, good or evil. He must always be prepared to say what makes it right or wrong, good or evil, when and if his assertion is challenged. If he cannot meet the challenge by giving a reason or if the reason he gives is unacceptable (false or unfounded), then the thing in question must be presumed to be morally neutral. There is a kind of presumption of "innocent until proved guilty"— "neutral until proved right or wrong"—that provides the framework of ethical discourse. The reason is that if there is nothing to make an act or activity right or wrong, good or evil, then for logical reasons, it cannot be right or wrong, good or evil. If reasons cannot be given, it must be presumed that there are none.

It follows from this rule, as outlined, that appeals to self-evidence, intuitions, gut-feelings, or authority, i.e., *ipse dixits* of various sorts, are an *ignoratio elenchi*, or beside the point. For none of these *ipse dixits* can function as a right-making or wrong-making characteristic. There are, of course, other reasons for rejecting them as premises in an ethical argument.(13)

The dialectical nature of ethical argumentation is reflected in the fact that it proceeds developmentally, through a series of assertions and challenges. Unlike some other intellectual procedures, such as the solving of puzzles, the procedure involved here does not start from a question or a state of doubt. It always begins with an assertion or claim, which in turn is subjected to challenge. As the dialectic develops, if a challenge cannot be met, the original assertion loses its support and is thereby defeated, or negated. (The analogies to law are obvious: if a claim cannot be defended when challenged, then it must be rejected.) On the other hand, if the challenges are met, then the assertion in question may be regarded as established.

It is clear that in adopting this procedure we are using a logical rule that is inconsistent with the ordinary rule of formal logic known as the fallacy of denying the antecedent, i.e., fallacious inference from the falsity of the premises of an argument to the falsity of the conclusion. The new rule is in that sense clearly incompatible with the rules, say, of an extensional logic. That is why the present procedure is called "dialectical."(14)

In defense of the *onus probandi* rule, as presented here, I would argue that this is the natural, normal way we use to refute moral claims of one sort or another. Since I have already excluded the possibility of arguing from opposites, that way is not open to us. A purely negative argument must operate differently, e.g., by the *onus probandi* rule. Consider, for example, how you would argue against someone who claimed that walking on the cracks on a sidewalk was morally wrong. Would not, in the end, the only argument be a question: why should it be wrong? For want of a reason, the claim collapses. (To say, in response, that it will break your grandma's back is not a good reason simply because it is empirically false.)

Applying the *onus probandi* rule to the claim that scientific activity is a moral activity means that we must begin by asking: why? what makes it moral? And then, we must scrutinize each of the answers in turn, weighing its credibility—its empirical confirmability and warrant. Considering the immensity of the present subject and the generality of the claim, it will be impossible to deal with the question of the morality of science in the detail that it deserves. Therefore, what follows must be viewed as programmatic rather than definitive.

With this proviso, there seem to be two different kinds of argument that need to be considered for the position that science is a moral activity. The first argues from the almost invariable benefits of scientific knowledge and the second argues from the intrinsic worth to man of scientific activity considered as an intellectual activity. I shall discuss each of these arguments in turn.

V. Argument from the Universal Benefits of Science

We may regard scientific activity as a kind of intellectual activity aimed at producing scientific knowledge. In this sense, science is what Aristotle called a *poiesis*—a making or production—rather than a *praxis*—an activity valued for its own sake.(15) (Of course, it might be both, as Plato thought when he included science under things valued both for their own sake and for the sake of their consequences.) When regarded in this light, the value of scientific activity is a function of the value of its product, scientific knowledge. Accordingly, a good scientist is someone who produces good science; a worthwhile scientific project is one that leads directly or indirectly to good science; good scientific hypotheses, experiments, and observations are good if and only if they lead to good scientific results. People, their actions, thoughts, and relationships—all their activities in relation to science—are evaluated in terms of their scientific productivity. As in other examples of productive activity, the personality and motivation of the producer, and his moral character, are, strictly speaking, irrelevant to the quality of the product. The moral quality of the activity derives from the moral value of the product, and it is assumed as far as science is concerned that the product is always valuable!

One way of stating the argument in question is to say that all scientific knowledge is useful, either directly or indirectly, by leading to other scientific knowledge which in turn is useful. And in the long run scientific knowledge itself is almost invariably useful for mankind. In this regard science is like some other good things such as food or health.

It should be observed that the claim for science is quite comprehensive: it applies to *all* science. Other things being equal, scientific knowledge *per se* is good, for there is a high probability that almost any bit of successful scientific activity will turn out to be beneficial. Therefore, in order to vindicate this extreme claim, it is not enough to show that some scientific knowledge, such as certain medical discoveries, has been beneficial in the past. We are asked to accept the proposition that the pursuit of science is invariably worthwhile on the grounds that in the long run it will inevitably lead to worthwhile results. Since the claim to be moral is a wholesale claim, the support for it must be wholesale also.

To support the wholesale claim, its advocates point to spectacular discoveries in the past due to the accidental discovery of something else that had seemed at the time to be trivial or irrelevant. The unpredictability of future scientific discoveries may be granted. The question is whether or not it is sufficient to justify the general claim under consideration. Claims for long-range benefits are notoriously plausible for believers and implausible for nonbelievers. They are like Pascal's wager; you cannot lose. How much of this is blind faith is an open question; surely even the most optimistic defender of science must admit to the largely unempirical basis of his prediction of the inevitable benefits of science.

There are two parts to the hypothesis of expected benefits; first, what might be called the chain-reaction thesis—that one advance in science inevitably leads to further advances of science and that any discovery, however trivial, tends not only to increase the sum total of knowledge but to contribute to the growth of knowledge in depth as well. Whether or not science always develops in this way is a question that is beyond my competence to decide. But the fact that in some areas, such as molecular biology, one discovery has led to another cannot be used to establish the more general and all-encompassing thesis that any bit of scientific knowledge will be useful in the advance of science.

The second part of the hypothesis is that the scientific knowledge acquired will be beneficial to mankind. Here we are asked to consider the long-range rather than the short-range benefits. Nuclear physics, it is true, may have brought us the atomic bomb and the tragedy of Hiroshima, but we are asked to disregard them and to think instead of the long-range benefits from the use of nuclear energy in more constructive areas. The harmful side effects of scientific discoveries are systematically discounted.

The claim that science almost invariably brings benefits to mankind raises further questions: what kinds of benefits does it bring? It is easy to see that certain medical advances are good for mankind, although many of these advances—the elimination of certain diseases—create new social problems, such as overpopulation. It is not easy to know where we stand concerning the costs and benefits to society at large of much of science.

I suspect that underlying the optimistic view of science is an argument somewhat like the following: (1) The more we can control natural processes, the better it is for mankind; for then we can bend nature to our will and use it for our own welfare. (2) Science gives us progressively greater control over nature. (3) Therefore, science is good for mankind. This kind of argument is discussed at length by Passmore in his *Man's Responsibility for Nature.* He calls it the Baconian-Cartesian approach to nature, which he traces to the earlier Stoic-Christian doctrine that nature exists to serve man.(16) The argument that whatever is useful for man is good and that science is useful for man, QED, is so slippery that only someone already convinced would find it plausible.

In sum, it is not very difficult to think of many unanswerable questions regarding the thesis of the invariable beneficial character of science, if it is taken as a universal and all-encompassing claim. It seems more plausible to suppose that science *per se* is morally neutral and that sometimes it is beneficial and sometimes not. Indeed, the same bit of scientific information may at one time be beneficial, and at other times injurious.

Other questions appear at this point: for example, whether certain kinds of scientific endeavors may not themselves be intrinsically moral or, on the other hand, intrinsically immoral. Logically some of the activities we call science may involve reference to the purposes for which they are pursued, for example, science in the area of biological warfare or behavior control. But an adequate treatment of these issues would require a more extensive discussion of what science is, something that I am not prepared to undertake here. In any case, we may tentatively conclude that the benefits-to-mankind argument has serious holes.

VI. Argument from the Intrinsic Value of Scientific Activity

We still have to consider the other half of the argument for the moral value of scientific activity, namely, that science as an intellectual activity is good for its own sake. The *locus classicus* for this position is, of course, Book X of Aristotle's *Ethics*. I need not repeat the arguments; the main contention is that science (*theoria*) is a distinctly human activity and makes men like the gods.(17) Later versions emphasize the concepts of self-fulfillment, self-realization, perfecting human nature, and so on. All of them maintain that "Science is man's noblest pursuit." Not only is science what distinguishes man from the animals but it also distinguishes the civilized world from the world of the barbarians, and makes us morally superior to the cave man and to primitive people in general.

I find all these conceptions distressingly vague and confused. It is easy to understand that scientific discovery and creativity, or simply the possession of scientific knowledge, might be highly satisfying, exhilarating, exciting, moving, awesome, and wonderful in many ways that would be of great value to many individuals. But in this regard scientific activity is not unique; music, art, and other sorts of cultural activities have the same features. Furthermore, excitement is not restricted to scientific discoveries like that of the double helix; exploits like Lindbergh's flight across the Atlantic are equally exciting. Creativity in the arts may be as rare and wonderful as it is in the sciences. Mozart is not second to Newton in this regard. There is no reason why science should have the first place in things of the human spirit as Aristotle thinks it has. In any case we need further argument to convince us that science has a morally superior status that is in some respects unique.

At this point, one is tempted to ask: what *kinds* of arguments would be convincing, and what would they prove? Since we have separated the argument from intrinsic value from the argument from benefits to mankind, we must be careful not to slip from one of these arguments to the other when one of them begins to appear weak. Panegyrics apart, a survey of the history of philosophy, including philosophers like Plato and Spinoza, indicates that most of the arguments for the intrinsic value of science conceive of it as bringing salvation or liberation for the possessor. Possibly this kind of rationale for science may be out of date, if one considers the highly technical nature of modern science.

Obviously, a much more detailed study of these arguments and of other possible ones would be required before reaching any sort of definitive conclusion. Two preliminary philosophical questions might be mentioned that relate to the question of the intrinsic value of scientific activity. First, one might ask whether or not some sort of distinction ought be drawn between types or realms of values (moral values and spiritual values); if so, then one might admit that science is not a moral value, but nevertheless claim that it has an intrinsic value of a very high order (like art or religion)? Perhaps that is what is meant by calling it "man's noblest pursuit."

Closely related is the second question: does not the exaltation of science as a moral activity in itself reflect an élitist conception of ethics? Historically, as in the case of Plato, the scientist often regarded himself as a member of an ethical élite and not of *hoi polloi*; perhaps he ought to be regarded as a secular saint or an intellectual hero. One could well ask whether or not this kind of superior status is an acceptable ethical category.

To conclude this part of the paper, I want to stress that all that I have tried to do here is to indicate what kinds of questions someone who advocates the position that science *per se* is a moral activity ought to be prepared to answer. If these questions cannot be answered satisfactorily, we must conclude that science *per se* is morally neutral.

VII. Logical Incompatibility Between
Conduct-Systems

We now come to our last question. If science *per se* is not a moral activity, as I have tentatively concluded, then is it logically compatible with morality (simply morally neutral), or is it logically incompatible with it? If it is logically incompatible, then some of the things required by pursuit of science, such as the scientific imperative, would be inconsistent with the requirements of morality. Does the scientific imperative require the *denial* of some of the precepts of morality?

In order to understand the issue involved, a few further observations concerning logical incompatibility will be required. What we need to show is that the acceptance of one set of precepts entails the denial of another set of precepts. For example, science (in the sense of what is prescribed by the scientific imperative) and morality would be logically incompatible if the scientific imperative meant that certain morally wrong acts or activities are not morally wrong and that certain morally neutral acts or activities are required to be done or omitted. Underlying the notion of logical incompatibility is the systematic character of "systems" like morality and the scientific ethos. By their "systematic character" I mean that they comprise sets of precepts, rules, principles, and categories that are interrelated logically through relationships of derivation, and so on.(18)

The way in which the notion of logical incompatibility functions can be understood most easily if we examine it in connection with moral conduct in the playing of games. Many games, especially competitive ones, permit or even require acts that are ordinarily prohibited by morality, for example, hitting, deceiving, or "doing one's opponent in." Such acts, although *per se* wrong morally, cease to be wrong when performed in the game. In James's words, while playing a game one goes on a "moral holiday." There is a kind of "suspension of the ethical," to use another well-known phrase, even in a supposedly tame game like croquet! The rules for games such as boxing, poker, and wrestling, often are, strictly speaking, logically incompatible with morality. Not only is there a logical incompatibility between the respective rules relating to overt acts, but also with regard to their general evaluation of conduct and of persons. A "good" poker player excels at deceiving others; a "good" boxer is one who knocks out his opponent.

It might be contended that the motive makes a difference; in playing a game the motives for performing certain acts are different from those in "real life." In the game, one player hits another only in order to win the game, rather than to hurt him. In fact, however, if one distinguishes between actual motives and supposed motives, it is clear that being "in a game" is often used to cover up bad motives; being in a game provides a good excuse for undesirable behavior. For example, one can legitimately lose one's temper at one's opponent in a game; in fact, it may help one to win. It is only too obvious that people often use the game as an outlet for their suppressed feelings of hostility and aggression or, as the case may be, for their greediness or suppressed sexual desires. All of this, however, simply confirms my thesis, namely, that things are permitted in games that are forbidden in real life: the ethical is suspended.

There is indeed a trivial sense in which conduct in compliance with the rules and objectives of a game might be construed as moral: a player might have entered into the game for moral reasons of one sort or another—through having promised to play the game, or in order to make someone else happy. In such cases the derivatively moral character of game-playing might make some of our examples cases of contingent rather than logical incompatibility. For present purposes, let us disregard ramifications of this sort.

The saving grace is, of course, that playing a game is restricted activity; it is circumscribed as to time and place, the role that it plays in a person's life, the seriousness with which it is undertaken, and the kind of injuries permitted. (If one includes dueling and Russian roulette, the injuries might be considerable!) The moral holiday that one takes in playing a game is ordinarily a brief one.

Nevertheless, disregarding these limitations, rules relating to playing a game (of these sorts) and those relating to morality are strictly speaking logically incompatible; that is, within the game acts are permitted (and approved) that are prohibited by morality and acts permitted morally are forbidden (and disapproved) in the game. We are dealing here with logical, not contingent incompatibility, for they involve two different and logically incompatible sets of rules, standards, and criteria for the evaluation of conduct. I shall refer to such a set of rules, standards and criteria of evaluation as a "conduct-system," where "conduct" is intended to designate not only acts and activities but also attitudes, purposes, goals, motives, and all the other kinds of things that are subject to prescription and evaluation in the context of action.

There are many different varieties of conduct-system in this broad sense. They differ in structure and in their interrelationships. Some systems are highly structured and articulated (such as chess); others are vague and fuzzy (such as etiquette). Some systems are open systems and others are closed. They are closed in the sense that there are decision procedures by which it can be determined what does and what does not belong to the system. Morality and law are typical instances of open conduct-systems; games, on the other hand, are typical instances of closed conduct-systems.

One variety of conduct-system that is particularly noteworthy consists of those conduct-systems that make absolute and categorical demands on a person's conduct and that, as such, have no built-in limitations like those possessed by games. Such conduct-systems are sometimes called "alternate moralities," "ideologies," or "value-systems." Elsewhere I have called them "moral codes." (19) Such conduct-systems would include the conduct-systems of the Mayans, Nazis, Hindus, Navahos, and so on. Since each of these systems claims absolute allegiance, as it were, they are logically incompatible with each other; for the acceptance of the precepts and norms of one entails the denial of the precepts and norms of the other, if only in the sense that the denial is a denial of the absoluteness of another system's claims.

The essential difference between unrestricted conduct-systems and games is that the former are mutually exclusive, unconditional, and absolute. They demand that their rules and principles be given priority over other rules and principles, personal preferences, and so on. Therefore in an important sense it is logically impossible to be a good Mayan and, say, a good Christian; although, by contrast, it is possible for both a Mayan and a Christian to play the same game. The reason is that most people are willing to subordinate the demands of a game to the demands of morality (or their supreme conduct-system).

It is impossible in the present paper to provide a complete analysis of the notion of logical incompatibility that is involved here; for to do so would require a thoroughgoing analysis of the logical structure of systems of this type. As I have already suggested, systems like natural moralities are open systems and the relationship between various elements in the system is loose and variable. Consequently, there are in actuality overlappings and crossings that make fruitful communication between adherents of natural alternate systems entirely feasible. The more structured and closed a system, the more stringent is the logical incompatibility between the elements of that system and those of another system. Thus, some versions of utilitarianism, which represent closed systems of this type, are more likely to comprise elements that are logically incompatible with other supreme conduct-systems.

As I have suggested, science may be conceived as a conduct-system, that is, as a system of rules, principles, standards, and evaluations based on the scientific imperative. As such, in comparison to "natural moralities," the system is relatively closed. If it is established that its requirements are not moral requirements, as I have suggested might be the case, then we must ask whether this system is or is not logically incompatible with morality. If it is, we must ask whether it is incompatible with morality only in the restricted sense in which some games are incompatible with it or in the broader sense, in which, say, Mayan cannibalism is incompatible with morality. The last question amounts to asking: is the ideology of science an alternative morality, a substitute for ordinary morality?

In view of the slipperiness of the subject, it is difficult to find any clear-cut, systematic statements of the position which we would have to examine in order to be able to answer these questions. Writers on science who make exalted claims and demands for science are not at all clear about what they are trying to do. Hence, at this point, it is easier to leave the reader with a set of questions to be answered rather than with speculative conclusions. The only thing that can be said in this regard is that the categorical claims and demands made on behalf of science make sense in general only if they are understood as part of a supreme conduct-system based on the scientific imperative. If that is so, then the legitimation of deception, abridgment of liberty or privacy, and so on, as approved, advocated, and practiced for the sake of science is an essential, rather than an accidental, feature of the scientific conduct-system. More likely than not, then, we are faced with a set of demands and claims that are logically incompatible with ordinary morality. The ideology of science asks us, then, to give up our old morality and to accept a new one—the morality of science.

The denial of the absolute claim for science, what I have called the "ideology of science," by no means entails that science *per se* is immoral or even that it is for the most part immoral. It is quite possible to accept science *per se* as morally neutral. If science is morally neutral, like all other morally neutral activities, it is subject to the constraints of morality. In particular, when the scientific enterprise demands that certain moral considerations be set aside in the interests of the advancement of science, the demand should be rejected as immoral. In a sense, therefore, we are dealing with a rather strong requirement; for it appears to call into question the morality of many scientific enterprises. Most important of all, however, is the obligation that it imposes on all scientists to reflect on the moral implications of what they are doing in general, and in particular and in detail. A scientist must always be prepared to answer the question: what are you trying to find out? why? and for what purpose? In this regard the appeal to self-evidence or intuition is not enough; indeed, as I have argued, it is an *ignoratio elenchi*.

VIII. Why Science Cannot be a Moral Activity

I should like to offer a few observations in closing on why science cannot be a moral activity in itself. My purpose here is to provide an explanation of the moral neutrality of science for which I have already argued. In my view, there are certain key elements missing in science that are essential for morality. Clearly, what I have to say in this regard is based on my own conception of morality. It is not possible to defend this conception of morality here, although I think that a detailed defense is possible. Indeed, according to the *onus probandi* rule mentioned earlier, the conception would be legitimate only if I can provide good reasons for accepting it and I believe that I can do so, although not in the present essay. Accordingly, my remarks may be taken hypothetically, that is, if a certain conception of morality, which I shall provisionally call Kantian, is valid, then we can see why science cannot itself be a moral activity. (Of course, I do not wish to deny that, like many other things, it can be used for moral purposes.)

To begin with, scientific activity, unlike morality itself, is achievement-oriented. That is, it operates on the principle that the end justifies the means; the end, scientific knowledge, is good; therefore, other things being equal, the means to it are good and ought to be used. I think the case of the defective infant mentioned at the beginning is an example of the application of this principle. (Many other examples may be found in Katz.) The teleological ethics implied here is subject to all the customary objections to that type of ethics. It makes persons, their conduct, and their morality into mere means rather than ends in themselves.

Another difficulty in squaring science and morality is that they employ entirely different categories. Science and the norms governing scientific activity make no place for the essential categories of morality, such as the categories of person, motive, social relationship, and responsibility. The concept of a person, for example, which is basic to ethics, is not a possible concept in medical *science* (as contrasted with clinical practice); the subject matter of medical science is always organisms of some kind: diseases, bodies, or organs. That is why doctors are often said to treat cases, not persons. As scientists no other alternative is possible. By the same token, science does not need to use the categories of motive, character, and social relationship in the evaluation of scientific conduct. Unlike morality, success is all that counts in science.

Finally, if we take science as a conduct-system, we find that it excludes the concept of responsibility in the sense of social responsibility.(20) A scientist *qua* scientist is required to ignore the wider ramifications of what he is doing. In this sense, a scientist must be "irresponsible." A good scientist has to give his exclusive attention to what he is doing, to his theorizing and experimentation; he must follow the thread without regard to where it leads. It is easy, therefore, for a scientist to disengage himself from the consequences of his discoveries. He says: "My job is to do science, it is the discovery of truth; what is done with what I discover is someone else's business, not mine." This attitude, which is not atypical, is about as irresponsible as leaving time bombs around to explode.

Morality, as I conceive it, arises out of and is directed toward relationships between persons. Science, on the other hand, is concerned with things, nonpersons. One could say that we are dealing with two entirely different sets of concepts, or languages: the language of morality and the language of science. Moral virtues such as compassion and concern as well as moral vices such as cruelty and indifference are outside the conceptual framework of science. Unlike science, however, these categories do enter into law and politics. And in contradistinction to medical science, they also enter into the practice of medicine.

In our culture there are many spheres of activity, like games, that demand and receive moral immunity of a certain sort. Their moral immunity makes them free from moral criticism and evaluation. This culturally approved mechanism for freeing one-self from moral and social responsibility by taking on a role is pervasive throughout our society. It represents one of the threats to its integrity. The excuse of role-playing was used by those participating in the Vietnam war, even though in private they had doubts about its rightness. It appeared again in the Watergate plots. These political fiascos have forced us to rethink the question of the immunity of government and its officials from moral accountability. Perhaps the time has come to reexamine the pretensions of scientists to the same kind of immunity that was claimed by our politicians.

NOTES

1. "... and what better basis is there for the moral imperatives which guide our society?" Interview with Philip Handler, reprinted in Jay Katz, *Experimentation with Human Beings* (New York: Russell Sage Foundation, 1972), p. 121. This section of Katz's collection contains many such statements. Further documentation seems unnecessary.

2. *Dictionary of Quotable Definitions* (Englewood Cliffs, N.J.: Prentice-Hall, 1970), p. 514.

3. Precisely the same position is echoed in a letter to *The New York Times Magazine*, June 8, 1975, p. 50.

4. A discussion of the "morality" of institutions may be found in my "Morality and the Ideal of Rationality in Formal Organizations," MONIST 54:4 (October 1970), 488-516. The "bureaucratization" of science is the basic theme of Harvey Wheeler's "Science's Slippery Slope," *The Center Magazine* VIII:1 (January-February 1975), 64-67. "There is hardly any but the bureaucratic way to do contemporary science" (p. 66).

5. The opening sentence of Katz, *Experimentation with Human Beings*, begins: "When science takes man as its subject, tensions arise between two values basic to western society..." (p. 1). Note the play on the word "value," which is noted in the following paragraphs of this paper.

6. John Rawls, "Outline of a Decision Procedure for Ethics," *Philosophical Review* 66 (1957), 177-97. Reprinted in Judith J. Thomson and Gerald Dworkin, *Ethics* (New York: Harper & Row, 1968), p. 59.

7. See Ralph Barton Perry, *General Theory of Value* (Cambridge, Mass.: Harvard University Press, 1926), *passim*. One of Perry's early books was entitled *The Moral Economy* (New York: Scribner's, 1909).

8. In Brian Barry's terms this dogma treats *wants* as the unit of social evaluation. See his *The Liberal Theory of Justice; A Critical Examination of the Principal Doctrines in "A Theory of Justice" by John Rawls* (Oxford: Clarendon Press, 1973), p. 21 and *passim*.

9. This distinction is set forth in greater detail in my "Remarks on the Conflict of Obligations," *Journal of Philosophy* 55 (September 11, 1958) Some of the present discussion makes use of ideas presented in that article.

10. See Michael Walzer, "Political Action: The Problem of Dirty Hands," *Philosophy and Public Affairs* 2:2 (Winter 1973); and Bas van Fraasen, "Values and the Heart's Command," *Journal of Philosophy* 70 (January 11, 1973), p. 166.

11. See Walzer, "Political Action," p. 166. "We know he is doing right when he makes the deal because he knows he is doing wrong. . . . If he is the good man I am imagining him to be, he will feel guilty, that is, he will believe himself to be guilty. That is what it means to have dirty hands."

12. Chaim Perelman and L. Olbrechts-Tyteca, *The New Rhetoric: A Treatise on Argumentation*, J. Wilkinson and P. Weaver, trans. (Notre Dame: University of Notre Dame Press, 1971).

13. "The self-evident, as the criterion of validity, is the authority for discrediting all *argumentation*. . . ." Perelman and Olbrechts-Tyteca, *The New Rhetoric*, p. 464. See also pp. 3, 11, 510.

14. It should be observed that the term "dialectical" is used here in a classical, Aristotelian rather than in a Hegelian-Marxian sense. See, for example, Aristotle, *Topics* 100^{a}30 and *Rhetoric* 1354^a 1-20. Perelman and Olbrechts-Tyteca prefer the term "rhetoric" in order to avoid the Hegelian connotations of "dialectic." For an English-speaking audience, on the other hand, the term "rhetoric" has undesirable connotations, whereas the term "dialectical" is relatively innocuous.

15. Aristotle, *Nicomachean Ethics*, Bk 1, Ch. 1 and Bk VI, Ch. 4.

16. John Passmore, *Man's Responsibility for Nature* (New York: Charles Scribner's Sons, 1974), Chapter I, "Man as Despot."

17. "The life of the intellect is the best and pleasantest for man, because the intellect more than anything else *is* man." Aristotle, *Nicomachean Ethics*, 1178^{a}5.

18. For some of the conceptions used in this section, I have drawn on my work, *The Structure of a Moral Code*. (Cambridge, Mass: Harvard University Press, 1957). For additional remarks on the game analogy, see my "Legal and Moral Obligation," in J. Roland Pennock and John W. Chapman, eds. *Political and Legal Obligation*: NOMOS XII (New York: Atherton Press, 1970).

19. See Ladd, *The Structure of a Moral Code*.

20. I have tried to explain this concept of responsibility—responsibility in the normative sense—in my "The Ethics of Participation" in J. Roland Pennock and John W. Chapman, eds. *Participation*: NOMOS XVI. (New York: Atherton-Lieber Press, 1975).

Commentary

An Alternate Conduct-System

Amnon Goldworth

PROFESSOR LADD'S QUESTION, "Are science and ethics compatible?" is an important one, given the present heavy social investment in science and the considerable impact of modern science on societies. However, there are certain matters in Ladd's approach to this question which require revision.

Ever since the Nazi experience, there has been a concern whether there are questions which science may not raise. I submit that there are no such questions if these, in principle at least, are capable of being answered by scientific procedures. There is nothing in what Ladd calls "science *per se*"—the scientific motive of seeking knowledge or scientific methodology—which allows us to distinguish between acceptable and nonacceptable scientifically answerable questions. Furthermore, there is nothing in the nature of the answers obtained by science which guarantees that they will be used for humane or moral purposes.

Thus, examining science in the abstract will not provide a sufficient answer to Ladd's question. We must look at what a particular form of scientific activity aims to achieve and the means it employs to satisfy this aim. Doing this gives us mixed results. Let me cite one instance. What the Nazis aimed to achieve by scientifically investigating the various means of exterminating human beings was evil. So were the experimental means used to determine the human survival threshold to extremes of cold. Yet, the question of that threshold is a scientific one which is not evil *per se*. Indeed, if means other than inhumane ones had been used by the Nazi scientists, the answers obtained might today be viewed as a positive good. (*Note:* Some of these points are alluded to by Professors Gorovitz and MacIntyre in their paper in this volume in order to reject the internal and external norms distinction accepted by scientists. Although I am persuaded by their argument, I do not believe that what I said requires a commitment to either the scientists or their position.)

In the light of these remarks, it would be better if Ladd's question was considered within a historical perspective, bearing in mind the nature and consequence of the practice of science as institutionalized and sustained by social forces. Some historical perspective is evident in Ladd's references to such matters as human experimentation and science as an alternate conduct-system. These are discussed in the context of contemporary science as evidently practiced in the United States. But a more particularized perspective (or perhaps set of perspectives) would be useful if Ladd's question is to be dealt with adequately. This will become more evident in my discussion of science as an alternate conduct-system.

After some prefatory analysis, Ladd refines his original question by asking: (1) whether scientific activity is only contingently incompatible with morality; (2) whether scientific activity as such is morally neutral but not incompatible with morality; (3) whether scientific activity is logically incompatible with morality; and if so, how. Ladd's strategy is to suggest strongly that scientific activity is morally neutral, thus focusing attention on (2) and (3). He then sharpens the issue by considering the logical incompatibility of scientific activity and morality in the light of the logical incompatibility of games (such as poker and wrestling) and of alternative conduct-systems (such as those of the Mayans or Nazis) and morality.

Although Ladd mainly attends to the issue of logical incompatibility, he does not explicitly decide between (2) and (3). His object is to make clear the kind of questions that anyone must be prepared to answer who "makes an extreme claim for science." However, his observations are influenced by views concerning the relationship between games and morality, on the one hand, and the relationship between alternate conduct-systems and morality, on the other, that are misleading or insufficient.

Morality fulfills human needs as a conflict-reducing or conflict-resolving instrumentality. Games fulfill human needs, but not by reducing or eliminating conflict—at least not directly or intentionally. Indeed, whatever conflict exists in a game is generated by what the game rules permit or require. It is true, as Ladd observes, using James's words, that we take a "moral holiday" in playing games, but only with respect to certain moral rules. One does not kill an opponent in a game of poker. And even in the potentially lethal games of Russian roulette or dueling, one does not load all the chambers with bullets or shoot one's opponent in the back. The moral holiday is permitted because the game rules clearly determine the level and extent of conflict, and this conflict is viewed as morally permissible. If it were not, then it would be banned, as has happened in the cases of dueling and Russian roulette.

Thus, when Ladd remarks that ". . . playing a game (of these sorts) and morality are strictly speaking logically incompatible; that is, within the game acts are permitted (and approved) that are prohibited by morality and acts permitted morally are forbidden (and disapproved) in the game," he overlooks the fact that it is our moral judgment which permits the playing of games. If moral judgment allows for the purported "suspension of the ethical," it is so because it is the game as a whole that comes under our moral scrutiny and not each one of the game rules in free-floating isolation from the others. Whether or not scientific activities are games, what I have said suggests that we could pass favorable moral judgment on a scientific practice which included moves that, in isolation, would be logically incompatible with specific moral imperatives.

This considerably complicates moral assessments of scientific activities. For we no longer can decide, as Ladd does, to morally reject a scientific enterprise merely because some of its actions are logically inconsistent with moral tenets. Rather, it is the enterprise as a whole, involving its plans, purposes, actions, and achievements which requires moral scrutiny.

In discussing a logical incompatibility of morality and alternate conduct-systems, Ladd brings matters to a head by asking whether scientific ideology creates an alternate conduct-system. I find this question to be too vague as it stands. Rephrasing an earlier remark I would say that there is nothing either in the scientific motive of seeking knowledge or scientific methodology, as these are recognized by contemporary scientists, that points either in a moral or immoral direction. Whether this should be so is better understood in the context of Professors Gorowitz and MacIntyre's article (pp. 248-74). If, on the other hand, we are concerned with the question of how scientific methodology is or can be employed in the securing of knowledge, and how that knowledge is or can be used, we must look at practices in actual places at actual times. And what such historical investigations suggest is that the ideology of science does not create an alternate conduct-system, but rather, the social ideology of the wider community, as embodied in a conduct system, determines the manner in which the science of that community is practiced.

The social ideology of Nazi Germany was in part based on a distinction between *Menschen und Untermenschen*. And it was this recognized distinction that permitted a Nazi scientist, who most likely behaved in a perfectly moral fashion toward his fellow Nazis, to treat the *Untermensch* with an utter disregard for his or her humanity. Present American social ideology, by comparison, is in a more confused state, as reflected in the variety of attitudes toward blacks, prison inmates, and "gooks" as these combine with traditionally sanctioned and presently espoused human ideals. Yet, a narrower view reveals that the American scientist's proclivity for classing human beings as "subjects" or "cases," while dehumanizing, does not presently preclude or prevent a concern for the subjects or cases as human beings whatever their color, class, race, or nationality.

It can be said that science has helped orchestrate the development of particular social ideologies. It can equally be said that the manner in which the ideology of science has been actualized is dependent on the character of social ideologies over which science has no direct control. Indeed, it would appear that whatever exclusive ideology is created within the confines of the scientific establishment cannot predominantly be out of phase with socially established attitudes and practices without science suffering the powerful sanctions of society. Thus, the question of a logical incompatibility of science and morality can only be answered by observing the degree to which a given social ideology as reflected in a social conduct system adheres to the tenets of morality.

Commentary

Science and Moral Neutrality: Some Notes on Ladd's Method of Logical Negation

E. D. Pellegrino

COMMENTARIES ON SCHOLARLY PAPERS can fall into two categories. In one, the commentator attends briefly to the author's argument and then proceeds to write his own paper on the same subject. In the other, the commentator tries genuinely to understand the author's argument and confines his remarks to its validity and its implications.

I will take the latter course, since Professor Ladd has taken pains to set forth his reasoning about the moral value of science and has proposed his method as an instrument for assessing all ethical claims and theories. The purity of my intent will, I admit, be slightly compromised by my *obiter dicta* on some of the corollary points to the main argument.

More than half the paper is devoted to a careful setting of the logical framework within which the claim of science to be a moral activity will be examined. I will adhere closely to the organization of the paper, considering first the general line of the argument and its logical propaedeutic, and then its application to the specific issue of science as a moral activity.

I. The Line of Argument
and Its Logical Propaedeutic

The question is stated at the outset: can the claim of moral value for science be substantiated? If so, what follows? If not, what follows?

Professor Ladd deals analytically with the question in the manner he prefers for ethical discourse—as a practical, rational discipline, and not as a mode of theoretical knowledge.(1) He proposes a logical schema—his "methodological ethical skepticism"—as a method for assessing ethical claims and theories. The method argues negatively, using the principle of *onus probandi*, and eschews any use of positive counterarguments. His aim is to avoid dogmatism in evaluating ethical claims.

This method rests on a logical propaedeutic of several important distinctions. The first is the distinction between two conceptions of the conflicts of values—the conflict between objects of value and the conflict between peoples' differing opinions about what is valuable. The first conflict is usually resolved by ordering one value against another, choosing the higher. The second type of conflict is such that holding one value entails denial of the other, and conflict is resolvable only by force or persuasion.

Another distinction, related to the first, is between the contingent and logical incompatibility of ethical claims. He is considering incompatibilities between propositions and valuations, not activities themselves. Contingent incompatibility occurs when two desirable states cannot coexist because of circumstances; logical incompatibility occurs when the assertion of one claim entails the denial of the other. Most arguments about cost-benefit, Ladd avers, arise from contingent incompatibility; while arguments about rightness and not-rightness, wrongness and not-wrongness are cast in the frame of logical incompatibility. Logical incompatibilities are contradictories, not contraries. The proof of the contrary cannot serve to prove, the negation of a moral proposition.

Ladd focuses the remainder of his argument on logical incompatibilities, since this is the proper realm for evaluating ethical claims—not contingent incompatibilities. He shows that certain conduct-systems, like games and cultural ideologies, are logically incompatible with morality in the ordinary sense. They claim "moral immunity" for some or all of their actions. Games involve restricted moral immunity, and supreme conduct-systems claim unrestricted immunity and superiority over all other systems; they are thus alternate moral systems.

The original question is then recast in terms of this logical schema: is science a part of ordinary morality, or logically incompatible with it? If it is logically incompatible, is it in the restricted sense as in a game, or in the unrestricted sense as an alternate moral system?

Using the principle of *onus probandi*, Ladd then answers his own question only in part. He rebuts the usual reasons for claiming science to be a moral activity, so far as its product goes, and concludes that scientific knowledge is morally neutral. He leaves unanswered the moral claims of science as an activity for its own sake.

Ladd's argument is incomplete so far as the latter half of his own rephrased question is concerned—whether science is logically incompatible with ordinary morality as a game or as an alternate moral system. Since no claim in this direction is clearly enunciated, he cannot deal with this issue by the method of *onus probandi*. Instead, Ladd does so tangentially and by tentative counterassertions, suggesting that some scientific activity is incompatible logically, as in a game, and some as in an alternate moral system. His method leaves us in doubt on perhaps the most important point in the discussion.

II. Methodological Ethical Skepticism
as a Logical Framework

I have taken some trouble to reconstruct both the logical propaedeutics and the line of argument Ladd uses, since he is suggesting this method is generalizable to all ethical claims as well as the claim of science. Is this logical apparatus useful and justifiable for such purposes? What does it permit us to conclude, and with what validity and what limitations? First, we will look at the method and then at its application in the specific case of science.

Ladd's methodological ethical skepticism is modulated by the positions he has taken elsewhere with reference to the nature of ethics and ethical discourse. He does not regard ethics as a specific body of knowledge susceptible to epistemic analysis. He prefers to think of it as a rational, practical discipline open to rigorous logical analysis.(2) Further, he wishes to purge ethical discourse of opinions of right and wrong of conceptions of what is valuable. Ethics depends rather ". . . on the nature of the acts themselves and the situations in which they take place."(3) To this end, he postulates what he calls the reality principle: "This principle forbids the adoption of false beliefs into one's ethical thinking, and asserts that, if a conclusion is founded on false beliefs, then it must be rejected as invalid and unacceptable. The reality principle may be summarized by saying that ethics must be realistic."(4)

The reality principle requires that we reject a moral claim if it contains empirically untenable propositions. Violation of the principle is a sufficient, though not a necessary, condition for rejection since other ways may exist. Though not specifically stated, Ladd uses this principle to refute the claim that scientific activity is a moral activity.

A central feature in Ladd's methodological ethical skepticism is the way he combines these two principles with a special use of the method of *onus probandi*. This is one of the oldest methods in dialectical reasoning. He who makes a claim or an assertion can be challenged to prove it to the satisfaction of his listener. The method is essential in clarifying propositions and encouraging critical reflection and judgment. It is deeply rooted in Plato's and Aristotle's attempts to show how we can reason from premises which are merely probable rather than certain. Ladd combines features of the elenchus of the earlier Socrates (*Meno* and *Protagoras*), with certain features of Aristotle's *Rhetoric* and *Topics*.(5,6)

But Ladd applies the method of *onus probandi* to moral claims in a special way. He asserts not only that an ethical claim that cannot be proven must be rejected but also that it is morally neutral. What is more, he even suggests that failure to prove a claim is tantamount to a presumption of falsity in the same way that failure to prove title to a house presumes that one does not have title. This amounts to a denial of the usual distinction between truth and correct thinking. In ordinary logic, it is recognized that a true conclusion may follow from false premises. This is a pertinent possibility in dialectical as opposed to demonstrative reasoning. In dialectical reasoning, we deal by definition with merely probable premises. Our conclusions, therefore, are rarely free of the possibility that the opposite may be true even when the conclusion follows rigorously from the premises. But Ladd clearly states that the rule of the falsity of denying the antecedent does not apply in his concept of negative ethical argumentation.

Suspending the rules of formal logic as Ladd does, what is the meaning of a failure to sustain rightness or wrongness of an activity? It is one thing to say either in logic or law that the evidence for an assertion is "weak," "insufficient," or "unacceptable," but it is quite another thing to say the act in question is "neutral"—that it is like Aquinas's example of picking a blade of grass. Should not moral neutrality also be proven by the same rules for the method of *onus probandi*? Moral neutrality is an assertion itself subject to challenge, and it cannot be concluded by default.

After all, there must somewhere be a connection between the realms of logic and behavior in so human an endeavor as ethics. Is it not more stringent to say that the moral rightness or wrongness of an activity has not been proven and that the individual must fall back on other criteria? Pain and deception may be morally neutral as scientific activity, but they are logically incompatible with ordinary morality. At some point, we must reconcile the meaning of moral neutrality of acts in science when they collide with ordinary morality.

What, then, is the utility of the conclusion of moral neutrality? Ladd is at great pains to state at the outset that he plans to challenge the "scientific imperative," the assertion that science is one of the "highest" of human activities. He equates "highest" incidentally with "moral"—another assertion we might want to test with the *onus probandi* principle. Granting that he has disposed of the pretentious claims of science, which incidentally all scientists do not hold, does he make unnecessary difficulties for himself by insisting first on "neutrality" and then on logical incompatibility as a system with morality?

Is there not a less hazardous way of establishing moral neutrality, quite apart from its relationship to the scientific imperative, though we can return to that in a moment? This is an important question, since Ladd says his method is applicable to all moral discourse. Some of us, for example, would define moral neutrality as the domain of acts which *do not* involve a relationship between individuals or between individuals and society in which rights and responsibilities play a significant part. Moral acts are human acts and grow out of the relationships of human beings. Some of the acts are morally neutral—washing your car—but washing your car when there is a water shortage or with your neighbor's hose and water supply is not morally neutral.

In science there are acts in the domain of morality even within the rules of science as an activity of its own. For example, we must report honest observations; we must report unfavorable as well as favorable results; we cannot use another man's data without permission, and so forth. This is a part of the scientific imperative, though not its full extent, of course. Is Ladd's refutation, therefore, a sufficient one? Does he not predetermine the outcome by the global way he states the pretensions of science?

Those who hold for science as a moral activity cover a considerable spectrum. Some identify the ethics of science as integrity in the use of the scientific method (honesty of observation and reporting). Others demand that the claims for morality of an act are admissible only if they meet the rules of scientific evidence. Still others subscribe to science as an alternate system of morality. It is this latter group who are most directly defeated by Ladd's negative logical argumentation.

The scientific imperative is not a monolithic concept. Showing its most extreme pretensions to be morally neutral and then logically incompatible with ordinary morality can apply only to a portion of the spectrum. In short, we have something of a straw man in the way the original question is framed.

Ladd's method assumes that a moral claim is sustainable if the evidence for it is acceptable to reasonable men. Who are the reasonable men? How many reasonable men in history have accepted the rightness and wrongness of an act in the face of its denial by other equally reasonable men? A verdict of moral neutrality can be reached because of empirical error in the premises, simple lack of evidence, ineptness in marshaling the available evidence, or the incapacity of the listener to comprehend the evidence or deception. The method of *onus probandi* can detect some of these but not all of them.

Moreover, "conviction" is a subjective state in which reason impels us to assent to an assertion. Nonetheless, even with reasonable men, conviction is compounded of many factors of mind, psyche, culture, and life situation. Our assent to the idea or the will of another is a complicated phenomenological problem in need of better understanding.

If we are to break out of the inevitable subjectivity inherent in "accepting or rejecting" an assertion, we need some explicit expression in advance of what constitutes the conditions of proof or rejection—a bench mark against which to use *onus probandi*. We need also a clear comprehension of what judgments we can safely make about a failure to meet the requirements of proof Ladd sets forth. The only judgment we can validly make is that of "unproved"—the question must remain moot.

To follow the legal analogy, the guilt of the defendant has not been proven. This does not mean he may not be guilty but only that the case for his guilt is not strong enough to convict him. But in this legal instance, we accepted beforehand not only the principle of *onus probandi*—which binds the prosecution—but also a prior principle—"not guilty until proven otherwise." In our society, most people accept this principle as an axiom, and presumably it has met the requirements of *onus probandi*. In the case of moral claims, as Ladd argues, there is no prior principle except "morally neutral until proven otherwise." But he has not sustained that notion. It is an assertion still subject itself to the principle of *onus probandi*.

The method of logical negation suffers from its passivity. It can counter and dispel claims brought to it. Strictly followed, it must wait for an assertion to be brought forth. The kinds of questions considered, their scope and phrasing rest with the one making the ethical claim. Ladd himself finds it necessary to depart from a negative stance when he argues that science *per se* cannot be considered a moral activity. Here he makes assertions of his own which he admittedly does not test by the method of *onus probandi*.

Ethical skepticism as espoused by Ladd is a useful exercise acting as an astringent to reduce the emotive content so common in ethical claims. Well used, it can prevent the uncritical acceptance of facile eristics. It is an essential prologue to positive forms of argumentation if its limitations are recognized.

How helpful is the concept of moral neutrality which eventuates from the method? It certainly acts as a restraint to deontologic pronouncements and sensitizes us to the possibility of logical incompatibility between different conduct-systems. The caveats I have expressed about the dubiety of such a concept as "moral neutrality" in human acts are not intended to rebut the position that moral claims be justified. When they fail to convince, moral judgments can at least be suspended, so that capricious obligations are not imposed.

We still face the practical question of whether a particular act is moral or not. At some point, in the world of practical affairs we must choose between alternate conduct-systems since they often are logically incompatible with each other. If, for example, we arrive at the conclusion that abortion is morally neutral because the arguments advanced for its wrongness do not convince, we are interpreted as giving tacit approval, no matter how fastidiously we argue that refuting the claim to wrongness does not prove rightness of an act. We cannot, therefore, avoid the ultimate intersection of the logical and the real, separable though these realms might be for purposes of ethical discourse. To paraphrase Ladd, I agree that at some point we must ground ethics on "the nature of the acts themselves and the situations in which they take place."(7)

III. Application of the Schema
    of Logical Skepticism

These criticisms of Ladd's method can now be examined a little more closely as they are applied to the way in which he examines the presumed claim of science to be a moral activity.

He divides the arguments in support of this claim into two: those which purport to show that science is beneficial for man, and those which argue for its value *per se* as intellectual activity.

He makes a very strict demand for proof—namely, that every last bit of scientific knowledge must be shown to have been directly or indirectly beneficial to man. Since this cannot be proven empirically, and since *some* scientific knowledge is harmful to man, the claim is rejected. Science, Ladd says, is therefore morally neutral. What he feels he has refuted is the claim of science to be an exalted, overriding moral system. Moral neutrality in this instance means it is subject to the constraints of morality.

This is a stringent test. It illustrates the difficulty with the principle of *onus probandi* discussed above—the conditions of proof can vary so widely that almost any claim can be defeated. Law, the ministry, teaching, scholarship, philanthropy—all would fail a similar test. These activities also claim at times that they are an "exalted moral activity" in the sense that their values should prevail over others in certain circumstances. What branch of human knowledge could show that it has invariably been good for mankind?

What Ladd has shown is that *no* human activity can claim to be an exalted moral activity. If he applies the same rigid criterion to these activities as to science, he is consistent within his schema, and we cannot complain as to method. But then science is no different from other human activities, and the effort to deflate the "exalted" moral claims of science seem discriminatory even though Ladd denies any such intention.

The matter becomes even stickier when Ladd examines the claim for science as an activity good in itself. He concludes with a less certain judgment and asks for "further argument." But he gets there by simply ruling the arguments as "excessively vague and confusing" without a detailed examination of them by any empiric or logical test. Here again, one wonders about the prior question of the conditions of proof and how subjective they may or may not be.

A disconcerting feature of Ladd's reasoning is the way in which the meaning of the original question is subtly shaped to satisfy the logical schema. Thus, he purports to examine if science and ethics are compatible. In this first paragraph, it is the "presumed exalted moral status" of science he questions. This he defines as the presumption that, if science encounters ordinary morality in a situation of contingent incompatibility, science will insist that its system of values predominate. Shortly thereafter, he says it is really the "scientific imperative" which is being questioned—namely, the drive to "maximize scientific knowledge." Then again, he purports to show that science as intellectual activity has no claim to being a "unique" morally exalted activity.

These transformations of the question introduce different nuances and assumptions. Moreover, Ladd uses the term "science" itself in equivocal ways. He seems to be speaking for the most part of the modern conception of science as theory, observation, experiment, and so on. Yet, when he rejects the idea of the intrinsic value of science itself, he attacks Aristotle's conception. But, for Aristotle, the term "science" was more inclusive than the modern term. As considered in a variety of places—the *Posterior Analytics*, the *Ethics*, and the *Metaphysics*—science is, for Aristotle, a special kind of knowledge, that is, a knowledge of causes, of what is necessary and eternal and demonstrative. In the *Ethics*, he specifically says, "Scientific knowledge is judgment about things that are universal and necessary."(8) Philosophy—metaphysics in particular—is a branch of science for Aristotle. In Book X of the *Ethics*, he discusses happiness and says, in the highest sense, it is the contemplative life—not science as Ladd would have it.(9) In the *Ethics* he defines "wisdom" as the most "finished" of the forms of knowledge—not science.(10) Wisdom is philosophy, and it consists of "intuitive reason combined with knowledge."(11)

What arguments does he, therefore, find "excessively vague and equivocal"? Are they the arguments for modern science? Those for Aristotle's conception of science? Or is it wisdom whose claims as man's highest activity are being refuted? For, it is wisdom and contemplation—philosophy—that Aristotle exalts in Book X of the *Ethics*—not science *per se*.

Maritain deals very cogently with the distinction between the ancient and modern concepts of science.(12)

Ladd says that science is morally neutral since both arguments fail the test of *onus probandi*. This means that science is subject to the constraints of ordinary morality. This would make "ordinary morality" an exalted moral system. This may be so, but it is not defined or justified as such in the paper.

If the exalted claim of science to be a moral activity is refuted, what about the less exalted claim that some, or most, of its efforts are indeed beneficial for mankind? Presumably, in this sense, science could be a limited system of morality. We would then have to deal with the intersection of its claims with those of other limited moral systems. Logical incompatibilities between systems could exist and still require resolution.

Finally, is the game analogy really acceptable as a paradigm for the activities of science? Are games and science analogous as conduct-systems? Even in games all the rules of ordinary morality are not suspended. One must abide by the rules of the game—a principle which comes from ordinary morality; one must not cheat, lie, or "fix" the results. Obviously, games are subject to some of the rules of morality and so is science, even as a supreme conduct-system. Wholesale refutation obscures the fact that there are degrees of morality in scientific activities, and these are not always logically incompatible with morality either as a game or a supreme conduct-system.

Ladd closes with an interesting departure from his promise not to employ positive counterarguments. He devotes a postlude to assert that science is incompatible with morality on positive grounds as well as on the grounds of negating its claims. He finds science lacking in several elements essential to a moral system—it uses ends to justify means; it has no room for moral categories like "person"; it ignores social consequences; it is interested in things, not people. The implication is that science is not only morally neutral but amoral or antimoral. Each of these assertions is debatable and subject, of course, to the *onus probandi* test.

This postlude is less objective in tone than the body of the paper. Resorting to positive counterargument—and in so summary a fashion—leads to an impression of "overkill' and weakens the case for the method of logical negation in ethics.

Taken as a whole, however, Professor Ladd has made an important, provocative, and interesting contribution to the criteria for ethical discourse. His proposal of the method of logical negation and methodological skepticism is well argued and clear enough to reveal its advantages and its limitations. He offers us an indispensable device, useful at every stage of argumentation, whether it be in the ethical or the more general domain.

NOTES

1. John Ladd, "The Issue of Relativism," *Ethical Relativism*, John Ladd, ed. (Belmont, Calif.: Wadsworth Publishing Company, 1973), pp. 108-09.
2. *Ibid.*
3. John Ladd, "Comments on Abraham Edel's Patterns of Use of Science in Ethics," Boston Studies in the Philosophy of Science, Proceedings of the Boston Colloquium for the Philosophy of Science, IV, 388.
4. *Ibid.*
5. R. Robinson, "Plato's Earlier Dialectic" (Oxford: Clarendon Press, 1953), p. 122, quoted in J. E. Raven, *Plato's Thought in the Making* (Cambridge: Cambridge University Press, 1975), pp. 62-63.
6. N. D. Ross, "Aristotle: A Complete Exposition of his Works and Thought," (New York: Meridian Books, 1959), pp. 58-59 and 262-63.
7. Ladd, "Comments on Abraham Edel's Patterns. . . ."
8. Aristotle, *Nicomachean Ethics*, 6.6114[b] 31-32, *Basic Works of Aristotle*, Richard McKeon, ed. (New York: Random House, 1968).
9. *Ibid.*, Book X, Chapter 7, 8.
10. *Ibid.*, 6.5,1141[a], 17-18.
11. *Ibid.*, 6.5,1141[a], 18-19.
12. Jacques Maritain, *The Degrees of Knowledge* (New York: Charles Scribner's Sons, 1959), pp. 22-23.

The Non-neutrality of Hypothesis Formulation

Marc Lappé

I. Freedom of Inquiry

Critics and proponents of science alike consider hypotheses the free ground upon which scientific inquiry takes place. Hypotheses become the jousting grounds of criticism where ideological adversaries tilt at each other, intent at toppling insecure concepts or weak formulations. The *generation* of a hypothesis is in this view a value-free enterprise; values come into play only after the fact, when hypothesis-testing is conducted according to rules of procedure which demand both intellectual and ethical rigor. Thus for some, the formulation of a hypothesis itself is envisioned as taking place in a quasi-Camelot, where pure ideas spring fully armed from the head of the scientist.

In such an idealized world, hypotheses are seen as being "struck like sparks from unaccountable hunches or quirks of the mind, from an idiosyncratic penchant for the pleasing form or agreeable order."(1) Karl Popper reinforces this value-neutral view in advocating the imperative of freedom of conjecture as part of scientific advance.(2) For Popper, it is only *after* their formulation that hypotheses are to be subjected to normative tests. If we take this view, scientific scrutiny and criticism are essential to the process of justification, not that of discovery.

96

This view of science conveys a sense of the germinal period of scientific innovation as one in which total abandon is permitted, and even encouraged. As George Wald put it, "The scientist is willing to plunge blindly, the better to plunge. . . . The logic is left to be repaired later."(3) Dangerous stuff that, in a world in which the domination of any one hypothesis can hold sway for decades (or in Copernicus's time, centuries) before illogical or faulty construction becomes apparent. More dangerous still, when expropriation of hypothetical formulations (about presumptive genetic bases of criminality, for example) threaten traditional notions of human autonomy or liberty. However, if the problem of value-laden hypotheses were purely one of misuse, this analysis would stop here—no one questions that ideas can be misappropriated for nefarious purposes. It is rather the stronger claim, that some hypotheses in and of themselves can be inappropriately preferred, that I am addressing here. The source of error to be examined is not one of misuse, but of factors internal to the hypothesis itself—the source of its assumptions, its predictions, its required tests. In sum, the cultural and historical forces which precondition a mind (or an historic period) toward a world view.

At any time, a novel hypothesis poses a risk of dislocating human attention from one set of problems to another. Whether the later appropriation of its verified predictions leads to social decay or flourishing is rarely, if ever, in the hands or mind of the scientist who first formulates his idea. But this first formulation may be laden with cultural and political baggage. The heuristic appeal of a hypothesis all too often capitalizes on a world view which is already socially conditioned—and is thus subject to cultural biasing factors. For instance, the notion that people as well as plants might be perfectable in an inheritable fashion through environmental manipulations was an idea which inevitably linked Marxian ideals to Lamarckian genetics(4)—and thence to Lysenkoism.

II. Disaffection from Science

I would agree that the progress of science requires that hypothesis formulation embody irrational elements to ensure that it goes beyond the bounds of existing knowledge. The critical question remains whether or not constraints can or should be imposed on this process. Often the claim is made that exercises in creativity should not be subject to the same kind of scrutiny reserved for their products. Even those counted among the most politically radical have tended to concur with this view.

James Shapiro, who with Lawrence Eron, Jonathan Beckwith, and others, isolated a gene (the *lac* operon) for the first time, created a stir in 1969 by announcing that he was leaving science for politics. In a letter to *Nature*, Shapiro, Eron, and Beckwith gave a surprisingly docile view of their scientific work before critiquing the social and political context in which it might be abused. They said, "In and of itself our work is morally neutral; it can lead either to benefits or dangers to mankind. . . ."(5)

Why this reluctance to question the roots of science? The solution to the paradox of political radicalism in the company of scientific conservatism is not hard to find. In a different setting, Shapiro was asked why he did the work in the first place. His answer: "We did this work for scientific reasons, also because it was interesting to do. But scientists generally have the tendency not to think too much about the consequences of their work while doing it. But now that we have, we are not entirely happy with it."(6) It appears that Shapiro, Eron, and Beckwith were scientists first and political radicals a far second. The questioning of fundamental assumptions of freedom of inquiry cannot be done by those who have benefited by that practice.

Some would say that if Shapiro *et al.* truly were concerned with the political implications of their work, they would have questioned their priorities in choosing a genetic system for study which could not foreseeably yield benefits as much as harms. But that view misses the central point of doing science itself. In order for a scientist to question the roots of his own work, he must profess disinterest in the very matter which sets his tasks apart from the purely political: the quest for truth. In this case, Shapiro, Eron, and Beckwith quite understandably subordinated their political ideologies to the sudden accessibility of a "truth" which they found possible through development of a novel technique. They were able to discount any ethical cost implicit in the work itself, by projecting concern to its probable misuse at some later time. But the very *selection* of a problem raises questions of resource allocation which conflicts strongly with the ideology of free inquiry. A scientist trained in one narrow discipline may not be able to adopt a new priority system to select hypotheses based on moral values.

III. Instability of the Central Dogmas

Surprisingly, Shapiro's disaffection created a major furor. To understand why one member's quitting could cause such a dislocation in the scientific establishment requires an understanding of science as a collective activity. The four norms of scientific activity given by Robert Merton (organized skepticism, universalism, communality, and disinterestedness) have become highly unstable. Israel Sheffler recently observed that:

> The notion of a fixed observational given, of a constant descriptive language, of a shared methodology of investigation, or a rational community advancing its knowledge of the real world—all have been subjected to severe and mounting criticism from a variety of directions.
>
> The overall tendency of such criticism has been to call into question the very conception of scientific thought as a responsible exercise of reasonable men. . . .(7)

An instability of internal structure makes it possible for the "normal" processes of hypothesis formulation to become destabilized. A possible result, already realized in transplantation immunology,(8) is that heuristic but unsubstantiable hypotheses will gain greater currency. More important perhaps, a period of instability affords an opportunity for scientists to inspect their premises and assumptions about the nature of hypothesis formulation.

IV. Descriptive Elements

To analyze the basis for instability, it is useful to bifurcate the scientific enterprise by distinguishing processes unique to the elaboration of scientific hypotheses and those entailed in the process of corroboration or refutation of those hypotheses.

As Stephen Brush has pointed out,(9) the first of these processes comprise the "context of discovery," the second, the "context of justification." Errors and unethical conduct in the latter have been well documented recently(10) and show that errors of judgment persist. But the nature of the errors which might be made in the context of discovery has not, to my knowledge, been systematically explored. Certainly, acts of omission may occur because of human fallibility, so at first examination it appears difficult to define the conditions under which morally responsible errors occur.

Under what circumstances then is hypothesis formulation (as distinct from hypothesis testing) itself appropriately scrutinized for its value content? Since the ordinary process of hypothesis formulation does not embody moral rules, where do value constructs, if any, come from? Does hypothesis formulation include value conditions? The problem is first one of descriptive, rather than normative, ethics. To state the problem in Stephen Toulmin's words:

> Where a dominant direction of variation [in new lines of scientific thought] can be observed within any particular science, or where some particular direction of innovation appears to have been excessively neglected, a new type of issue arises. Within the total volume of intellectual variants under discussion, what factors determine which types of option are, and which are not pursued?
>
> We are asking how scientists come to take certain kinds of new suggestions seriously in the first place—considering them to be worthy of investigation at all—rather than [what] standards they apply in deciding that those suggestions are in fact sound and acceptable.(11)

Toulmin recognizes that in many cases the justification for taking a particular kind of scientific hypothesis seriously has to be sought outside the intellectual content of the particular science. Like many historians of science, Toulmin recognizes that the selection criteria for hypotheses are so embedded in social and historical factors that it may be unrealistic to expect that they be extricated.

How do the traditional selection criteria for hypotheses stand up to the scrutiny of the historian or sociologist? Abner

Shimony delineates four criteria intended to keep hypothesis formulation value-free.(12) By providing conduct rules for hypothesis formulation that keep biasing factors in view, Shimony hopes to keep the process part of the internal norm of science. His list includes the following provisos:

1. That the hypothesis be clearly stated;
2. That the motivation for proposing it be explained;
3. That the explanation in some way acknowledge (but not necessarily accept) a recognized body of propositions regarding the subject; and
4. That it not be an arbitrary choice from a family of hypotheses which answer the same motivation.

Two of these factors—consciousness of motivating factors and freedom from arbitrariness—are by definition factors which cannot be objectively delineated, especially as they apply to complex phenomena, and are hence value constructs. Shimony's other tests for hypotheses are similarly limited, perhaps because Shimony may be more interested in demonstrating the internal consistency of science than in constructing ethical tests for the acceptability of its procedures.

Thus, rather than propose an external measure for hypothesis acceptability (such as social utility or consistency with established norms), Shimony would have the researcher assign priorities to hypotheses based on calculations of prior probabilities of likelihood of success in describing unexplained phenomena. His world of "tempered personalism" assigns each seriously proposed hypothesis a rank order in which no hypothesis is excluded from consideration. This idealized construct is one in which the researcher holds varying degrees of commitment to rival hypotheses, rather than allegiance to a central one. Such a system conflicts strongly with the expedient needs of scientific inquiry, which often mandate adherence to a single hypothesis until self-testing leads to refutation. But more important, it simply reinforces whatever modeling system worked in the past (for on what else will prior probabilities be derived?), and works within the traditional goal-model: that elucidation of truth for truth's sake is the rightful function of science.

V. Normative Questions
in Hypothesis Selection

The conduct rules for the practices involved in empirical testing of hypotheses are well defined and do not appear to me to present novel categories of ethical inquiry. What constitutes "proper" conduct in the elaboration of hypotheses, however, is not well understood. What can be said? First, that it is impractical and wrongheaded to base an attack solely on freedom of inquiry or cultural biasing factors. Second, that it is evident that some discretionary latitude is necessary in different sciences to ensure an adequate complexity and richness in generation of scientific ideas. Third, that culturally influenced ideas and decisions are not in and of themselves objectionable; these may be the source of hypotheses which are particularly fruitful because they are based on experiential elements unique to a particular class of persons. (Fabre's observations and hypothesis-testing among the social insects are a classic example of a unique interplay between culture, ideology, and science.) But the assumption that hypothesis formulation is value-neutral when its objective is individuals (in the sense MacIntyre uses the word to embrace multilevel phenomena) is likely to be mistaken. As MacIntyre and Gorovitz observe: "The study of individuals cannot be nonevaluative in the way that properties is." Every "central question" of a science often embraces value constructs which force the language, thinking, and conceptualizations used to formulate them into new molds. This has proven especially true in genetics.

VI. Genetic Science as a Special Case

At face value, genetics appears to be a science which moves forward by proffering hypotheses which attempt to explain the causal network of molecular constructs which underlie all natural phenomena. A sociologist of science might ask first if there were value-related elements in this process which evoke certain classes of hypotheses for testing and not others. He might then ask if these elements were identifiable with specific cultural features of the class of persons who do the work. Finally, he might examine the implicit assumptions made by the formulators as to the degree of confidence they attach to the presuppositions of genetic test systems.

In part, because the relationships which genetics seeks to establish are between "individuals" (expressed as phenotypes) and their genotypic and environmental substrates, there is a high probability that genetics will be used as a causal nexus for explaining a spectrum of human conditions, attributes, or behaviors which do *not* necessarily have internal causes; for example, social deviancy or mental disorders. Second, because genetics is in its infancy, competing hypotheses will proliferate and adherents will be marshalled in part according to their world views. This point was made clear by Richard Lewontin in his most recent work with regard to genetic variation.

> Indeed the whole history of the problem of genetic variation is a vivid illustration of the role that deeply embedded ideological assumptions play in determining scientific "truth" and the direction of scientific inquiry. . . . It is not the facts but a world-view that is at issue, a divergence between those who, on the one hand, see the dynamical processes in populations as essentially conservative, purifying and protecting an adapted and rational *status quo* from the nonadaptive, corrupting, and irrational forces of random mutation, and those, on the other, for whom nature is process, and every existing order is unstable in the long run, who see as did Denis Diderot that *Tout change, tout passe, il n'y a que le tout qui reste.*(13)

A third problem is that the categorization of human behaviors is in itself a value-based activity. The techniques chosen for measuring behavioral traits themselves delimit the scope of the attribute being tested, and in the process, rule out other traits which might warrant study. More important, as behavioral geneticists Fuller and Thompson point out, measuring devices may determine the nature of the traits which can be found.(14) In part, this means that the tests used to measure behaviors may come to define the phenomena they seek to measure (IQ test results come to be equated with intelligence). But the need to put behaviors into categories for explication violates the basic biological norm developed by Ernst Mayr which demands that characteristics which are continuously varying not be considered typologically. In Fuller and Thompson's words, the behavior and biology of animals "do not readily fit into categories." Classical Mendelian genetics, of course, deals solely with categories.

A further complicating force is that even non-Mendelian genetic hypotheses must often attempt to explain a complex human trait in terms of simplifying assumptions which forcibly displace attention to the roots of causation from external factors to internal ones. This takes place, for example, whenever a complex (polygenic) condition like diabetes becomes ascribed to single genes with "reduced penetrance." The search for environmental correlates of the condition may then be suspended while intensive study is done on the putative genetic hypothesis. Geneticists often apply Occam's razor inappropriately to complex human conditions like diabetes, hypertension, or neural tube defects. Why is this so?

Admittedly, in order to "do" genetics in the laboratory, it is important to be able to exclude competing models or paradigms, and to suspend temporarily consideration of alternative hypotheses. For experimental systems, it is acceptable, even desirable, to isolate putative genetic factors from their environmental overlay; but in humans, this separation is difficult to attain in theory, if not impossible to achieve in practice. Moreover, isolation of environmental variables may violate ethical norms, as when testing to determine an intrinsic (i.e., genetic) basis for a malabsorption syndrome such as sprue, calls for institution of a diet known to cause intestinal injury. Since these and other limitations greatly restrict the ability of the environmentalist scientist to *dis*prove a genetic hypothesis, deciding to use a genetic model for explaining human ability or disability virtually assures a tenure of visibility of the hypothesis. Hence a major ethical issue in choosing any hypothesis for study which is not subject to refutation is the cost incurred in suppressing competing and potentially valid hypotheses.

For example, because heritability estimates of human IQ scores are restricted in their validity to measurements within groups sharing relatively common environments, between-group comparisons (for example, between whites and blacks) are likely to be unscientific and possibly invidious. The absence of any reliable means of deriving and measuring heritability for nonmetric traits, and the dearth of any means of measuring white admixture among blacks further preclude a valid test of the proposition of the genetic basis of white/black IQ score differentials.

The decision to treat variations of human attributes like intelligence as primarily a problem in genetics, rather than a complex biological/cultural/economic/political problem, places the need to discern first causes above that of the persons they affect. The behavioral geneticist knows in advance that genetic differences for a given form of behavior cannot be discerned if the environment is sufficiently suppressive of that trait. In the face of analyses which question the validity of heritability estimates,(15) attempting to derive heritability data on IQ scores among general ghetto populations becomes not merely a questionable scientific enterprise, but a morally suspect one.

At least part of the problem is wrapped up in the understandable need of the scientist to lift out and isolate a portion of a larger problem which is fit for study (that is, quantitation) from its larger context. But treating a scientific problem in isolation when its object of study is a complex phenomenon courts omission of critical evaluative factors, for three reasons. First, as Whitehead has emphasized: "No science can be more secure than the unconscious metaphysics which tacitly it presupposes. The individual thing is necessarily a modification of its environment, and cannot be understood in disjunction."(16) Second, the description of phenomena on the basis of idealized physical systems excludes interactional components and "bridging" rules which relate those systems to the behavior in question as it is evinced under real-world conditions.(17) Third, isolating the phenomenon may inadvertently exclude or downgrade one or more contributing factors, such as environmental factors in IQ scoring.

This threefold analysis suggests the kinds of value premises entailed in the exclusion of alternative hypotheses in favor of genetic ones. Genetic models may lead to an organization of the social world according to certain internal qualities unique to genetic systems, such as fixity, predetermination, and strong biological determinism. Such a view in its broadest sense may diminish the attention given to powerful but subtle environmental influences or social factors which modify the expression of a trait. One such example is the intrauterine environment, or postnatal milieu, both of which potentially affect the prospect of normal biological and psychological development. Genetic hypotheses also embody a sense of determinism which conflicts with norms that the society may be deeply committed to, by virtue of its laws, mores, and general moral structure. By embodying the injunction that we are somehow obliged to restructure society along lines which recognize the primacy of fixed biological potentialities, attributes, and traits, genetic hypotheses work to deemphasize the moral, unfixed elements of humanness which have been integral to the emergence of culture and religion.

VII. Exclusion of Competing Hypotheses

A first-level test for the appropriateness of seriously putting forth a given hypothesis should include an estimation of the moral costs of not testing a competing one. Even where those competing hypotheses embody more difficult or complex refutation or other testing procedures, they should be evaluated on the basis of their *moral content* before being displaced. A second-level test has to do with the degree of human good which *acting out* the predictions of the hypothesis will likely engender. In the case of genetic hypotheses, their heuristic appeal and simplifying assumptions may make them better candidates for scientific inquiry than are environmental ones.(18) How are we to choose between "good" hypotheses which are good for scientific reasons and those which are good for moral ones? Which approach benefits society more?

In Table 1, I have outlined some of the more commonly used reasons for accepting hypotheses on the basis of scientific criteria. (I would emphasize that a hypothesis which is "good" in the scientific context usually embodies several of these features.)

Using criteria such as these generally ensures no more than that the hypothesis chosen can do what it claims to do—provide a set of testable predictions which embrace enough previously

TABLE 1
Examples of Scientific Criteria for Hypotheses

A. Falsifiability
B. Simplicity and parsimony
C. Heuristic appeal
D. Predictive power (scope and variety of predictions)
E. Exclusion of competing models
F. Mensurate qualities (availability of suitable instruments, equations, etc.)
G. Explanatory power (ability to account for more than one set of phenomena)

unexplained phenomena such that its solution will be scientifically meaningful. This simplified construction points to several weaknesses of hypothesis-formulation: first, that the scientific formulation assumes that it is unnecessary to evaluate the costs of what is left out by isolating a phenomena in terms of its physical systems; second, that it excludes the tests for appropriate mechanisms which lead to choosing a specific area and form of inquiry. These are part of the moral content of hypotheses. Examples of the nature of the input necessary to begin to analyze and weigh "moral content" are shown in Table 2.

Items listed in this second table would be used to gauge the moral content of the scientific criteria. For example, "heuristic appeal" would be scrutinized for its cultural loading factors (item A). The exclusion of competing hypotheses would be

TABLE 2
Identification of Value-Based Tests
for Hypothesis Formulation and Testing

A. Identification and weighting of cultural biasing factors
B. Assessment of the costs of hypothesis selection
C. Assessment of the costs of performing the tests necessary for corroboration or refutation
D. Consideration of the moral factors attendant on verification
E. Projection of possible societal dislocations

subjected to analyses of its moral implications (item B). Evaluation of the possible ethical questions (experimental systems needed, etc.) raised by testing the predictions of the hypothesis would be made (item C). The possible costs as well as benefits of hypothesis verification would be weighed (items D and E).

This formulation immediately raises some vexing problems. Are we really saying that we should disallow some scientifically promising hypotheses or experiments because they are morally threatening? Whom do we expect to perform these analyses? How ought we balance the scientific criteria against the moral ones? How important a consideration should the moral content of any hypothesis be and how do we go about demonstrating it? A set of case studies may illuminate some of these apparent dilemmas.

It should be evident that the major class of hypotheses being considered involve predictions or assumptions that impinge more or less directly on human nature and social conditions. A set of examples from the interface between the "hard" biologic sciences (genetics) and the "soft" ones (sociology, psychiatry) will highlight the complexities of the thesis that moral considerations are an obligatory part of the construction of hypotheses.

VIII. A Classification Scheme for Assigning Moral Weights to Hypothesis Formulation

A. Class I: Hypotheses which are intrinsically dangerous. At face value, this is the simplest class of hypotheses to evaluate. Rules for abstaining from doing direct harm or injury are seemingly self-evident. As George Barnard Shaw noted in *The Doctor's Dilemma*, "No man is allowed to put his mother in the stove because he desires to know how long an adult woman will survive the temperature of 500 degrees Fahrenheit, no matter how important or interesting that particular addition to the store of human knowledge may be." However, in practice it may be difficult to project and weigh the class of harms which might ensue should an initial hypothesis be verified. For example, the need to construct a probe which could test the construction of human genomes led to the development of DNA hybridization techniques which then became part of the technology needed to develop bacterial "plasmids" which could make multiple copies of mammalian gene sequences. This work immediately lent itself to the introduction of genes into a plasmid, which could confer oncogenicity (tumor-producing) or virulence (killing power) on a host cell. This potentiality, coupled with other unforeseen possibilities, led to the Berg letter in *Science* which called for a moratorium of genetic research on certain plasmid systems.(19) Thus, although testing the concept that virulence can be conferred to an intestinal bacterium may be "dangerous," the development of the technique itself could have been justified on the grounds of its fundamental worthwhileness for advancing molecular biology. Indeed, this is what was done.

B. Class II: Hypotheses which are mischievous. A "mischievous" hypothesis is one in which any logical sequence of testing generates equally unsatisfactory moral outcomes. A mischievous hypothesis is also one which is intrinsically untestable (that is, not subject to falsification). However, mischievousness might also involve a moral ascertainment, for example, that there has been an attempt to deceive, or that some morally weighted predictions of the hypothesis were formulated *prior* to the hypothetical construct itself.

Take, for instance, a hypothesis which proposes that heredity is the principal reason for success in business. If confirmed, the hypothesis would predict that businessmen achieved their status on the basis of inherited properties. But the presumed properties which lead to business success have never been systematically defined, nor the possibility of performing quantitative tests to determine their distribution in the population determined. Genetic markers for these nonexistent properties are unknown. By taking "business success" as a unitary phenomenon, one accepts this class of behaviors as scientifically defined. By agreeing to "test" such a hypothesis over time, there is every possibility that the scientist will have conferred a degree of respectability to a system he may never have intended to support.

C. Class III: Hypotheses which are socially invidious. An invidious hypothesis is one which posits properties or relationships among persons which imply the existence of morally questionable traits, characteristics, or behaviors. For example, the hypothesis that a specific ethnic group or population is inclined to deviant behavior for biologic or intrinsic reasons is invidious because it violates norms and assumptions about the autonomy of individuals who are members of groups or classes. A representative hypothesis here, for example, is one which posits that low IQ and race can be predicted on the basis of chromosome banding patterns.(20) Because both of the traits in question (race and IQ) are suspect classifications for what they purport to represent or measure, this hypothesis, like others in its class, will likely be disqualified for both scientific *and* moral reasons.

D. Class IV: Hypotheses which are holistically threatening. This class is characterized by hypotheses which posit a world view which violates social and moral norms. Here, it is critical to distinguish hypotheses which are holistically threatening by virtue of their *moral* content from those which ostensibly pose the same threat because of their revolutionary constructs. For example, Galileo's world view could be considered holistically threatening because of the perturbation it portended for man's theological view of himself, in contrast to the hypothesis of a growing number of health workers that genetic predisposition to disease (as, for example, determined by HL-A markers) is responsible for a large part of human disability,(21) is threatening because it abruptly shifts the burden of proof of being free from disease-producing conditions away from the society and to the individual. This latter shift in world view is thus holistically threatening in a different way from Galileo's.

By replacing a view of social causation of illness or disability with a genetic one, the genetic susceptibility hypothesis could threaten those segments of society which still have appreciable amounts of environmentally related disease. Individuals who were susceptible to disease by virtue of their social and economic conditions would thus be heavily penalized. Thus, whereas an emphasis on such epidemiologic hypotheses could conceivably move society toward better standards of long-term medical prevention and ascertainment, the replacement of a world view which sees medicine as primarily serving individual needs in the present with one which sees medicine serving future needs obviously requires moral analysis.

That these two viewpoints represent assessments of hypotheses in the real world can be seen in an editorial in *The Lancet*(22) in which the mind-set of different health workers is described. The editorial writer makes the observation that there are "global-minded" and "research-minded" workers who compete for hypotheses on the grounds that the value of health services as a whole be given precedence (in the first instance) or that the value of individual patient-lives takes priority (the latter). Not only might one expect that different solutions to similar problems might be proposed by the two groups (the point of this editorial), but also that the weight given to recognizing the value of different approaches will differ depending upon the social conditions and acculturation that each group experiences. In this instance, as in most hypothesis formulation in the health sciences, the choice of a hypothesis may be not merely socially conditioned, but socially driving in terms of the attention given to solutions.

IX. Conclusion

From even this preliminary analysis, it should be evident that assigning a determinative or even contributory role to the moral content of hypotheses in selection of models for testing scientific propositions is fraught with difficulty. The balance point between what is morally threatening (compare categories in Table 2) and what is scientifically promising (see Table 1) may be impossible to determine with assurance. Not only are incommensurables being juxtaposed, but also the value system of the observer can shift the emphasis given to one set of priorities to the other, both within and between classes of criteria.

Whatever the ultimate value of a more refined system, it should be abundantly clear that the proliferation of scientific hypotheses under the rubric of freedom of inquiry can no longer proceed unexamined.

NOTES

1. Theodore Roszak, *Where the Wasteland Ends* (New York: Doubleday & Co., 1973) p. 142.
2. Karl Popper, *The Logic of Scientific Discovery* (New York: Basic Books, 1959).
3. George Wald, "Innovation in Biology," *Scientific American* 199 (September 1958), 100-13.
4. Conway Zirkle, *Marxian Biology and the Social Scene* (Philadelphia: University of Pennsylvania Press, 1959).
5. James Shapiro, L. Eron, and J. Beckwith, "Letter to the Editor," *Nature* (December 1969), p. 1337.
6. James Shapiro, quoted by James U. Glassman, "Harvard Researcher Quits Science for Politics," *Science* 167 (1970), 964-65.
7. Israel Sheffler, *Science and Subjectivity* (Indianapolis: Bobbs-Merrill Co., 1967), pp. v-vi. Cited in Stephen Brush, "Should the History of Science be Rated X?" *Science* 183 (1974), 1160-72.
8. Marc Lappé, "Accountability in Science" (Letter to the Editor), *Science* 187 (February 28, 1975), pp. 696-99.
9. Brush, "Should the History of Science be Rated X?"
10. Jerry Gaston, *Originality and Competition in Science: A Study of the British High Energy Physics Community* (Chicago: University of Chicago Press, 1974; Salvador Luria, "What Makes a Scientist Cheat," *Prism* (May 1975) pp. 15-18, 44; "The Sloan-Kettering Affair: Could It Have Happened Anywhere?" *JAMA* 229 (1974), 1391-1410.
11. Stephen Toulmin, "The Evolutionary Development of Natural Science," *American Scientist* 55 (1967), 456-71.
12. Abner Shimony, "Scientific Inference," in *The Nature and Function of Scientific Theories*, R. G. Colodny, ed. (Pittsburgh: University of Pittsburgh Press, 1970), pp. 79-172.
13. Richard Lewontin, *The Genetic Basis of Evolutionary Change* (New York: Columbia University Press, 1974), p. 157.
14. John Fuller and W. Robert Thompson, *Behavior Genetics* (New York: John Wiley & Sons, 1960).
15. David Layzer, "Heritability Analyses of IQ Scores: Science or Numerology?" *Science* 183 (1974), 1259-66. See also P. A. P. Moran, "A Note on Heritability and the Correlation Between Relatives," *Annals of Human Genetics* 37 (1973), 217, in which it is proven that a coefficient of heritability cannot be validly derived.
16. Alfred North Whitehead, *Adventures of Ideas* (Cambridge: Cambridge University Press, 1933), p. 154.

17. Frederick Suppe, "What's Wrong With the Received View on the Structure of Scientific Theories?" *Philosophy of Science* 39 (1972), 1-9.
18. Qutub Quazi and T. Reed, "A Possible Major Contribution to Mental Retardation in the General Population by Gene for Microcephaly," *Internal Journal of Clinical Genetics* 7 (1975), 85-90.
19. Paul Berg *et al.*, "Potential Biohazards of Recombinant DNA Molecules," *Science* 185 (1974), 303.
20. H. Lubs *et al.*, "Correlations Between Low IQ, Race and Variations in Q and C Banding," *American Journal of Human Genetics* 25 (1974), 47A.
21. Arne Svejgaard *et al.*, "HL-A and Disease Associations—A Survey," *Transplantation Reviews* 22 (1975), 3-43.
22. "Measuring Health and Disease," *Lancet* (June 9, 1973), pp. 1293-94.

Commentary

Hypothesis Formulation: Another "Inviolate" Realm Open for Ethical Inquiry?

E. D. Pellegrino

ONE OF THE MOST DIFFICULT things for scientists to accept is the examination of science itself, particularly by those outside science. Yet, the public concern for the moral and social implications of the unprecedented capabilities of science and technology is a commonplace today. Philosophers, ethicists, and scientists themselves are questioning the ideology of science as a value system, whenever it appears to demand prerogatives no other human endeavor can be allowed.

The essay by Dr. Lappé takes the inquiry into the usually inviolate realm of hypothesis formulation, suggesting that nonscientific values of moral and social significance should modulate the choice of hypotheses and the problems they generate. The troublous overtones of thought-control, censorship, and inhibition of creativity will worry every morally responsive scientist. Nonetheless, self-righteously to deny the validity of a critical inquiry into every facet of science is to deny the scientific attitude itself. Lappé's paper is therefore timely, and though quite preliminary, it deserves careful cogitation, particularly by those who use human beings as subjects.

Lappé's thesis is straightforward and simply set out. He avers that the formulation of scientific hypotheses and the selection of problems for study are importantly determined by non-scientific factors in the cultural, psychosocial, and personal realms. The long-presumed value-free state of hypothesis formulation is challenged. Lappé deems it socially responsible, and necessary, to interject value considerations into the selection of hypotheses. Some hypotheses and problems should be pursued; and others—because of their unfavorable impact on particular groups in society—ought not to be pursued, or at least should be held in abeyance.

Lappé draws his major examples from genetics and particularly behavioral genetics. His particular concern is with hypotheses which postulate genetic bases for complex phenomena such as intelligence. In such cases, the possibility of suggestions of inferiority of any social group can have serious practical impact. The interplay of nature and nurture in human behavior is too easily neglected in the interests of hypotheses and experiments which might have scientific feasibility. The more complex hypotheses which would more closely relate internal and external factors often cannot satisfy the criteria of scientific nicety.

To obviate some of these difficulties, Lappé proposes that the usual criteria for a scientifically sound hypothesis be modulated by a second set derived from the social-ethical realm and that these be "weighted" for their impact on the social well-being of individuals and groups. Presumably, the scientist would be expected to choose hypotheses and problems which could optimize both human and scientific values.

The difficulties and the dangers of implementing such a proposal are clear, and the temptation is to discard the suggestion out-of-hand. This is, unfortunately, the mood of quite a few scientists in the midst of an "ethical backlash" which has grown out of the current intensive inquiry into bio- and medical ethics by ethicists, philosophers, legislators, and the general public. To succumb to the negative stance that the "backlash" engenders is to reinforce the critics of science who contend that science and ethics are incompatible. Scientists must learn to distinguish between a defense of science as an ideology and science as a means for investigating reality. Science, in the first sense, would oppose Lappé by apodictic pronouncements. But science, in the second sense, would agree that science itself is a legitimate subject of inquiry. It is in this latter spirit that Lappé's paper should be examined.

What is being challenged is the absolute freedom scientists have enjoyed to ask the widest range of possible questions about man and nature. Even the seemingly irrational or preposterous statement can become a useful tool by the way it stimulates intellectual discourse and experiment to disprove it. This encroachment on the personal creativity of scientists must be understood in the wider context of the move today toward limiting the discretionary latitude of all who possess special knowledge. This is itself an expression of the even more fundamental anxiety in society that those with knowledge not available to all might not use it in the public interest. Lappé, therefore, opens the question in an atmosphere of considerable distrust for science.

To begin with, there is a serious question about whether we have—or will have—valid and verifiable information to make the *a priori* decisions Lappé's schema requires. Even in the scientific dimension, the criteria for a good hypothesis are in part subjective and debatable. When we add the criteria he proposes in Table 2, we encounter greater difficulties. How can we accurately identify and weigh cultural factors, the social cost of hypothesis selection, or the cost of verification? How can one validate *a priori* estimates in the value realm? Even if we try to envision the hypothesis as proven, how useful is the estimate of its social impact? Is this not begging the question and leaving the field open for prejudicial judgments?

Even more troublesome are the judgments that an hypothesis does or does not have moral consequences in terms of the weighting system in the classification schema Lappé proposes. Again, what valid way is there to determine when an hypothesis is inherently dangerous, mischievous, socially invidious, or holistically threatening? Would any research in behavioral genetics pass this test? Some group or other might well be placed in an unfavorable light temporarily. Even if this is not obvious in advance, some might argue that we must not entertain hypotheses in which such an outcome is even remotely possible. Yet, research in human behavior may be the most significant way mankind can deal with differences among people and build a better society which neutralizes the debilitating and discriminatory differences.

Even more serious is the question of who will make the determinations and on what authority and by what means they will enforce them. Is this to be the responsibility of individual scientists, institutions, or governments? Who will determine the delicate balance between scientific probity and social value of an hypothesis? Since the answers must be obtained in advance, the possibilities for endless ideological conflict and repression by extremists on the right or left are tremendous.

Concern about the damaging social consequences of hypotheses is valid. Granting this, however, does not negate the value of scientifically disproving a socially "dangerous" hypothesis. Should we sacrifice the social benefits of countering false notions once they arise? Now that questions about the interrelationships of genetics, race, intelligence, and behavior have been raised, the myths must be separated from the facts. The deficiencies of intelligence testing and the interrelationship of genetically determined and environmentally conditioned factors need to be better understood. What other means are there for defeating half-truths and prejudicial opinions?

There are some good reasons for exploring hypotheses which might reveal an inherent disadvantage of some human group. Those who might be the victims of a genetic deficit which impairs their capacity to cope with life on equal terms with the majority want, in the long run, to know it and to know how to overcome it. Rather than eliminating an hypothesis from consideration, it might be more socially responsible to explore it as rigorously as possible. Little is gained by a disadvantaged group if the source of its disadvantaged state is left in question or politely submerged. Is anything more patronizing or paternalistic than to protect a minority from accurate knowledge of its condition? If a debility exists, it should be known and treated or compensated for by social means. If it does not exist, that fact must be known as soon as possible. In either case, knowledge and not ignorance is the socially beneficial course.

More important than suppressing an hypothesis is the assurance that it is advanced with full knowledge of its dangers and with every safeguard that the knowledge obtained will be reliable and pertinent. Indeed, most of the examples Lappé uses are examples of poor scientific thinking. To come to conclusions about the predominating effect of genetic factors when the environmental factors have not been rigorously studied is poor science as much as it is poor ethics. Clearly the question of social impact of any hypothesis imposes a moral imperative on investigators and their peers not to support hypotheses in which the interplay of all relevant factors is not fully taken into account. No political or sociological strategy can protect us against poor science. The scientists' unique moral responsibility in this matter lies here.

This becomes particularly apparent in trying to apply a criterion as sweeping as "holistically threatening"—Class IV in Lappé's schema. Galileo's work was suppressed because it was in fact threatening to the dominant world view of his society. So were the ideas of Darwin, Freud, and Mendel, whose hypotheses threatened man's conceptions of his own nature. In each of these instances, the "dangerous" ideas had been considered before they were concretely addressed. Suppressing Galileo or Darwin would only have postponed the eventual exploration of their hypotheses while denying us their conceptual richness.

To try to determine what is a "holistic threat" leaves society open to the worst evils of an institutional or bureaucratic morality. We have seen too much already in our times of the way institutions assume a morality of their own—often in direct contravention to the best interests of society at large.

All of these difficulties notwithstanding, Lappé has opened up a series of questions that will not soon disappear. A deeper inquiry, together with some means for containing the more overtly threatening hypotheses, will be pressed upon scientists. Socially responsible ways of working with potentially dangerous hypotheses must be sought. Instead of inhibiting hypothesis formulation, I would prefer to improve our society's capabilities to deal with tentative ideas and ambiguous states of knowledge in more mature ways.

We should deepen and sharpen the questions Lappé has raised. Simultaneously, we must develop socially acceptable mechanisms to deal effectively and humanely with the differences among men—respecting those which do not debilitate and eradicating those that do. These distinctions cannot be made without creativity in hypothesis formulation, even if these hypotheses seem at first to be threatening to our world view or our social group.

We need a wider discussion of the values which underlie our way of life. Some operational definition of priorities is required if the new knowledge uncovered by medicine and science is to be humanely applied. Some combination of free hypothesis formulation, social monitoring of problems to be pursued, and a means for discontinuing hypotheses or experiments which are, in fact, threatening or dangerous must eventuate.

Social and legal methods for constraining scientific endeavors will be self-defeating without a heightening of the sense of moral responsibility of each investigator. The fine balance between a further loss of discretionary latitude, on the one hand, and a return to unrestrained scientific effort on the other, must be struck.

After all, it has never been possible to curb human thought. New ideas seem to work at a subconscious level amidst men and women of common interest and suddenly reach maturity in several places at the same time. The socially sensitive (or publicly regulated) scientist might reject the dangerous hypothesis, but the idea would still be discussed. The potential mischief of a damaging hypothesis could still be perpetrated. The moderation and modulation an ethical investigator could bring to the question would be lost.

I hope Lappé's paper can receive careful and rigorous debate by scientists and ethicists as well as philosophers, historians, and public policy-makers. His "hypothesis" is, itself, threatening to the world view of scientists. To inhibit its discussion is to admit tacitly that some ideas are too dangerous to handle—something no scholar or scientist should lightly admit.

Human Well-being and Medicine: Some Basic Value-Judgments in the Biomedical Sciences

H. Tristram Engelhardt, Jr.

THE CONCEPTS OF WELL-BEING and the good life have been of central interest for philosophy. These notions have also been addressed in part by the law and by social institutions. Of the latter, medicine and health care have been engaged in the achievement of the good life, human well-being, in distinctive ways: they have addressed themselves to cure and care. But educators cure ignorance, and congressmen care for their home districts. What then is the special character of the health professions? How is the good of health distinct from the good of an education or that of a just society? Though broken arms are neither vices nor states of ignorance, some states of ill health seem difficult to distinguish from virtue and ignorance. For example, are psychopaths congenitally vicious or are they ill, and how are we to understand the persistent heavy smoker who develops chronic lung disease, or the individual with a phobia whose habits can be corrected by behavior therapy?

These somewhat heterogeneous questions have in common an accent on the ambiguity of both the concept of health and that of disease. Or, to put it another way, the health professions are

120

goal-oriented enterprises focused on the preservation of and/or reestablishment of human well-being, with the nature of that well-being left somewhat vague. But, at least to begin with, one can distinguish the endeavors of the health professions from education and moral discourse in that the former are engaged in explanation, prediction, and control—diagnosis, prognosis, and therapy. The health professions presume that the phenomena they address, whether psychological or somatic, are bound together in nomological regularities. That is, the health professions presuppose at least the possibility of health sciences—that it is possible to study and give scientific accounts in terms of pathology and psychopathology. They deal with empirical regularities, not primarily with blame and praise—with freedom. Thus, the health sciences and professions are not, as such, exercises in applied ethics.

It might seem, then, that biomedical endeavors could be easily distinguished from normative discourse. But both normative ethics and medicine tell one what the good life is (virtue in the one case and health in the other), and how to act so as to maximize the good life (virtue and health) by avoiding or correcting that which mars human life (vice and disease). To say that something is a disease commits one to saying something about human nature and the nature of human well-being. Further, such talk involves choices among human goods. Thus, to characterize polydactylia, for example, as a disease, is to say that six fingers on a hand is profoundly ugly; or to characterize color blindness as a disease, is to say that seeing colors is a human good. The question of the choice among goods is most problematic in the case of mental diseases, in that psychiatry tends to compass a broader range of human life than other medical specialties. Thus, disorders such as homosexuality,(1) masturbation,(2) and frigidity(3) have been at times classified as diseases.

In short, discussions about what counts as health and disease involve consideration of what counts as the proper human state, and the latter is caught up with value-judgments which are both explicit and implicit. Insofar as health and disease are concepts that structure the context or life-world not only of health professionals, but of all of us who orient ourselves with regard to our sickness and well-being, value-judgments about human conditions structure reality. In deciding, for example, that sickle cell anemia is a disease, one opens up the possibility of programs for detection and prevention which influence attitudes toward persons with the disease, as well as those who possess the trait. Being told that one has sickle cell trait may then have impact on one's attitudes toward reproduction, even the choice of one's mate. Health and disease are concepts which direct us and help us in the formation of our life-projects—the goals we set for our lives and the ways in which we pursue them.

The purpose of this paper will be to speak to this issue: the role and nature of value-judgments in defining the realities described by pathology and psychopathology. The paper contains three sections: the first addresses the concepts of well-being and disease; the second focuses on the role of value-judgments in sorting out symptoms and sign complexes (syndromes) and their place in the development of explanatory models in medicine; and the third states a few summary conclusions.

I. Well-being and Disease

The concept of health is central to medicine and the conduct of human life but is complex and ambiguous. The ambiguity turns in part on the ambiguity in the concept of human well-being. It turns, too, on the fact that it is not clear what dimensions of human well-being are meant to be encompassed in the concept of health. Consider, for example, the definition of health given by the World Health Organization: "Health is a state of complete physical, mental, and social well-being and not merely the absence of disease or infirmity."(4) This definition, it would seem, is broad enough to encompass both moral and political well-being. Further, on the basis of the concept of complete well-being, few, if any, humans are healthy. Thus, this concept seems to function as an ideal rather than an achievable norm: it indicates how humans *should* live rather than merely indicating how they could, in fact, live.

The relationship between the concepts of health and disease is also unclear. Is there only one concept of health, or are there, on the other hand, numerous concepts of health, each corresponding to a particular concept of disease? The World Health Organization's definition of health as "not merely the absence of disease or infirmity," but "a state of complete physical, mental, and social well-being" addresses this question by suggesting that there is only one standard of health, though there are many ways in which one's health can be deficient, ways in which one can be diseased. In that case, every definition of disease, or of a particular disease, would presuppose a different element of health. To say that asthma and peptic ulcer are disease states presupposes that ease in breathing and in digestion are elements of health. But those judgments imply that one knows what functions, under what conditions, are proper to human nature. On this issue, for example, turn the questions of the meaning of aging and the significance of widely distributed phenomena such as acne—are they diseases? Do they constitute the absence of "normal" human well-being?

And so the questions seem to multiply without end. One might be tempted to think, then, that such questions are merely academic quibbles to be sorted out at leisure, and that they have little practical significance. But if aging, for example, is considered a disease rather than a normal phenomenon, then one is likely to "treat" aging in a different fashion. The phrase "premature aging" indicates that some aging is proper, other aging is not. If one conceives of menopause as a proper, natural phenomenon, one may, for example, treat changes in the vaginal mucosa of postmenopausal women in a different way than if one regards such changes as diseases to be avoided.(5) That is, if one conceives of postmenopausal women as normally sexually active beings, whose function as such should be preserved as long as possible, one has implicitly made a decision according to a concept of the nature of human well-being.

These issues move into a whole domain and spectrum of states: presbyopia, elevated cholesterol levels, baldness, the morbidity associated with normal teething—the frequent if not usual wear-and-tear and changes associated with living. To some extent, judgments about these states depend on the context: phenylketonuria would never exist as a disease if humans usually ate diets free of phenylalanine. Such considerations suggest that one aspect of health is a successful adaptation to one's environment and that disease is maladaptation. Such judgments are based on the usual state of things, and on what one should be adapted to do or to be. Humans, for example, usually do not eat phenylalanine-free diets. But, again, such judgments cannot merely be made in terms of the usual state as a statistical norm, because even if, for example, presbyopia is the usual state for persons over forty, one may still wish to call such conditions states of disease.

Adaptation is a goal-oriented concept which presupposes that one knows what activities humans should be adapted to engage in and under what conditions. For example, sickle cell trait may be a state of health in an environment where falciparum malaria is endemic and antimalarial drugs are not available; the same trait would be a disease in high mountain villages with low oxygen pressure. Or, to take another example, humans, unlike rats, are not adapted to living on a Vitamin C-free diet, though it does not follow from this fact that all humans are diseased (though a rat which could not synthesize Vitamin C would be considered diseased). What is crucial in understanding adaptation is not the environment or organism as such but the purposes or goals which one holds that the organism should be able to achieve. Human well-being in the sense of health comes to identify a physical or psychological condition of humans that enables them to engage in the activities proper to them as humans. What will count as health, as a result, becomes dependent in part on the range of activity one considers to be a proper element of human life. As a positive concept, the concept of health refers to one's ability to engage in the range of activities or be in the range of states which should be open to other members of one's species, even though, in fact, not all members of the species do engage in such activities. To say that X is healthy is to say that X does not have a physical or psychological inability to do those things that humans should be able to do (or be like—e. g., not have acne).(6)

One must, then, give an account of what is proper to humans in order to give a sketch of the concept of health. The account is circular. One decides what humans should be able to do by deciding what will count as physical and psychological well-being (health) and one decides what should be physical and psychological well-being on the basis of what will count as the projects proper to humans. The nature of health and the scope of human projects are closely bound, for health is a necessary condition for whatever endeavors humans wish to engage in. Painting pictures, building houses, hunting for food, tilling the soil, having sex, bearing children, reading books, conceiving of new ideas—all to varying extents presuppose a state of health. The delineation of the scope of health depends on what one judges to be the elements of normal human life. Moreover, the elements appear not only to be multiple, but diverse. One is forced thus to examine the meaning of a normal human lifestyle in a piecemeal fashion. That is, by seeing what counts as diseases, by seeing what elements of the life process when absent would not support well-being, we might be able to understand what is meant by health. Even if health may not be merely the absence of disease, what we take to be diseases can help us to understand the scope of the concept of health. By recognizing what is not health, we can sketch in the boundaries or limits of health. We will move, thus, to consider the concept of health in a "backwards" fashion—through the concept of disease.

What will count as a proper human goal is open-ended and turns on a decision concerning what humans should be, as well as what they are. Even if 95 percent of the human population developed juvenile diabetes, and the "normals" were thus statistically deviant, one could still decide that diabetes is a disease. Similarly, aging can be seen as a disease if one wants to decide that a particular life-span, free of certain limitations upon action, should exist. The less pain is involved, and the less widely distributed the limitation on action, then the more the judgment that a particular condition (a particular limitation on free, rational action) is a disease is open to cultural variability. Thus, whether or not color blindness, or the inability to roll the sides of one's tongue inwards, will count as diseases will depend upon what a group of people decide should be the goals of man.

The decision is a group decision. To call someone ill is a social judgment involving particular social roles. But how do groups decide upon the proper goals of humans (and thus upon the geography of health and disease), and are there ways in which one might say a group decided wrongly (or rightly)? The last question is fundamental to the issue of the nature of disease. At least two general types of answers are forthcoming. First, proper human goals can be defined in terms of what is conducive to the long-range survival of the species.(7) This has the advantage of giving an evolutionary aura to the criterion— health is that which is conducive to the long-range adaptability and success of the species.

There are difficulties with such an answer, however. For example, given such an interpretation, persons with sickle cell disease could not be said to be diseased, in the absence of antimalarial drugs and the presence of falciparum malaria (sickle cell trait appears to give adaptive advantage to individuals in environments where there is a great deal of falciparum malaria and thus to be an element of normal function).(8) Their discomfort, and even death, would simply be the price of group survival and a part of the adaptability of the species. Such an analysis presupposes, of course, that long-term survival of the species is a fundamental or overriding goal—a goal that may or may not be accepted by individual humans or even the community of humans. In fact, one might somewhat perversely turn this naturalistic argument around and point out that it is natural for species to die out. For example, merely possible future humans, as not actually humans, would not be treated as means merely if we decided not to bring them into existence and, instead, consume for ourselves the resources available which they could have claimed, had they come into existence, become actual persons.

Further, human nature is not necessarily adapted to human goals. Or, to quote Sir Peter Medawar, " . . . nature does *not* know best,"(9) but creates a " . . . tale of woe [including] anaphylactic shock, allergy, and hypersensitivity,"(10) due to the character of human nature. What nature imposes often is not at all what reasonable humans would choose as goals. The proper or essential human goals to which healthy human processes contribute are those in accord with human judgments about what should be the case, which obliquely makes a Kantian point: the truly human is rational free agency and what contributes to that is healthy and what does not is diseased. But, of course, there are a great number of ways to be rational and free, and hence the ambiguity with respect to specifying essential or proper human goals in this fashion.

This brings us to the second method of deciding what counts as essential or proper human goals. Humans are distinguished from other species in being rational free agents. Rational free action is *the* proper human goal, in terms of which all other human purposes are best pursued, including moments of impetuous abandon. In such terms, those states that augment rational free action would count as health and those that restrict the basis of such activity would be diseases. This answer has both advantages and disadvantages. On the one hand, it helps explain the plasticity of the definition of health and disease: the goal of rational free agency is abstract and can be specified in many fashions. Thus, though anything that impeded intelligence (such as schizophrenia) or limited action (such as paralysis) would, *prima facie*, count as a disease state, the diseases of homosexuality or color blindness would remain moot. Decisions as to what would be a disease would then to a great extent hinge on the finitude which humans as finite agents would accept and the character of the life they wished to live. Thus one sees, for example, discussions of aging which really amount to considerations of the amount of aging one will accept and what amount one will treat as a disease.

The second answer also forces a clearer delineation of medical problems from political or moral problems which might circumscribe free agency as well. That is, if medical problems are not problems for which one is responsible as one is for one's moral problems, how are the lines to be drawn? Siegler and Osmond give a summary of Talcott Parsons' sketch of the sick role that highlights the fact that though being sick is not a state of affairs for which one is immediately responsible, it is a state for which one is responsible for seeking treatment. "First, depending on the nature and severity of the illness, the sick person is exempted from some or all of his normal social role responsibilities. Second, the sick person cannot help being ill, and cannot get well by an act of decision or will. Third, the sick person is expected to want to get well as soon as possible. Fourth, he is expected to seek appropriate help, usually that of a physician, and cooperate with that help toward the end of getting well."(11) The division between lack of responsibility for having the disease and responsibility for treating the disease is not as clear-cut as this sketch may suggest. One is also responsible for not having prevented the diseases one has, insofar as such prevention was possible. In short, it is hard to sift out the elements of moral responsibility with respect to disease.

On the one hand, having a disease cannot be an immediate result of an act of the will, like stealing a car or telling a lie. Otherwise, it would be appropriate to say to the diseased person, "Stop that at once!" Yet, one can be responsible for one's disease, as a smoker can be responsible for having bronchogenic carcinoma, or a person with angina can be responsible for an attack if he imprudently runs up a flight of stairs. Such responsibility for one's illness is liable to increase as it becomes easier to predict what available actions will lead to or prevent illness. Thus, a smoker can be properly blamed for getting cancer. Further, if he or she requires treatment that is a burden on the general community, one has a basis for saying that he or she acted immorally with respect to the responsibility to avoid cancer and its public costs. One can imagine increasing the tax on cigarettes specifically to pay for the cost of treating the diseases of smokers. They have a special duty to pay for the costs that have resulted from their acquiring a disease they could have avoided. They are to blame. The same conclusions can be made with respect to drug addicts. One can blame them for *becoming* addicted, though one could not blame them for *being* addicted.

In short, with respect to disease, one wishes both to blame and not to blame. The distinctions turn on the fact that diseases, mental and physical, are as such held to be due to a fabric of causal events imposed upon the person afflicted, even if that person may have initiated the causal sequence (the smoking which led to the disease). Thus, to say that someone is responsible for having a disease is to say that one has a condition (mental or physical) at time t_0, which is causally imposed independently of one's volition at t_0, though at a previous time, t_{-1}, one could have avoided initiating the causal sequence that led to the disease. As a result, it makes sense to blame a person with angina for developing the disease if a different diet would have prevented it, and for blaming the anginal patient for a present attack if more prudent behavior would have avoided it. But one cannot hold him responsible for having angina (in the sense of "keeping" the angina) with respect to any of his or her choices at that present time at which he or she already has the disease.

Judgments concerning disease states thus have complex social implications. They are the basis for both excusing and for blaming, for saying that having a disease is not dependent upon human volition, though acquiring a disease may be the result of human negligence. The problem of defining the scope of the groups which share common judgments about the proper goals of humans is a task for medical sociologists. It is a task of describing social groups that share a lifeworld in which certain abilities and human activities are seen as essential to the human condition. But cross-cultural criticism is still possible when and if concepts of disease fail to distinguish political and moral judgments from medical judgments. Criticism would, for example, be possible if a group held that exceptionally high intelligence or clarity in making decisions were diseases. Such judgments would fly in the face of the nature of being human, of being a rational agent.(12) Finally, expectations with respect to health that did not recognize the limits of human life (those who might want to speak of death itself as something to be overcome by medicine) could be judged as mistaken. Death itself should, for example, never count as a disease.(13)

One is thus confronted with a spectrum of diseases ranging from those which obviously limit humans in some essential fashion in their capacity as agents (coronary artery disease, carcinoma) to those states which may or may not be seen as limitations (homosexuality, color blindness). Norms as far as they can be had are thus somewhat abstract: the proper goal of humans is to act freely and rationally. But there are many ways to achieve that goal, and so only the more severe limitations on its pursuit show themselves unambiguously to be diseases. In other cases, the choice is open to variations, such as those with respect to whether alcoholism or drug addiction or obesity should count as diseases. This is not to say that choices of whether or not such states should be considered diseases are arbitrary, but only that they are much less clear-cut.

Medicine is thus involved in deciding the nature and geography of human well-being. The geography is, as the above attests, heterogeneous. Many things are gathered under the rubric disease and for diverse reasons: considerations of teleology, pain, and aesthetics. Beyond that, there is a whole clan of loosely related usages: "He has a disease," "He has a congenital deformity," "He has a birth defect," "He has a deformity of his hand due to an auto accident . . . due to surgery . . . due to an infection." Are all these conditions to be spoken of as disease states in some extended sense? Is an amputee to be said to be suffering from a disease (the absence of a leg), and does it matter whether the amputation resulted from the injury of an accident or was performed because of osteogenic carcinoma?

Dorland's Dictionary defines disease as "a definite morbid process having a characteristic train of symptoms," and a syndrome as "a set of symptoms which occur together."(14) Thus, there may be a point in saying that the person who has a gunshot wound has a syndrome, though not a disease—the process that caused the damage was not immediately part of a physiological or psychological train of causality (though that may incidentally be the case—the person who did the shooting may have been psychotic). The gunshot wound, though, constitutes a syndrome, a collect of morbid symptoms and signs which are the business of medicine to address. The amputee may or may not be in a similar circumstance, depending on the extent to which he or she is still crippled or rehabilitated by a prosthesis. Syndromes, the patterns of observables which medicine addresses with treatment, are patterns of physical and/or mental limitations accountable (or at least held theoretically to be accountable) in terms of physiological and/or psychological laws—even the state of affairs treated for other than a pathological process (loss of a limb from shark bite).

In short, the language of medicine is complex and exceeds the language of its nosologies. "He is crippled because he lost his right leg in an auto accident," and "He is crippled because his right leg was amputated because of osteogenic carcinoma" identify states of nonhealth illness so that it is possible to recognize both individuals as being in a state properly the object of medical concern, even if the individuals are not diseased in the sense of still being subject to a "morbid process." One can be sick (fulfill Talcott Parsons' criteria for the sick role) without being diseased, if one uses the term "disease" in the restricted fashion prominent in some of the ordinary usages of "disease" ("He is crippled but he is not diseased," or "He is crippled but does not have a disease"). Finally, at this juncture one more qualification or reminder is perhaps needed: not all morbid states are the results of presently active morbid processes. Morbid states can be the end stages of long-ceased morbid processes (the scars of smallpox), or of nondisease processes (the scars of a burn). Consequently, one can say of someone, "He is not in perfect health; after all, he is a paraplegic because of his accident, but he does not have any diseases."

The concepts of health and illness are more ample than the concept of disease. Disease language involves a move to generate scientific explanations of syndromes by reference to some ongoing processes leading to those syndromes. In contrast, some people are ill, not healthy, because of diseases long ended or because of accidents. But the disorders, disabilities, and syndromes to which medicine does turn its attention, define by contrast the geography of health and indicate the various groups of evaluations which identify the elements of human well-being. This geography is a heterogeneous domain of concerns, presupposing variously related judgments about human well-being and its absence.

II. Discovering the Pathological

But how does one recognize a particular state as a state of illness, open to being explained as a disease, given the general conditions outlined above? To begin with, in recognizing clusters of phenomena as syndromes, one engages in evaluation, not description alone. One identifies a complex of signs and symptoms, a constellation of complaints and associated physical findings, as morbid—that is, as constituting a recognizable pattern that should be treated. The pattern is not merely recognized as a pattern, but as one which is in some way wrong and which should, if possible, be corrected. Syndromes are, as I will consider them, collections of observables considered apart from any explicit theoretical account of their nature and composition. They are identified through collections of reports of pain and discomfort, as well as observations of dysfunction and deformity. At the level of syndrome identification, there are important evaluative judgments as to what is unpleasant, dysfunctional, or deforming. The judgment as to what should be brought within the scope of a syndrome turns on what coheres as a pattern of signs and symptoms, as well as whether the pattern is an illness, a disagreeable state attributable to somatic or psychological dysfunction rather than to willful obstinacy (a common fit of anger), or a planned deception (a case of malingering), or the action of supernatural powers (a demonic possession). Syndromes are thus observable patterns in search of a medical explanation. They presuppose that the cluster of observables constitutes a pattern which can be explained in terms of the laws of pathology and/or psychology. As a consequence, a subset of the universe of observation statements is mapped onto the universe of explanations insofar as a cluster of observables is identified as morbid (as an illness) and is then given a disease explanation.(15)

To call a state of affairs an illness is not simply to identify the state, but also to characterize it as being in some sense bad. The types of evaluative judgments involved in such selections of clusters of phenomena as syndromes (illnesses) are diverse. They can, however, be arrayed into at least three groups: the teleological, the algesic, the aesthetic—each concerned with a different aspect of human well-being. The first, the teleological, speak to the issue of those functions proper to humans; they concern the goals humans should be adapted to achieve. In this first group one might, for example, place toxic amaurosis, blindness following exposure to such agents as wood alcohol. One presumes seeing to be a proper function of humans, and the blindness to be caused, not feigned. But specifying the scope of that natural function brings one to borderline cases which emphasize the role of evaluative judgments concerning the proper range of human abilities. There is thus the question of whether color blindness is a disease: is seeing colors an ability the lack of which would count as a disease? That judgment seems in part to turn on the fact that most humans can see color. Because no humans are adapted (able) to see ultraviolet, "blindness" to ultraviolet is not a disease (and is thus, in a sense, not blindness at all). Whether color blindness is a disease thus depends on what we hold are the proper goals of humans.

Such teleological judgments also play a role in deciding whether aging is a disease, whether the pain of normal childbirth is pathological, whether respiratory distress when climbing a mountain is normal or an indication of disease. In each case, one is deciding whether the discomfort is to be accepted or to be treated as abnormal. Judgments of these sorts are complex, but can be put this way: X is (under these criteria) a disease state, (1) if and only if it is a state arising out of physiological and/or psychological processes of an individual beyond the direct control at that time of the person afflicted; and (2) if that state precludes a proper or essential human goal.(16) Thus, if seeing color is part of being a human, color blindness is a disease. If being able to see colors is not an essential or proper function, then being able to see colors turns out to be merely an ability which enhances, but is not central to, human well-being.

The use of terms such as "function" or "dysfunction" indicates that such judgments concerning what will count as a disease presuppose judgments concerning goals to be served. Thus, the fact that a large number of individuals cannot taste phenylthiocarbamide is, most likely, not going to cause anyone to call them diseased.(17) Tasting phenylthiocarbamide is just not important to any human goals in the same way that seeing colors is. The same can be said with regard to the genetic trait of being able to roll the edges of one's tongue inwards.(18) Whether or not such functions are important enough so that their absence would constitute a disease depends on what one considers to be proper human goals and abilities. In short, judgments concerning disease states involve a whole range of more or less subtle judgments concerning the activities humans should be able to perform, the goals they should be able to achieve. Humans should be able to walk up five flights of stairs if they are not ninety; they should be able to make precise movements with their hands; they should be able to balance themselves with great precision; they should be able to taste and enjoy their food, enjoy sex, see the world, and hear a certain range of sounds.

For example, if, as Dr. Robert Heath maintains, marijuana is pathogenic because it causes a decrease in interest and drive, then there is a presupposition that humans should be able to accomplish a certain quantity or quality of things in order to be healthy, to realize the proper goals of humans.(19) Or, to place the issue in a different perspective, if it is important to have a natural resistance to many of the effects of the falciparum malaria, sickle cell trait becomes a state of health, and sickle cell disease becomes the cost to a population of being healthy.

One should also notice that the pattern of a syndrome can be such as to collect mental as well as physical signs and symptoms. Behavior patterns can be judged to be pathological as, for example, are schizophrenia and obsessive-compulsive neuroses, even though there are not well-established causal accounts of these phenomena. They count as diseases (at least as syndromes), not only because they are dysfunctional (untreated schizophrenics cannot do abstract thinking well, or participate well in the affairs of life; obsessive-compulsive neurotics find their compulsions interfering with their activities, goals, and projects), but also because people with these states find them unpleasant (painful in an extended sense).

The notorious difficulties in deciding with regard to the character of natural teleology should also be noted here. The nosologic standing of homosexuality is a good example. The judgment that homosexuality is a disease was made in part on the basis of an alleged dysteleological character of such sexuality (it is not natural), and in part on its compulsive character.(20) Yet, on the second point, heterosexuals seem as compelled in their behavior as do homosexuals. Again, these difficulties in specifying what is normal with regard to psychological syndromes are, it should be added, not unknown with regard to somatic conditions. Persons who are color-blind tend to discriminate differences in intensity much better than those who see colors, and thus, among other things, are good at detecting camouflage.(21) The noncolor-blind thus have a disadvantage as well. In short, the difficulty of specifying goals is widespread.

The second type of judgments made with regard to disease states are made in terms of their being painful. A migraine headache counts as an illness in terms of pain alone, independently of any regard to loss of function. One might term these algesic criteria. These can be overridden in the case of painful activities held to be essential to proper goals of humans: childbirth, teething, pain after unaccustomed exercise. Here the judgment appears to be that X is a disease (under these criteria) (1) if and only if the state (here that of pain) arises out of a physiological and/or psychological process beyond the direct control at that time of the person afflicted; and (2) if the state of pain is not part of a process conducive to a proper or essential human goal. Of the three factors used in sorting out clusters of phenomena as diseases, the algesic appear to be the least variant: a pain is a pain even if cultural circumstances influence its evaluation. Morover, as a relatively simple reaction to stimuli, there has been fair success in identifying its physiological substrata. Thus, broken legs, angina, and colitis show themselves relatively unproblematically to be disease states: they are appreciated as collections of phenomena which involve pain held to be due to physiological processes beyond the direct control of the persons affected (and the same could be said with regard to pain associated with similarly uncontrollable psychological processes).

The third set of criteria is aesthetic. Some states of affairs are taken to be disease states because of aesthetic judgments like "Polydactylia is a disease," or "Supernumerary breasts is a deformity." A woman and her society might very well consider alopecia areata a disease since women in our culture, even more than men, seem to be perturbed by becoming bald, even if only partially. Further, as David Mechanic points out, one South American tribe considers anyone not marked by the colored spots of dyschromic spirochetosis to be diseased and excludes the person from marriage.(22) The aesthetic is the most evasive of the criteria. It is very difficult (if not impossible) to specify what counts as a human deformity or, to reverse the statement, what counts as physical well-being with respect to human form and appearance. Are achondroplastic dwarfs diseased because they are dwarfs? What are proper human proportions? In any event, the judgment here again requires that the state of affairs held to be a disease or pathologic deformity not be under the direct control of the person afflicted and that the state of affairs be appreciated as abnormal, as a deviant form.

As heterogeneous as these judgments may appear, they draw the line between physiology and pathology; they isolate and associate clusters of phenomena for medicine and the biomedical sciences to explain. They define implicitly what *pathos*, suffering, is.

III. Some Conclusions

This series of considerations of the concept of human well-being and medicine leads to at best a very general concept of health, namely, a state of possessing the physiological and psychological prerequisites (or substrata) of rational free agency. But one can be free in so many ways and rationally pursue so many goals that only very general things can be said beyond the judgment that rational free agency, and, *a fortiori*, its physical and mental preconditions, are the cardinal goods for the health of any person. Thus any physiological or psychological processes or states not under the immediate control of a person which (1) preclude the goals chosen as integral to the general life of humans (inability to engage in the range of physical activity held integral to human life); (2) cause pain (if that pain is not integral to a process leading to goals held to be integral to human life); (3) preclude a physical form that other humans would hold to be normal (not deformed)—will count as diseases. One should notice that much of the ambiguity of the concepts of health and disease stems from the fact that what is said about human well-being would be true of embodied persons generally, not just human persons. This essay has given an account of the well-being of embodied persons insofar as that well-being can be considered by medicine. Anything more concrete will have to be provided by a medical-sociological and anthropological study of the goals humans accept as integral to their physiological and psychological well-being. Surely much awaits an interdisciplinary effort by philosophers, medical sociologists, and anthropologists. Humans are animals which make their own nature, set their own standards of health and disease, and thus raise core issues concerning the directions and goods of life. They raise issues which are ineluctably both philosophical and scientific.

NOTES

This paper is drawn in part from a lecture given in the Matchette Lecture Series, Southern Methodist University, Dallas, Texas, December 9, 1974. I am in many respects in the debt of recent publications concerning the concept of health and disease: Lester S. King, "What Is Disease?" *Philosophy of Science* 21 (July 1954), 193-203; Horocio Fabrega, "Concepts of Disease: Logical Features and Social Implications," *Perspectives in Biology and Medicine* 15 (Summer 1972), 583-616; Robert P. Hudson, "The Concept of Disease," *Annals of Internal Medicine* 65 (September 1966), 595-601; *Hastings Center Studies* 1:3 (1973), "The Concept of Health"; Ruth Macklin, "Mental Health and Mental Illness: Some Problems of Definition and Concept Formation," Philosophy of Science 39 (September 1972), 341-65; Owsei Temkin, "The Scientific Approach to Disease: Specific Entity and Individual Sickness," in *Scientific Changes* A. C. Crombie, ed. (London: Heinemann, 1961), pp. 629-47; Henry Cohen, *Concepts of Medicine* (Oxford: Pergamon Press, 1960), p. 160; and Stewart Wolf, "Disease as a Way of Life: Neural Integration in Systematic Pathology," *Perspectives in Biology and Medicine* 4 (Spring 1961), 288-305. I am particularly in debt to Lester King and Laurence B. McCullough for their suggestions concerning this paper.

1. American Psychiatric Association, "Sexual Deviation," *Diagnostic and Statistical Manual: Mental Disorders* (Washington, D.C.: American Psychiatric Association, 1952), pp. 38-39.
2. H. Tristram Engelhardt, Jr., "The Disease of Masturbation: Values and the Concept of Disease," *Bulletin of the History of Medicine* 48 (Summer 1974), 234-48.

138   H. TRISTRAM ENGELHARDT, JR.

3. *American Handbook of Psychiatry*, Silvano Arieti, ed. (New York: Basic Books, 1959), I, 719.
4. Constitution of the World Health Organization (preamble). *The First Ten Years of the World Health Organization* (Geneva: World Health Organization, 1958), p. 459.
5. Robert W. Kistner, "The Menopause," *Clinical Obstetrics and Gynecology* 16 (December 1973), 107-29; Robert A. Wilson, Raimondo E. Brevetti, and Thelma A. Wilson, "Specific Procedures for the Elimination of the Menopause," *Western Journal of Surgery, Obstetrics, and Gynecology* 71 (May-June 1963), 110-21.
6. The accent must fall on one's physical or psychological state, rather than on one's moral state, with the presumption that the first, unlike the second, is properly described in terms of psychological and physiological regularities and nomological structures; and the second is described in terms of one's free actions or states open to alterations immediately through one's exercise of free choice. For example, one's ability to survive under physical stress may be a sign of health, even though that condition is the result of free action, such as being in good physical condition due to frequent exercise. That state of good health, though, is only mediately the result of one's free choice— namely, the choice is mediated by the physical exercise. A moral resolution, though, is immediately connected to one's free choice.
7. Chauncey D. Leake and Patrick Romanell, *Can We Agree?* (Austin: University of Texas Press, 1950).
8. F. B. Livingstone, "The Distributions of the Abnormal Hemoglobin Genes and Their Significance for Human Evolution," *Evolution* 18 (1964), 685.
9. Peter Brian Medawar, *The Future of Man* (London: Methuen and Company, 1960), p. 100.
10. *Ibid.*, p. 101.
11. Miriam Siegler and Humphry Osmond, "The 'Sick Role' Revisited," *Hastings Center Studies* 1:3 (1973), 41.
12. It should be noted that these boundaries of the natural for humans as free agents are the boundaries for persons as such, not only human persons. That is, they would apply to all persons, whether human or not. This implies that what is important here is not human nature, but the nature of persons. In particular, human persons can for good reasons change human nature as, for example, is done with birth control, which divorces the social and biological dimensions of sexuality. Human nature becomes something for human persons to modify and change.

13. To fail to recognize death as a natural limit would be to fail to recognize the necessary contingency of human life. It would thus, in a sense, be irrational. See H. Tristram Engelhardt, Jr., "The Counsels of Finitude," *Hastings Center Report* 5:2 (April 1975), 29-35.
14. *Dorland's Illustrated Medical Dictionary*, 24th ed., s.v. "disease."
15. One could thus distinguish illness and disease as *explanandum* and *explanans*, the first belonging to the universe of observation statements, the second belonging to the universe of explanatory statements. A suggestion in this vein is made by Alvan Feinstein, *Clinical Judgment* (Huntington, N.Y.: Robert E. Krieger Publishing Co., 1967). In this paper I will somewhat loosely use the terms "illness," "disease state," and "syndrome" as equivalent statements identifying a complex of phenomena recognized as morbid. In fact, syndromes will often simply be called "diseases" to indicate that they are illnesses subject to a disease explanation.
16. The reference to the state of disease being beyond direct control of the individual rules out calling states such as not being able to see because one's eyes are closed, diseases.
17. This condition may, though, be correlated with diseases. H. Harris, H. Kalmus, and W. R. Trotter, "Taste Sensitivity to Phenylthiourea in Goitre and Diabetes," *Lancet* 2 (1949), 1038.
18. Amram Scheinfeld, *Your Heredity and Environment* (Philadelphia: J. B. Lippincott, 1965), pp. 480-81.
19. *People* 2 (December 9, 1974), 12-13.
20. Morton Prince, "Sexual Perversion or Vice? A Pathological and Therapeutic Inquiry," *Journal of Nervous and Mental Disease* 25 (1898); 237-65.
21. Richard H. Post, "Population Differences in Red and Green Color Vision Deficiency: A Review, and a Query on Selection Relaxation," *Eugenics Quarterly* 9 (March 1962), 131-46.
22. David Mechanic, *Medical Sociology* (New York: The Free Press, 1968), p. 16.

Commentary

Historical Notes on Levels
of Disease Conceptualization

Guenter B. Risse

RATHER THAN ANALYZING Professor Engelhardt's arguments from a philosophical point of view, my task as a historian has been to deal with the process of disease conceptualization as reflected by the medical past. Needless to say, the ambiguity of both the concepts of health and disease and their dependence on value judgments are readily confirmed through a survey of the historical record. A useful method of examining Professor Engelhardt's value judgments in their role of defining the pathological is to superimpose them on the actual biological reality present during a given historical period. This reality should be properly viewed as a shifting ecological balance between the human organism and a host of potentially harmful microorganisms, an equilibrium variously determined by geographical location, climate, and human activity and organization.(1)

A review of contemporary primitive cultures, in part mirroring prehistoric settings, reveals the presence of symptom clusters involving pain, disability, and even deformity. Cosmological beliefs and religious values largely determine the way in which the causal agents thought to be responsible for such symptoms are defined. Hence, certain syndromes are lumped together as coherent units, and are believed to have been inflicted by individualized agents—a witch, god, or demon. By contrast, other clusters of symptoms, involving perhaps a similar degree of pain and disability, are viewed in naturalistic causal terms. These manifestations generally reflect traumatic ailments, acquired during hunting, warfare, and even agricultural pursuits.

Whether magico-religious or naturalistic in origin, many symptom sequences are distinguished as clearly as possible, lifted out of the confusing and complex array of dysfunctional perceptions, and given a specific name. Such crude ontological conceptualizations of disease, which occur in practically all primitive societies, are highly useful. They provide a focus for specific therapy while assigning meaning to a series of disagreeable sensations, thereby lessening the patient's fear and anxiety.(2)

A higher level of sophistication in the discernment of symptom clusters or clearly defined syndromes occurred in the ancient Near East. Limited records obtained from Mesopotamia—for example, the forty tablets edited by the French Assyriologist René Labat—seem to confirm this. In those texts, the magical healer or *ashipu* selected a certain pattern of distress in order to arrive at a diagnosis, the naming of an illness. Most of the sequences were ordered according to the parts of the body in which were observed the prominent symptoms ("If he suffers in his middle and his belly"), thereby closely relating discomfort and loss of function with certain bodily regions.(3)

Similarly, we can detect more clearly defined symptom clusters in ancient Egypt, especially those of traumatic origin, which were therefore viewed in naturalistic rather than purely magico-religious terms. "One with a gaping wound in his head which has penetrated to the bone, denting the sutures of his skull, the end of his mandible is contracted, he discharges blood from both his nostrils and ears, he suffers stiffness in his neck . . .," reads a case in the Edwin Smith papyrus.(4)

With the Mesopotamian and Egyptian examples, one can see already that the early ontological concept of disease is buttressed by the linking of specific clusters of signs and symptoms to certain organs or parts of the body and an impairment of their structural integrities. In the case of Egypt, such a view was strongly reinforced by a religion which assigned protective deities to certain human organs, and by funerary practices confirming their presence. Moreover, the reality of infectious diseases and traumatic conditions seemed to be validated by epidemics and the vast array of lesions occurring during warfare and monumental construction projects.

However, ancient Egypt also allows a glimpse at a subsequent step in disease conceptualization: the appearance of a general operative principle called WHDW. A comparison of various identifiable syndromes leads to the establishment of general physiopathological mechanisms—in the case of WHDW a peccant matter which is responsible for many diseases and must be eliminated.(5)

Such an attempt to conceptualize the pathological establishes the so-called *physiological* concept of disease. The distinguishing lines between individual diseases become somewhat blurred as efforts are made to understand the physiological unity of the human organism and its range of responses to a variety of diseases. The medical ideas of ancient India and China reflect such a shift to speculative bodily principles derived from comprehensive philosophies of nature.

The Indian *Dosas*—air, bile, and phlegm—were seen as bodily secretions and principles supporting the activity of the organism.(6) Conversely, the Chinese *Yin* and *Yang* forces presided over a healthy equilibrium of the bodily elements.(7) This system of explanations places more stress on individual psychophysical characteristics and how they really determine patterns of distress.

About the same time, ancient Greece engaged in similar conceptualizations, borrowing ideas from the contemporary philosophy of nature. As in India, bodily humors played essential roles in guaranteeing functional integrity; furthermore, societal values such as harmony, symmetry, and balance shaped the ideal of health and the humoral theory of disease.

Through the use of speculative explanations, Hippocratic medicine viewed each individual as possessing a particular humoral mix, giving him relative health and predisposing him to certain imbalances. The patient's discomfort and biological struggle with the environment were, therefore, deemed unique—the result of lifestyle, geographic location, and climate. Hence, the focus of disease was the diseased individual.(8)

The new biological conditions affecting the Roman Empire and later medieval Europe forced a gradual shift in the concept of disease. Thousands of human beings afflicted by similar symptom clusters and physical signs favored the reestablishment of an ontological concept of disease.

Epidemics such as the "Black Death" of 1348 clearly set up characteristic sequences of suffering which minimized the importance of individual responses. These clusters, reenacted thousands of times over a widely scattered territory, also tended to blur the distinctions made by individual physicians. In fact, the repetitious pattern prodded healers to seek further distinctions and search for specific etiology and treatment (see Girolamo Fracastoro's (1483-1553) concept of contagion(9).

Famous authors such as Paracelsus (1493-1541), a contemporary of Fracastoro, and van Helmont (1577-1644), reinforced the ontological concept of disease with their own theories. Paracelsus spoke of particular *seeds of disease* endowed with specific spiritual powers, an *Ens morbi* sown by God since the fall of man. These seeds, alien and extraneous to the organism, were capable of causing particular disease. Van Helmont expanded on these ideas; he conceived of disease as a specific and invisible idea which becomes flesh by battling a local or central principle of vitality in the body.(10)

Almost contemporary with van Helmont came William Harvey's (1578-1657) formulations, derived from his embryological studies. For Harvey diseases were parasites, animated by a vital principle of their own. Contagium was equated with the emission of semen, which remained alive once impregnated locally in the new host and was disseminated by virtue of its own vitality.(11)

Somewhat later, well into the seventeenth century, the physician Thomas Sydenham (1624-89) echoed most strongly the view that diseases have an existence of their own. One ought to remember that the last great plague epidemic, affecting London in 1665, occurred in his lifetime. Wrote Sydenham in the preface of his *Medical Observations concerning the History and Cure of Acute Diseases* of 1676: "It is necessary that all diseases be reduced to definite and certain species." For Sydenham each disease represented a distinguishable species, and sick individuals were merely expressions of the disease. He suggested intensive analysis of clinical cases to extract the essential sequence of symptoms that were pathognomonic for the disease in question.(12)

Sydenham's call was heeded by numerous physicians during the eighteenth century, who created a series of nosological systems. The perceived human diseases were classified into orders, families, genera, and species, as if they were realities like plants and animals.

In the early nineteenth century, the advent of large hospitals capable of housing thousands of patients recreated an artificial epidemic scenario, where an ontological conceptualization of disease was aided by linking specific gross pathological changes to certain diseases. Philippe Pinel's (1745-1826) call for analysis of distress sequences gave diseases a concrete existence, and made them rallying points for clinico-pathological research while deemphasizing individual biological responses.(13)

Subsequent advances in bacteriology greatly favored the ontological conceptualization. The invasion of specific microorganisms was viewed as the sole cause of disease, prompting the search for specific chemotherapies and immunizations. Discrete units of symptoms and signs provided enough visibility to facilitate public support for their eradication and prevention. Moreover, these diseases could be easily targeted for research and statistical analysis.

Similarly, new and detailed knowledge of normal and abnormal tissues as well as the natural evolution of disease states, stimulated a more successful study of function during the nineteenth and twentieth centuries. Greater knowledge of physiological systems operative across many disease boundaries—stress, for example—renewed interest in environmental, genetic, and immunological factors operative in the genesis of disease, and favored a physiological concept of disease. These studies allowed the psychophysiological individuality of each patient and a unique environment to reemerge as decisive factors in assessing and curing illness.

In conclusion, the history of medicine reflects a gradual fine-tuning of distress sequences which were established by a series of value judgments in response to certain biological conditions. Since the latter formed part of a changing ecological balance between man and a host of microorganisms, each culture used its own value judgments in assessing deviancy. Within such relativism, one can detect certain criteria, like the algesic one, as remaining largely uninfluenced by cultural factors. The same is true of common traumatic conditions which created rather stable patterns of pain and dysfunction. Both conceptualizations of disease, the ontological and the physiological, have thus been operative for millenia, reflecting the shifting tide of emphasis on either disease or the diseased individual.

NOTES

1. I am indebted to Professor William H. McNeill for his panoramic view of the shifting pattern of disease, which will appear soon in book form.
2. A short and comprehensive review of the essential characteristics of primitive medicine is in Erwin H. Ackerknecht, *Medicine and Ethnology* (Baltimore: Johns Hopkins Press, 1971), pp. 17-29.
3. René Labat, *Traité Akkadien de Diagnostics et Prognostics Médicaux*, I. (Transcription et traduction, Leiden: Brill, 1951).
4. See G. B. Risse, "Rational Egyptian Surgery: A Cranial Injury Discussed in the Edwin Smith Papyrus," *Bulletin of the New York Academy of Medicine* 48 (1972), 912-19.
5. R. O. Steuer, "WHDW, Aetiological Principle of Pyaemia in Ancient Egyptian Medicine," *Supplements to the Bulletin of the History of Medicine*, No. 10 (1948).
6. See P. Kutumbiah, "The Distinctive Contributions of Indian Medicine to the Progress of Medical Thought," *Indian Journal of History of Medicine* 9 (1964), 1-12.
7. I. Veith, "Traditional Chinese Medicine: Historical Review," in *Modern China and Traditional Chinese Medicine*, G. Risse, ed. (Springfield, Ill.: Charles C Thomas, 1973), pp. 13-29.
8. O. Temkin, "Die Krankheitsauffassung von Hippokrates und Sydenham in ihren, Epidemien,'" *Sudhoffs Archiv* 20 (1928), 327-52.
9. Girolamo Fracastoro, *De Contagione et Contagiosis Morbis et Eorum Curatione*, transl. and notes by W. C. Wright (New York: Putnam, 1930).

10. W. Pagel, "Van Helmont's Concept of Disease—To Be or Not To Be? The Influence of Paracelsus," *Bulletin of the History of Medicine* 46 (1972), 419-54.
11. W. Pagel and M. Winder, "Harvey and the 'Modern' Concept of Disease," *Bulletin of the History of Medicine* 42 (1968), 496-509.
12. Thomas Sydenham, "Medical Observations Concerning the History and Cure of Acute Diseases," in *The Works of Thomas Sydenham, M.D.*, 2 vols. (London: Sydenham Society, 1848), p. 13.
13. P. Pinel, "Analyse appliquée a la médecine," *Dictionaire des Sciences Médicales*, 2 (Paris: Panckoucke, 1812), 23-30.

5

Moral Thought in Clinical Practice: Applying the Abstract to the Usual

Eric J. Cassell

RECENT DISCUSSIONS OF ETHICS in medicine have concerned themselves with large problems in the care of the dying, transplantation, abortion, genetic manipulation, behavior control, and so forth. Each of these areas provides substantial questions for rigorous exercises in moral philosophy. Yet it is axiomatic that they are drawn from, and are, to one degree or another, the day-to-day concern of clinical medicine. This fact creates a sense of unease because of a belief that physicians have neither special competence nor training to make such moral decisions. That same disquiet should infuse discussions of medical ethicists with a certain urgency, but even more, with a desire to see the results of their work return to clinical practice. Yet, we are not at all certain how newly developed understandings in moral philosophy are brought back to the practice of medicine. We need, then, a better comprehension of what an applied moral philosophy would look, or, better, sound like. What more fitting place to examine such a question than clinical medicine, where there already exists applied anatomy, applied biochemistry, applied pathology, and so on.

One similarity that is already apparent between applied moral philosophy and applied anatomy or biochemistry, for example, is the impatience with physicians shared by philosophers, anatomists, biochemists, and others from pure disciplines. It is worth a few moments' reflection on why the philosopher or scientist might be irritated with the physician. In any intellectual pursuit the challenges lie in the large problems, at the blurred edge of the field, not at its established center, in the unusual, not the ordinary. The moral philosopher may struggle with the meaning of "the good" but is entirely able to say and hear the word "good" in everyday life—understanding and being understood without much difficulty. But that day-to-day life is the concern of the applied worker whose challenge may lie in applying the abstract to the usual. Similarly, the physician may struggle with problems such as where to use actinomycin-D (an antitumor agent), chlorpromazine (a tranquilizer) or imipramine hydrochloride (an antidepressant) without any awareness or even interest in the fact that, as different as are their effects on patients, they share certain similarities in structure which are intriguing in their specific relationship to the structure of DNA in the helix.

Thus, I ask, as an applied moral philosopher, a measure of tolerance for dealing with what may appear trivial, and tolerance for having plunged into the world of value thought apparently without regard to the keen fights over certain words and concepts that do not seem even to give me pause. But I think that we shall see that the trivial aspects of the nature of person that emerge in this discussion are very interesting, and that the need for plunging on toward a disciplined applied moral philosophy is great.

A second obstacle in the path of creating an applied moral thought lies in the failure to distinguish between the problems inherent in certain moral decisions—such as when to turn off the respirator—and the information from which those problems are formed and on which the decisions are based. Again, a similarity can be found in the sciences. If the biochemist is challenged by the chemistry of DNA and its relationship to the function of DNA, then he needs DNA to work with; and, except as it interferes with his experiments, he doesn't care if it comes from a man or a mouse, but the physician trying to use the results of those studies must be concerned because he works with men, not mice.

At a recent meeting of philosophers, a finely constructed argument was presented that dealt with population problems. One of the examples from which the argument was drawn was biologically impossible. That impossibility was not relevant to doing philosophy, but it was crucial to medicine. Medicine is not done, it is practiced. So I ask tolerance again, because I am going to deal primarily with how the physician acquires the moral particulars of day-to-day clinical problems, rather than how he operates on those particulars in making a decision.

Perhaps by definition, and almost certainly by general agreement, the nature of person is central to ethical problems in medicine. Agreement begins to evaporate with attempts to enumerate and characterize the predicates of the concept of "person." The correspondence in the *Hastings Center Report* in reply to Joseph Fletcher's "Tentative Profile of Man"(1) is informative in this regard. One writer states that Fletcher is too abstract, and not based in the biology of man, another that Fletcher is behavioristically biased, confusing a characteristic of personhood with measurement. I was not privy to the whole correspondence, but if I were, I could find, I am sure, many other disagreements and perhaps as many agreements. Nonetheless, we understand the drive behind Fletcher's attempt to set some standards—provide some guides to measurement in order that we might get down to the daily business of *making* the decisions rather than constantly discussing *how* the decisions are to be made. In his second essay in the *Report*,(2) Fletcher is trying to distill his list of fifteen positive and five negative indicators down to four more basic indicators of personhood. The many reasons for and against the criteria are argued and cited in his discussion which could, of course, have gone on to encyclopedic length without providing much more guidance to a physician at a bedside. The discussion is the business of moral philosophers, and, I presume, moves their field forward.

While the substance of the discussion at this point may not provide physicians with the guidance desired, the very *fact* of the discussion provides the most basic and important direction of all—that is, that the issue of personhood is relevant to a decision made at a bedside. Since that truth has been present since physicians and patients first came together, it may seem self-evident, but that is not at all true. My contention that medicine is basically a moral profession—or moral-technical, if you wish, based on the fact that physicians are directly concerned with the immediate welfare of other humans—is probably not all that self-evident to most of my colleagues, and may even be argued here. That is, while the large problems of death and dying, transplantation and so forth are acknowledged by most to be moral-technical issues, it is not so clear to all that even in the treatment of trivial illnesses and human problems, moral difficulties constantly arise and are disposed of for better or worse by physicians and patients acting jointly or severally.

In a previous essay,(3) I discussed some of the reasons why the moral nature of medicine is so obscure but here I would like to touch on another reason. Often the abstraction of ethical issues, apparently so necessary for their dissection and understanding by philosophers, tends to remove them from the arena of their origin. That is, by concentrating on the frontiers of ethical thinking represented by organ scarcity in heart transplantation, the philosophers allow the physician who cares for patients as his daily job (none of whom may ever get close to a transplantation center) to continue in his belief that those intellectually interesting discussions have nothing to do with his routine concerns. He may even be thankful that he doesn't have to make such difficult decisions. Telling a particular asthmatic patient that moving to Arizona would be good for his asthma is not seen to be part of the same universe of discourse; it is merely a technical decision about asthma.

But here, in the reverse direction, is precisely what is so troubling about Fletcher's fifteen or even four indicators of humanness or Engelhardt's three(4) or anybody's whatever number of criteria for personhood. In searching for the essential predicates of personhood, it is necessary to refer to the properties of persons as they are found in this world. But it is self-evident that the properties of a person are not like the properties of a rectangle. The properties, whether they sound precise, like "cerebral function," or do not even pretend to precision, like "awareness of self," are merely, to borrow from Robert Hartman,(5) metaphors. These property names, as metaphors, stand for the "totality of continuous transformations" of the root meaning of the word. We can never meet the person described by Fletcher's or anyone's indicators; he is merely the creature of the abstraction.

Physicians do not treat abstractions, they treat individual patients. They do not treat patients with the metaphor "self-awareness," they treat a person who, at that moment, contains one of the forms that self-awareness takes in the continuous transformation that is contained by the metaphor. And, further, the shape of self-awareness in that patient is itself undergoing continuous transformation, or at least so we believe. That may seem a complicated way of saying that physicians treat individuals—which we all knew anyway—but it leads to an important point about applied moral philosophy in contradistinction to applied physiology, for example. The point is that there is a basic difference between the nature of the properties of the body as shown in physiology and the nature of the properties of personhood.

The human body from time immemorial has contained all the physiology (at least that which is correct) that is described in modern textbooks of physiology. Further, astute physicians through the ages employed their experiential knowledge of that physiology in the care of patients. Its systematic discovery in the scientific era of medicine has vastly extended the practical utility of understanding human physiology largely through exact definition of phenomena. That is, it has become possible to correlate changes in physiology with disease states in a highly predictable manner only because the definitions of those aspects of physiology under study are sufficiently precise to allow reproducibility. But the definitions are in essence a consequence of the methods used to demonstrate the phenomenon. Thus, while it is possible to estimate blood pressure by feeling the pulse, such a method is not precise enough to allow duplication, and, in any case, is dependent on an awareness of blood pressure in the first place. The sphygmomanometer, however, measures blood pressure accurately enough to give the concept real clinical meaning. Clinical meaning implies that something can be measured in a practical manner, has predictive and explanatory value, and can thus enter into decision-making. Even though a definition is often a complete abstraction of what occurs naturally, it remains extremely useful. For example, forced expiratory volume/one second (FEV_1) is merely the maximum amount of air that can be forcibly expelled from the lungs in one second. In other words, the definition is essentially the method.

This is not the place to explore the very real problems introduced into understanding physiologic processes by such artificial definitions; suffice it to say that at present the advantages seem to outweigh the disadvantages. All these definitions, to a greater or lesser degree, enjoy precision and reproducibility. I avoid using the word "objective" in reference to those measurements, since it is an overworked word in clinical medicine, which, I believe, often has more sentimental value than substance. While we are aware that these physiologic measurements are a static representation of a dynamic process and that variation is the rule in body functions, the measurements usefully stand for the thing they measure. While the variation may be considerable, the universe affected by the variation is usually small enough so that the predictive and explanatory value of the measurement is not destroyed.

Just as the patient has always been complete in physiology, from time immemorial, he or she has also contained all the properties of personhood considered by modern ethicists. And, equally, astute physicians through the ages have employed their experiential knowledge of those properties in patient care. There the similarity ends. A distinguished cardiologist once said that, because of advances in technology, the neophyte physician of today is in many respects the equal of the experienced physician of yesterday; the same cannot be said of the neophyte physician in the moral aspects of his profession. And, aside from the awareness of the problems created by our present discussion or its importance to philosophy, nothing in the attempts to distill the essence of personhood—that one quintessential factor—predicts a brighter future. One is reminded of the attempts by Boerhaave, a famous Dutch physician of the eighteenth century, to find the basic factor, the defining feature of fever, something considered a disease at that time. He settled on an elevated pulse! Boerhaave was a brilliant physician and the apparent inanity of his conclusion suggests how muddy was the universe he was attempting to clarify. It took a century of observation and nosology to divide up the numerous, well-defined diseases that had previously been included in the rubric "fever." Precise definitions of the imprecise are not possible.

But in the nature of personhood, as opposed to physiology, because of the metaphorical nature of the names of the properties of person, attempts at precise definitions in the manner of the exact sciences would seem to me to lead away from, rather than closer to, understanding. Further, as I have noted, definitions useful in clinical medicine are dependent for their utility on the methodology that leads to the definition. For philosophy to develop a successful applied moral philosophy (and I will accept as the measure of success that the neophyte of the next generation be the equal of the present experienced practitioner) it would seem necessary to find methods by which the physician identifies the properties of personhood. In the light of the universal importance attached to the nature of person in moral decisions, those properties are moral data. Paul Ramsey objects to the word "data" used in conjunction with the word "moral" and I suspect that, in part, it is the implication of precision in the word "data" which offends him. It follows from Hartman's understanding of the metaphorical nature of the properties of personhood that no such precision is possible in the moral particulars of a person. Indeed, to seek precision in the physiologic sense, is, as I noted earlier, to move away from understanding in the moral. It may seem paradoxical to imply that greater understanding may come about by giving up the demand for preciseness. But there is a distinction between preciseness of thought and preciseness in the particulars on which the thought operates. To clarify that, it is necessary to refer to the differences between analytic thought and valuational thought as I have used those words in the discussion of thinking in medicine in "Preliminary Explorations of Thinking in Medicine".(6)

It follows from its reductionist nature that analytic thought can only be as exact as the definitions and data on which it is based. That is, if I demonstrate to you the distinctness of the forced expiratory volume one second from forced vital capacity and how each reflects different functions of the lung, and if you are to understand me and use the concepts, it is essential that each word have the same precise meaning for both of us. (It is clear that the meanings do not have to reflect the "truth" about the lung—precision and accuracy are not the same.)

Exactness in valuational thought lies in another direction, particularly when it deals with conceptions of self. There I am being precise when I am able to delineate those particulars which are specific to *your* conceptions of self from those which are part of *my* similarly labeled conceptions—when I do not confuse what you say about you with what I say about you or about myself. Exactness is also lost when interpretation is confused with observation. That is, when you tell me about yourself, I leap from *what* you tell me to *why* you tell me, and why your conception takes that form. The interpretations may be correct, they may even add weight to your words, but they are not the conception itself as you displayed it. (Indeed, interpretation of that nature is analytic, not valuational.)

Both defects in valuational thought—confusion of hearers' thought for speakers, and mistaking interpretation for observation—are extremely difficult to avoid, the former because the hearer's conception serves an interpreter function in valuational thought. Shared knowledge of the world is essential if one person is to understand another. (Put another way, metaphors cannot work without some common understanding.)

The latter defect—substituting interpretation for observation—may be inherent in thought itself, but in reference to the particulars of person is particularly common in these days of widespread psychological sophistication. It seems necessary at this point to make a distinction between the particulars of personhood and the psychology of a person, since the term "psychology" is now used so widely as to have virtually lost all meaning. An example of the effect on medicine of a nearly universal psychologism among doctors and students may be useful. A twenty-five-year-old man developed pain in his throat of unusual character and duration which worried him greatly. He saw several physicians and was treated without effect. No specific disease was found, but he could not be reassured. An adequate history revealed that his father had died six months earlier of cancer of the esophagus, and he felt his mother to be his primary responsibility since he was the only child still unmarried and at home. Armed with those facts and aware of the trivial nature of his symptoms, I was able to reassure him. I took his sense of responsibility toward his mother to be a particular in the moral sphere essential to a decision about his treatment.

When the case was related to some medical students, one of them noted that the patient probably had the symptoms because he felt guilty over the father's death and the fact that he had won the oedipal battle. Indeed, the student could have been correct. But she jumped over the patient's expressed sense of responsibility directly into the interpretation. I do not take the guilt to be a moral particular, since it is not known to me except by inference, but rather a psychological interpretation. And I certainly do not take the inferred oedipal conflict as a moral particular, but rather as a second-level psychological interpretation.

It is not my intention to belittle the interpretation that guilt secondary to oedipal conflicts underlay the patient's sense of responsibility. Indeed, I use this case with full awareness that the physical symptoms are most likely the result of psychological mechanisms—more probably pathological identification with the father than those suggested by the student—but that is irrelevant here. In fact, if the patient's illness was an inappropriate sense of responsibility (I am aware of the subjectivism implied in the word "inappropriate", but that, though important, is not my present topic), then understandings of "guilt" or "identification with father" might be essential to making the patient better. It is rather arbitrary to call the sense of responsibility a moral particular and relegate the guilt and oedipal conflict to the psychological, but it is important to the development of an applied moral philosophy, I believe, to make the distinction.

Another case may make the point more clearly. A woman with characteristic episodes of abdominal pain is found to have stones in her gallbladder; an operation is suggested. She says that, if at all possible, she would like to delay her operation until her aged mother, presently ill, gets better, because her mother is her responsibility since her father's recent death. Here we have no difficulty separating the sense of responsibility from the symptoms or cause of the illness. We recognize our need to accept the sense of responsibility apart from her gallbladder disease. And, if her life were to be threatened by a delay in operation, we acknowledge the necessity to help her balance her needs against those of her mother, in acceptance of the natural existence of such a sense of responsibility in daughters.

I take the sense of responsibility to be a part of the anatomy of the person just as the gallbladder is part of the anatomy of the body. A sense of responsibility, the ability to form relationships, curiosity, the need for control, the need for love, the need to be needed, the desire not to be a burden are all universally found among persons. The list is not meant to be complete; many other properties could be, and perhaps should be, listed. Here there may be a need for a list in order that those looking for the metaphorical meaning of those properties for an individual patient might know what to seek. No psychological system of which I am aware explains their presence in persons. A psychology may tell us how they develop, why one hypertrophies and another atrophies, or even the pathology that results when one of those factors is absent. Psychologies may even tell us why they are present in the sense (anthropomorphic or teleologic) that it is good for persons to have these factors—but nothing explains why they are there; they are simply part of the moral biology of mankind. It seems strange to me as I write this because I, too, am used to psychological interpretations. Odd, because I have no trouble distinguishing between an acknowledgment of the anatomical presence of the gallbladder and its evolution, embryology, physiology, and pathology.

In an applied moral philosophy, the particulars germane to moral decisions reside in the anatomy of the person as well as the body. A critical examination of such a particular (in the first case above, the sense of responsibility) may be benefited by knowledge of its pathology—inappropriately great, inappropriately small, or just an inappropriate sense of responsibility—

but the essential knowledge on which such a critical valuation is based is the appreciation of its existence in the person in the first place.

To return to the first example, one might wonder how the physician knew that the patient felt so responsible for his mother. Quite simply, the doctor asked the patient. The actual train of questions first established that the patient was unmarried, the youngest child, that his sister and brother were both married with children of their own, and that he lived with his mother. Just as the fact, time, and cause of the father's death were elicited as part of a routine initial medical history, so was his marital status. The remainder of the questions were part of a specific inquiry into that aspect of the nature of the patient that applied to the problem at hand. In short, the particulars germane to the moral case were elicited by communication between the two, more specifically, through intentional speech acts.

The basic method for finding particulars essential to ethical decision-making in medicine that is suggested by this case, indeed by me in general terms, is the use of language. It seems reasonable in searching for the shape of an applied moral philosophy and, in particular, for a systematic or disciplined manner by which the moral particulars of the person are to be found by the applied practitioner, to start with the analysis of medical conversation. For the inquiry by the physician to have taken place in the first place and for it to have been successful—that is, produce information relevant to the patient's problem (more precisely the physician's perception of the patient's problem) much is assumed about the nature of speech acts. The work of Searle,(7) Fraser,(8) and Grice(9) is pertinent. (Much is also assumed about the relationship between doctors and patients, but that is not our present problem.)

Certainly we expect the conversations between the doctor and patient to have had intelligible meaning to both of them. While we intuitively know that to be true, Grice has summarized the argument in favor of its truth in a manner sufficiently serviceable for us to expect that both participants are cooperating and that cooperation implies certain characteristics of conversation. That which is implied in normal (as opposed to pathological) conversation allows us to suppose that the content has reliability in context. That is, we do not expect the speaker either to lie, to be inappropriate, to say too much or too little, or to say it in an incomprehensible manner. What is more, we can expect that the hearer will often have to work (to infer) to determine what it is that the speaker means; it is often the case that we do not say in precise words what we mean.

While Grice's comments may not satisfy those searching for pure meaning in words, and there are definitely situations where his maxims of conversational implicature are flouted, or where they are inadequate, it is in the nature of any applied discipline, linguistics and philosophy included, that the discipline will be usefully employed if it is successful in the usual instance; it is not necessary that the logic of the discipline never fail.

But even if we accept that the conversation between doctor and patient is comprehensible, it is not at all clear (except intuitively) how the physician evoked the moral particular inherent in the patient's sense of responsibility. Here Searle (and Fraser on Searle) are helpful. Further conditions for successful conversational interaction on the part of the physician include his personal body of information; his background of knowledge, both technical and experiential; his knowledge of the culture of the patient; social conventions, how patients act; as well as the fact that he and the patient have shared knowledge of the world, that is, conceptions that they hold in common. Also important is his knowledge of the particular patient, from whatever source it may have come. Then there is the specific history of the previous aspects of the conversation in question. Also contributing to successful speech performance are the identity of both speakers and how they perceive each other's role in the interaction, how the patient sees physicians in general, and how the physician perceives patients in general.

In other words, to understand how the physician arrived at the particular of person, knew it for what it was, and was then able to use it, one cannot conceive of both arriving at the conversation like two *tabulae rasae*. But since we know that already, it is equally important to point out that a successful and disciplined applied moral philosophy cannot be based only on the untutored intuition of the applied moral philosopher.

The gentleman who found out he was writing prose did not have his prose improved because of that knowledge. In like manner, to point out to physicians that, when they have a conversation with a patient that leads them to make a decision based on both knowledge of person and knowledge of disease, they are applied moral philosophers, will not, by itself, improve the quality of their performance. There could be no performance if Grice's maxims and Searle's conditions did not hold to at least some degree, and it is equally true that increasing experience would very likely improve performance without any knowledge of the nature of speech.

But for the development and teaching of an applied moral philosophy, a systematic and disciplined approach to understanding speech would seem essential if we are to meet the criteria of success suggested initially: that is, the neophyte practitioner of the next generation is as good (at least in respect to the applied discipline) as the experienced practitioner of the present generation.

In this discussion, I have devoted myself to examining the particulars on which moral decisions are based rather than the mechanics of those decisions. In so doing, I have concluded that the basic source of information about the personhood of the patient is the patient's words. I am not saying only that one find out the details of personhood important to a particular patient by asking, for that seems at least partially self-evident (the degree that it is not self-evident is not my concern at this moment). Rather, I am saying that the patient will tell about himself, including particulars germane to moral choice without being asked. That such particulars, as part of ordinary clinical conversation, are there to be heard. The patient will, to some degree, display the particulars of his conceptions of self in the course of providing information about his illness.

But now we have come to a testable hypothesis. It seems to me, as I listen to the conversation between doctor and patient, that the facts of the patient's illness—the symptoms—are intertwined with the particulars of the patient's person. The physician, to make his diagnosis, is unraveling that fabric and is or is not discarding the particulars of person. If that is true, and can be demonstrated, as I think it can, we can begin to arrive at a methodology for obtaining the information on which moral decisions are based. Such a methodology or even the information derived from it does not tell us how decisions are made nor allow us to teach others how to make decisions. It does not, in other words, define or teach wisdom. But surely it satisfies the first step toward wisdom, which must be an awareness that judgment is necessary and an awareness of the information on which judgment is based. Finding such a methodology—teaching how to listen for the particulars of person—does not even ensure that it will be employed, but it satisfies the first requirement for an applied discipline—a method that allows the application of the insights of the pure field to the applied.

NOTES

1. Joseph Fletcher, "Indicators of Humanhood: A Tentative Profile of Man," *Hastings Center Report* 2 (1972), 1-4.
2. Joseph Fletcher, "Four Indicators of Humanhood—The Inquiry Matures," *Hastings Center Report* 4 (1974), 4-7.
3. Eric J. Cassell, "Making and Escaping Moral Decisions," *Hastings Center Studies* 1 (1973), 53-62.
4. H. Tristram Engelhardt, quoted by Fletcher, "Four Indicators of Humanhood," p. 6.
5. Robert Hartman, "The Axiomatic Structure of Intrinsic Value," *Journal of Value Inquiry* 8 (1974), 81-101.
6. Eric J. Cassell, "Preliminary Explorations of Thinking in Medicine," *Ethics in Science and Medicine* 2 (1975), 1-12.
7. John R. Searle, *Speech Acts* (Cambridge: Cambridge University Press, 1969), esp. pp. 64-71.
8. Bruce Fraser, "Review of John Searle's *Speech Acts*," *Foundations of Language* 4 (1974), 433-46.
9. H. P. Grice, "Logic and Conversation," unpublished mimeo.

Commentary

Moral Questions in a
Clinical Setting

Amnon Goldworth

THE PRACTICE OF MEDICINE can be viewed either as a predominantly moral activity supported by technological procedures or as a predominantly technological activity to which certain moral issues are related. When Dr. Cassell observes that "medicine is basically a moral profession—or moral-technical, if you wish . . .," he favors the first view. This is hardly a small matter, for the medicine-as-technology view delimits medical problems as those which can be expressed in technical language and which are resolvable in terms of efficiency. What is not capable of such expression and resolution is either disregarded or viewed as a nonmedical issue. In contrast, the medicine-as-moral activity view places each human being, in terms of his appetites and attitudes, at center stage and subordinates or sacrifices technical efficiency to some essentially human good.

I am inclined to agree with Cassell that medicine is fundamentally a moral activity. Thus, I am most sympathetic to his claim that it is as important for the physician to listen to the patient in order to determine his psychological anatomy as a person as it is for the physician to examine the patient's gallbladder in order to determine the state of his bodily anatomy.

161

Cassell was particularly interested in discussing those issues that need to be entertained in order to begin to apply morality in the medical setting. Someone who is psychologically-minded would perhaps be more interested in the specific role of the doctor-listener. Can he or she be viewed as counselor, much as the psychological therapist is? And what are the difficulties of being both a doctor who "lays hands" on the patient and one who serves as a therapist? My interest, as a philosopher, is to extend Cassell's topic by asking, "What are the sorts of moral situations that the physician is likely to encounter in the clinical setting, if he or she listens to the patient?" By answering this question we can sharpen our focus on the sorts of considerations that appropriately or necessarily arise in applying morality in the medical setting.

Several points of clarification are in order at this juncture. First, I will be concerned with situations in which people come to doctors for help concerning their physical condition. Obviously, listening is the first order of business when emotional problems bring people to psychologists. Equally obvious is the fact that moral problems can arise in the psychologist's office. In addition, it is clear that there are moral problems in medicine having to do, say, with public policy which are not of the clinical sort at all. Concern with psychological and public policy issues would take us far afield from what Cassell was discussing.

Second, in asking "What are the moral situations that the physician can encounter in a clinical setting if he or she listens to the patient?" I will not be attempting an exhaustive case survey. The cases I will introduce are intended to serve as markers across an applied morality spectrum. They are intended to be sufficiently paradigmatic and distinctive to provide something of a picture of what one can expect to encounter as morally relevant in a clinical setting. A truly representative picture would require other sorts of cases. But, those that I do discuss will be sufficient to exemplify the logic of my approach and its value in relationship to my main question.

Third, the answer to my question does not require an extended account of the doctor-patient relationship as provided, for instance, by P. Lain Entralgo in *Doctor and*

Patient,(1) or as discussed in terms of the concept of personal care by Charles Fried in *Medical Experimentation*.(2) I am concerned only with what listening to the patient produces from a moral standpoint. This rules out moral problems such as those generated by the use of the randomized clinical trial as illustrated in Fried's book.

Case I was suggested by Cassell. "A 25 year old man developed pain in his throat of unusual character and duration which worried him greatly. He saw several physicians and was treated without effect. No specific disease was found, but he could not be reassured. An adequate history revealed that his father had died six months earlier of cancer of the esophagus, and he felt his mother to be his primary responsibility since he was the only child still unmarried and at home. Armed with those facts and aware of the trivial nature of his symptoms, it was possible to reassure him."

What is morally relevant in this situation is the duty of the doctor to relieve the physical suffering of the patient. It is not important from the moral standpoint that a particular suffering is somatic, or, as in this case, psychosomatic in origin. What is important is that if the doctor is to function effectively in carrying out his duty, he must draw on all the relevant information. And in the case at hand this involves being informed about the personality and personal history of the patient.

Given that Case I illustrated some emotional or moral conflict in the patient, Case II is intended to illustrate the physician in conflict. A patient comes to a neurologist complaining of dizziness and nausea. In the course of examining the patient, the neurologist learns that the patient is a heavy smoker. The neurologist concludes that the dizziness is caused by a viral infection which will shortly disappear by itself. But he also recognizes that he has an opportunity effectively to influence the patient to stop smoking by telling him that the ingested smoke is affecting the normal oxygen flow to his brain, which in turn is causing the dizziness. Should the doctor lie in order to preserve the health of his patient? Does the doctor have the right to deceive his patient who did not come for advice about smoking but about dizzy spells?

Unlike my previous two cases, Case III involves a moral conflict between the doctor and the patient. A woman comes to a doctor in her first trimester of pregnancy seeking an abortion. The doctor examines the woman and listens carefully to what she has to say. He determines that this woman is married, financially well off, physically healthy, and psychologically untroubled. He also discovers that she wants the abortion for reasons of social convenience: were she to carry the fetus to full term, it would interfere with a planned trip to Bermuda. The doctor, who is not an antiabortionist, believes, in this instance, that the woman is too cavalier in her attitude toward a potential human life. He refuses to perform the abortion. Indeed, he feels that his refusal is morally therapeutic for the woman. What is ailing her is not her pregnancy but her lack of moral sensitivity.

Case I is illustrative of those clinical situations which call for the application of the single, albeit important, moral precept; namely, to help a patient may require as much attention to the patient as a person as to the functioning of his or her internal organs.

Case II is illustrative of clinical situations in which the actual or potential medical problem is correlated with specific modes of behavior. Other examples are the Type A personality with a potential or actual heart condition, the male homosexual with a potential or actual rectal infection, the heavy drinker with a potential or actual liver ailment. An alteration of each of these behavioral modes could prevent or relieve or cure a particular physical problem.

I am reminded at this point of an article by Robert J. Haggerty,(3) who was concerned with social and environmental factors, such as "the way we live, our diet, our pace of life, our housing, our political and social structure," as they contribute or fail to contribute to our health. In particular, he was concerned with whether the doctor should play a role in dealing with these factors. The fact that Haggerty and others have raised this, as yet, unresolved issue bears directly on the qualms that the doctor can feel when he or she recognizes that a change in the social and environmental settings of the patient can be more effective in preventing and eliminating illness than the essentially ameliorative techniques used by present-day physicians.

Haggerty's concern can be extended to include the issues raised in type II cases by asking how far can or must the doctor go, morally speaking, in intervening in the personal, as well as social and environmental, affairs of the patient in order to carry out his or her requirement to help the patient get well? Aside from social action, are deception or duplicity, withholding information, using the subtle and not-so-subtle status of profession, all morally fair game as instrumental values of the intrinsic value of health? Or is health subordinate to the values of the autonomy and the integrity of the patient as a person? How much intervention, whether it be elicited advice or coercion, is morally too much or too little? What appears central to these issues is the boundaries of health care (to borrow Haggerty's phrase) as they apply to the proper professional role of the doctor.

Case III represents a number of clinical situations which are of mixed moral interest. Case III itself is not particularly exciting from a moral standpoint. I suspect that the reason for this is that the pregnant woman is not ill. One is no more disturbed morally by the doctor's refusal to abort than one would be with a doctor's refusal, whatever the reason, to perform cosmetic surgery on the sagging face of a ninety-year-old person. But there are cases, such as the refusal on moral or religious grounds to subscribe to medical advice or procedures, which are morally interesting. To what extent can the notions of professional duty and moral right be used by the physician to interfere with or override the conflicting moral convictions of the patient?

The difference between Case II and Case III has to do with the parties to the moral conflict: the former being intrapersonal (or perhaps physician vs. conventional morality); the latter being interpersonal, between patient and physician. But, what they have in common is the interconnected issues of the justification of medical intervention into the affairs of people and the conflict between such values as truth-telling and personal autonomy, on the one hand, and the value of health, on the other. Thus, before we can adequately practice morality in those clinical settings which involve type II and III cases we will have to clarify and resolve these issues.

NOTES

1. P. Lain Entralgo, *Doctor and Patient* (New York: McGraw-Hill Book Company, 1969).
2. Charles Fried, *Medical Experimentation: Personal Integrity and Social Policy* (Amsterdam and Oxford: Norton-Holland Publishing Company, 1974).
3. Robert J. Haggerty, "The Boundaries of Health Care," *The Pharos* (July 1972), pp. 106-111.

The Mind's Eye and the Hand's Brain: Toward an Historical Epistemology of Medicine

Marx W. Wartofsky

I. Medicine as a Constitutive Mode of Human Knowledge

Medicine is a fundamental form of human knowledge. It is one of the earliest modes of human adaptation and serves as a crucial survival mechanism of the species. Together with food gathering, hunting, the production of artifacts—tools, weapons, clothing, shelter—and the development of modes of social organization, there developed also the techniques, artifacts, and institutional forms of medical practice: caring for the sick; healing wounds; hygienic techniques for dealing with infection and for preventing disease; and the range of practices dealing with birth, death, and sexuality. Medicine thus ranks with the primary modes of human social practice and provides a major context for a study of the origins and the development of the characteristic modes of human cognitive activity.

But why should one revert to an anthropological context, if the subject here is the epistemology of medicine? Why not begin with general epistemological considerations, concerning the forms or structures of human knowledge, the conditions for the acquisition of knowledge, and for the testing or validation of cognitive claims? After all, it may be argued, we do not have to begin constructing epistemology anew in order to deal with medical knowledge. There is a philosophical tradition of more than 2,500 years, in which such epistemological considerations, concerning knowledge in general, have been refined, theories developed, and certain problems—for example, of the nature of belief, of truth, of the relation of thought to perception—have been carefully and clearly formulated. One might suppose that a proper epistemological treatment of the nature of medical knowledge would simply proceed from general considerations to their more specific applications to medicine.

I propose to reject such an approach, and on epistemological grounds. What I will propose here is that the characteristic modes of human cognitive activity are not given, in some general form, from which philosophers can then reconstruct a general epistemology. Rather, cognitive activity is always context-bound: it is concerned with acquiring knowledge of a certain sort, for a certain purpose, and in a certain matrix of social and historical human life. My claim here is that our species has developed its *general* cognitive capacities (both in its biological evolution as a species, and in its postbiological or cultural evolution through various historical forms of social life) out of the specific demands made on cognition by different modes of praxis.(1) Further, I want to show that medicine is one such primary or fundamental mode of cognitive praxis, with distinctive structures and aims; and that therefore medicine is not a branch of human knowledge growing from some common tree which we can call "cognition in general," but is rather a root of this tree, and is therefore a *constituting* rather than a *derived* form of knowledge. I want to claim that the general forms of human cognition have been shaped by medical theory and practice; that our general cognitive culture bears the imprint of the distinctive modes of medicine; and that an epistemology of medicine is therefore an approach to general epistemological reflection, rather than something to be derived from it.

What emerges, even initially, from such an approach is a view that medicine is not an isolated or fragmented piece of human knowledge, added on to other pieces, as part of a curriculum put together from separable and replaceable parts; but rather, that as a primary or fundamental form of human cognitive praxis, medicine is a constituting mode of general human knowledge, and helps to shape the general ways in which we learn or acquire knowledge, the general conceptions of the aims or purposes of knowledge, and the general canons or norms by which we test or validate our cognitive claims. Thus, I do not approach the question in the more traditional way: namely, from the point of view of a general epistemology, from which one then approaches medicine as a specific mode. Rather, I approach the question of epistemology from the other direction: how are the characteristic human forms of cognitive activity generated by or constituted by the differential and concrete modes of cognitive praxis which emerge in the evolution and history of human life. This general approach I call "historical epistemology," and I will say more about it later.

My title, "The Mind's Eye and the Hand's Brain," is meant to connote the dialectical interplay between theory and practice in medicine. Though my approach to an epistemology of medicine derives from an examination of the structures or modes of medical praxis, I am not proposing that medical knowledge is simply a reflex in the mind (or in the brain) of external practical activity or skill, or that medical theory is simply the formal or conceptual articulation of practice. If one thing stands out as a feature of human knowledge, it is the extent to which the theoretical imagination insinuates itself into every aspect of practical activity or skill. This thesis in epistemology, concerning the active role of the theoretical intellect in our practical experience, has a venerable history—from Plato and Aristotle to Kant and Hegel. Its contemporary form, especially in the philosophy of science, is couched in the language of "the relation of theory to observation in the sciences," or in the characterization of observation as "theory-laden." This view was developed as a critique of the naive positivist empiricism which took our observation, or empirical access to the external

world as theory-neutral, and regarded such observation as a kind
of primitive raw material for which theory provided a proc-
essing mechanism. I will be dealing with this issue here, but not
in these terms, since I believe that the problem, formulated in
this way—whether observation is theory-laden or theory-neutral
—already proceeds from a false premise shared by both sides of
the dispute: namely, that the mode of acquisition of empirical
knowledge is observation, whether defined as a relatively passive
confrontation with the facts, where the only activity is the
looking and seeing (in the empiricist view); or defined as a
relatively active transformation of the facts, dependent upon
the constitutive activity of the mind, that is, as a mental activity
taking place, so to speak, in the head (in the mentalist or
rationalist view).

My own view is that the constitutive activity of the mind, in
the relation of theory to practice, takes place (if we are to use
the locative metaphor at all) at the fingertips—that is, in the
interaction of cognitive organism and environment—in the
human case, in the practical activity of intervention in the
world. Moreover, I would argue that this "world" is one which
has been reconstituted not simply in some reflective theoretical
image, but has been reconstituted or transformed in actuality
by human practice. The cognitive image of the world, constructed by theory, is therefore, not simply a mental image, but is
rather the world itself, objectively transformed by cognitive
practice. Whatever mental image or internal representation we
form of this world transformed *by* our activity is itself formed
in this activity, as a part of it.

In this sense, I will claim that the activity of the hand has, on
the one hand, become transformed into an internal "image" of
this activity: that the brain, both in its evolution, and in its
adaptation and transformation by current practice maps the
modes or forms of our external practice; and also, that such a
mapping acquires a relatively autonomous function in shaping
the modes of external practice. What we see is seen not by the
eye, but by the mind's eye—through the mediation of the
imagination, or by way of the theoretical constructs which are
the products of the activity of the imagination. But these
constructs themselves develop within the frame of forms of

cognition *originally* derived from an internalization of our modes of outward practical activity. Thus, the interplay between medical practice and medical theory is not simply one topic in an epistemology of medicine; it is the fundamental or categorial framework for the construction of such an epistemology.

One more prefatory remark may be made here. The genesis of medicine at the dawn of civilization needs to be reconstructed by the archaeologist and the anthropologist. The history of medicine, insofar as we have records and artifacts, is intertwined with the historical development of human social life in other modes—the historic forms of production and distribution, social organization, ritual and belief, art and technology, theoretical sciences and philosophy. The students of the history of medicine may be divided, as are historians, into internalists and externalists: those who follow the inner history and development of medical theory, or practice, or its institutional forms; and those who emphasize the social, cultural, or technological contexts of developments in medicine. But the only adequate historical account of medicine is one in which internal and external history are integrated, in which the subtle interplay of medicine and society is taken into full account, and in which we preserve the relative autonomy of medical development, as well as the relative autonomy of extramedical contexts and also show the dialectical interrelationship between the internal and the external.

What bearing does this have on an epistemology of medicine? From the point of view of an *a*historical epistemology— namely, one which takes the modes and structures of human cognition as essential, or unchanging and transhistorical species-characteristics, such considerations as genesis and history are irrelevant (or are relevant only in the stages of the biological evolution of the species, in which, it is supposed, such cognitive structures emerged as adaptive features). This we may characterize as a *pre*historical epistemology. From the point of view of an historical epistemology, however, it is not simply the content of knowledge which changes, but its forms or structures as well, that is, the modes of acquisition of knowledge, and also the very sense of what does and what does not constitute knowledge. From this point of view, the historical changes and development of the modes of social practice are seen to be correlated with such changes in cognitive mode. Thus, it is not only the *existence* of medical praxis which helps to constitute the characteristic forms of human knowledge; it is also the *changes and development* in the historic forms of medical praxis which contribute to the changes in cognitive mode. I would argue that this correlation is not accidental, but rather that it is in the interaction between medicine and society, between medical theory and theory-formation in other sciences and arts, between forms of thought and forms of life, that this correlation finds its complex formative context. What I hope to present here, then, is a sketch, admittedly programmatic, of those features of historical medical praxis which are the basis for the distinctive features of an epistemology of medicine, and which contribute to our general cognitive modes.

How should one formulate the *problematique* for such an inquiry? First, I would propose that one reconstruct the characteristic modes of activity or of the praxis of medicine. Since this is an historical project, what is important are the changes in the dominant modes of such activity, in different periods. What will remain invariant through such transformations will then appear as what may be characterized as general features of such activity in any period, if there are such general transhistorical characteristics.

Second, I would propose that one reconstruct the conceptions, or self-images of such medical praxis, as the conscious articulation of the aims and methods of medicine. These are not simply passive reflections or articulations of a given praxis, but also serve to shape and, sometimes, to change such praxis.

Third, one should place this history of medical forms of activity—their institutional forms, their ideologies, as well as the actual achievements in medical knowledge and technique—in the context of their social role, the position of the practitioner and of the patient in social life, the attitudes toward medicine and disease, the relations of medicine with politics, religion, and science.

Fourth, one ought to reconstruct from this the problems that are characteristically taken to be the central ones of medicine, the methods which are taken to be the canonical ones by which such problems are solved, and what come to be taken as, or to count as solutions to these problems. Changes in these characteristics will then provide an "internal" history of medicine, in which major shifts are seen as shifts in problem-frameworks and solution-frameworks.

I can offer in this preliminary sketch only the outlines of such a study, with some examples. But I propose it as a program for research in historical epistemology, in which the details will become all-important as tests of the program's fruitfulness. A successful case study, then, would be one in which something is revealed about the distinctive features of the medical knowledge of a given historical period which had not been realized earlier; and more important, perhaps, that the historical changes in medicine will come to be understood not simply as an indifferent sequence of discoveries and techniques, but rather as changes which can be understood and explained within the matrix of the interaction of medicine and society, and therefore as a constitutive part of general history.

To begin, then, let me identify those features of medical praxis which have epistemological import in such an inquiry. What are the characteristic forms or modes of medical activity or praxis? Though this is a general question, it does not have a general answer, except perhaps in the most abstract sense. Rather, the characteristic forms or modes of medical praxis are themselves historically changing. Though "medicine" may name a continuity in human praxis and knowledge, having to do with the treatment of disease, the concrete and particular forms of this praxis are historically differentiated; and it is an open question for me whether the development of medicine is continuous, or is shot through with discontinuities, when one pays attention to the details. For example, if we take the concept of "disease" as one which characterizes the object of medical treatment, we will find, I think, that what *counts* as disease differs radically in conception and treatment approach from one historical or cultural context to another. It is not simply a question of what specific diseases come to be known and treated, for here the answer is relatively simple: *diabetes mellitus*, known to the ancient Egyptians, is presumably the same disease we know today. What has changed is our understanding of it, and our treatment. This change, for example, is at a point of radical transition today, as the simpler insulin-deficiency model yields to a more complex account of the biochemical balancing and triggering mechanisms (glucagon), which apparently make the older model obsolete.(2) So I am referring not simply to the changes in knowledge and practice which mark the continuities in the development of medicine. Nor is the "discontinuity" which I hypothesize simply a matter of discovering *new* diseases, or of the disappearance of certain diseases. Rather, I am proposing that the very conception of what counts as disease, the very fundamental approaches to treatment, the basic relationship between patient and practitioner all undergo radical changes in the history of medicine.(3) There are, so to speak, "revolutions" in medicine, which are deeper than either new discoveries, or new treatments, but which go to the root of the very conception of what medicine is about.

Therefore, the question: "What are the characteristic forms and modes of medical praxis?" does not yield to a survey of present forms, as some synchronic account of medicine *per se* or of the "essence" of medical praxis, which can then be spread out diachronically as the criterion of what is and what is not medicine. Instead, the question requires, I think, a differential, historical approach, partly as a way of understanding how we have arrived at our present achievement by overcoming mistakes and misconceptions in the past; but partly also to effect a certain modesty with respect to the limits of our present conceptions and practices, and to the inevitability of their replacement by perhaps radically different ones.

The epistemological import of such an approach is that it is not only the content of medical knowledge which changes, but that what counts as medical knowledge, the very form and conception of what is medical knowledge itself, changes historically; and that it does so in some important connection with the social and institutional forms of medical praxis, and also in a deep relation to changes in social structure and praxis beyond medicine—in economic life, in politics, technology, religion, art, and science.

II. Medicine and Epistemology:
A Genetic-Historical Approach

Let me sketch, then, what I would take to be a *genetic* approach to the question of how medicine bears on epistemology. We may hypothesize that initially, care of the sick, tending of wounds, birth and death practices, and hygienic practices were common, rather than specialized practices. That is, we may assume that such functions, in primitive human forms of life, were either communal or familial ones. With division of labor, either in the family or in the tribe, such care and skills came to be vested in special persons. At what point disease came to be characterized in relation to other ills (famine, storms, and various ravages of nature), we do not know. But at that point, dealing with disease came to share the ritual forms of dealing with these other ills; and these ritual forms themselves became special skills, involving special powers and special status.

To me this marks a major epistemological change. Whereas caring for the sick, or tending wounds, takes as its object the human being, his or her pain or discomfort, his or her incapacitation as a personal and social fact in the daily life of the family or the tribe, the ritualization of this process marks a major shift: the medicine man now deals not with the human being as his object, but rather directly with the agent of the disease, with its *cause*. I take this objectification of the causal agent of the disease—in the form of an evil spirit or an angry god—to be the first major step toward the theorization of empirical medical practice: it abstracts from the patient as a particular case, and adduces a principle (albeit in a fetishistic form), which explains *why* the patient has the disease. It is the first attempt at explanation of the disease, as distinguished from merely applied practice.

The pharmacopoeia of ancient medicine included *ad hoc* technical knowledge of herbs, muds, various animal tissues and organs—the whole array of purges and poultices discovered by inductive practice. So too, surgical and hygienic techniques originated, I would suspect, in preritual forms of practice. One might hypothesize a stage of "naturalistic" medicine which predates the ritual forms of treatment. But it is not until ritual forms develop, and become vested in a priesthood, that a causal explanation of disease becomes part of systematic technique.

I would argue that just as the ritualization of tool production gives rise to the notion of a prototype (a model after which copies are fashioned), and thereby, to the first forms of universals (concepts that are embodied in an artifact, transmissible from master to apprentice, and from one generation to the next in this form), so too, the objectification of the causal agent of disease in a ritual artifact (in the conceptual or linguistic artifact of an evil spirit, an angry god, or a totem animal) provides one of the first forms of a *theoretical entity* taken as a *universal*, that is, as the common agent of the disease in its manifold appearances. Once the identification is made, it carries with it the ritual form of dealing with this entity: whether by incantation, or magic words, or by the use of the very same poultices and purges which are inherited from naturalistic empirical medicine. But now the technique of preparing the treatment, or of administering it becomes ritualized as well; that is, it becomes stereotypical, and rigorously controlled, so that it will always be done in the same way, or in the same sequence. This requires an institutional form, so that this regularized and ritualized method of treatment can be learned, preserved, and transmitted, and its powers protected against loss. The social function of medicine thus becomes a specialized function; its practitioners are set apart; its modes of practice are carefully preserved and kept secret. Medical knowledge becomes, in effect, an *object* to be tended, preserved, and transmitted (and often symbolized as such, in the fetishistic form of a particular dress, artifact, or marking).

III. Epistemological Features and Consequences of Early Forms of Medical Praxis

The foregoing suggests three epistemological features: (1) the move to *causal explanation*, and thereby the introduction of *causes* as *theoretical entities* (albeit in the forms of the imagination as picturable spirits); (2) the move to *universals*, since such causal agents are then taken to be prototypical: that is, the same agent causes the same disease in all instances; and finally (3) the genesis of the notion of a *body of knowledge*, or of knowledge as an *object* (a social object, in the form of modes of action, or ritual performance, or particular methods or skills), which transcends the practitioner, is separable from him, and therefore can be preserved and transmitted.

It may be argued that these are not distinctively *medical* characteristics, since the techniques of tool production or of agriculture and hunting may also be seen to have such common epistemological features, insofar as empirical skills come to be ritualized, and embodied in a special person or a special class. Indeed, it would seem from historical and anthropological evidence that the medicine man deals not simply with disease, but also with natural processes, praying for rain or a good harvest, and dealing not simply with the spirits which cause disease, but those which cause other nonmedical ills as well. But this is interesting in its own right. The grouping of medical ills with other nonmedical human ills suggests that the various forms of human suffering and need are not sharply divided, but are understood and dealt with as aspects of a single and integrated scheme of disvalues. To put it differently: disease is understood as only *one* form of human suffering, or of evil, or of punishment for transgression. Thus the normative context of medicine—that it deals with good and ill, with weal and woe—is not yet separated from other normative contexts, and medicine is seen as an integral part of a more general technique for dealing with human ills of every sort.

There are two epistemological consequences:

First, medicine, at least in this early stage, is not yet differentiated, as a practice, from other normative practices, and thereby shares a common technique for dealing with ills and a common ideology and value-scheme. Therefore, even in its earliest causal-explanatory mode, medicine is already a normative kind of knowledge, in the sense that it is knowledge for the sake of some good. It is, in short, not differentiated as disinterested theoretical knowledge for its own sake. The theory is for the sake of the practice, and the practice is for the sake of human weal. The test of the theory is therefore its success in effecting its ends, or its failure to do so (though we shall see how the ritual form preserves itself also against the effects of failures).

Second, another consequence of the identification of the treatment of disease with the treatment of other nonmedical ills is that, in this primitive form at least, the cognitive repertoire of techniques for dealing with disease is easily adapted to other contexts, and that of other contexts to that of disease. Medical knowledge is in easy interplay with other forms of knowledge, but only because no sharp separation of functions has yet taken place.

There is, however, a third consequence which is not in itself epistemological, but which provides the basis for an epistemological distinction between two forms of medical knowledge, namely, that form of applied, empirical, and nontheoretical skill which characterizes what I have called "naturalistic" medicine; and the causal-explanatory kind of medical knowledge which generates theory (initially in the form of embodied and personified agents of disease, but prototypically as theoretical entities). The consequence of this latter revolution in modes of medical practice cannot be overestimated; and I have elsewhere argued that its correlate form in other practices (tool production, social organization, artisanal skills) is the genesis of science.(4)

It is therefore worthwhile to analyze this move somewhat further, since it establishes a fundamental institutional structure which profoundly affects the basic modes of medical knowledge thereafter. What are the features of this transition to theoretical modes of knowledge?

First, it marks the fundamental division of labor with regard to care of the sick and wounded, the treatment of disease, and so on. Though the medical practioner may also have been involved as the representative or agent who deals with general weal and woe, both medical and extramedical, the specialization of this medical function is nevertheless introduced. This means (a) that the elaboration of medical techniques and medical theory becomes the province of *professionals*; and (b) that the responsibility and opportunity to preserve and transmit such techniques and theories becomes a distinctive and separate form of education. Attendant on this, there develops a codification of such knowledge, either in a secret oral tradition, or in symbolic or written form; and the educational techniques and social and ritual forms for the sharing of such knowledge develop (either as an inherited and mystical "power" handed on from master to apprentice, or as the common and secret knowledge of a religious brotherhood or a guild).

Thus we have for the first time the institutionalization of medicine, and coincident with it, the institutionalization of medical education. Now this rather obvious truth bears with it what I think are major consequences—some positive, some negative—for the epistemology of medicine. The first such consequence is the establishment of *authority* in medical knowledge, vested in an authority structure. Beliefs about disease, its treatment, and its explanation take on the fixity of tradition and of ritual: that is, they may not be changed, and deviations are regarded as transgressions. The theoretical account, moreover, is closely linked to religious and metaphysical beliefs, and insofar as these too have a social function of maintaining a coherence and stability of authority, medicine as an institution becomes closely linked with the whole network of fixed authority-structures of belief and practice. Medical knowledge, and in particular, the primitive forms of medical theory are therefore part and parcel of the general ideological, religious, and metaphysical world-view of the community—in particular, of its "establishment"—and this leads to an extraordinary conservatism in the growth or change of medical knowledge. The innovations which may derive from empirical practices and discoveries are viewed as challenges to authority; or are kept beyond the bounds of professional medicine, in the uninstitutionalized preserve of folk-medicine, family medicine, or in the forms of lay practice which may be permitted. Thus, medical theory—what I have characterized as the causal-explanatory body of medical knowledge—is often divorced from the freer arena of uninstitutionalized empirical medicine. In short, the relation between established theories and skills and those acquired by continuing folk practices is effectively weakened.(5)

I am suggesting that the historical development of medical theory and practice shows both a progressive shift toward theorization and universalization, in the institutionalization of medicine by the division of labor; and at the same time, a retrograde divorce between a ritualized and fixed body of beliefs and practices, and a looser and more empirical folk-practice. The imprint of this division persists in medical practice through much of its history, even to the present day.(6)

It is with secularization (or partial secularization) of medicine that this breach begins to be overcome, in the return to a "naturalistic" medical tradition, but in an institutionalized and specialized form—the development of the Greek medical tradition, with Alcmaeon and Hippocrates. The condition for such an early development of secular (or partially secular) medicine is the unique social form of the ancient Greek city-states, the *poleis*. The theoretical models of early Greek medicine, like the theoretical models of early Greek cosmology, abandon the fetishistic and anthropomorphic forms of theoretical explanation typical of a mythopoetic culture, and begin to adduce natural principles for the explanation of disease, in terms of a harmony of the four basic qualities common to Greek cosmology and to medical theory: the hot, the cold, the wet, and the dry. Moreover, with the shift to a naturalistic mode of explanation, the emphasis on what can be seen, felt or touched, smelled and tasted can come into its own.

The Hippocratic school is empirically oriented, and careful observation is stressed. However, this characterization may lead to the one-sided view that Hippocratic medicine, because it is empirical, is antitheoretical or nontheoretical. Such a view is, I think, false. In Hippocratic medicine, what replaced earlier animistic theory was a growing emphasis on naturalistic theory, but not a reversion to an atheoretical or blind empiricism. Still, what is innovative here (though it has roots also in older medical practices, for example, in Egypt) is the attention to careful observation and recording of empirical detail. In fact, Greek medicine becomes one of the major models of knowledge in Greek thought, combining as it does empirical and rational elements. It profoundly affects the formation of Greek philosophy, and the theory of knowledge which develops there in its first full flowering in the works of Plato and Aristotle. The medical model of human nature, as a harmony of elements, is that which Plato adopts for human nature in general; and the norm of right functioning as the proper balance between these elements comes to be adopted by Plato as his model of the

Good, in general; and in particular, as his model of Justice in the State. Aristotle is the direct heir of the empirical tradition, employing as his dominant philosophical model one derived from medical-biological notions of growth and development, of the passage from potentiality to actuality. He combines this with the model of artisanal skill, of the making of things for some purpose, as the way in which human labor or skill becomes rational practice, and develops as knowledge of principles, that is, as theoretical knowledge.

One of the earliest accounts of the difference between artisanal skill, or merely empirical knowledge, and rational or theoretical understanding in terms of universal principles is Aristotle's, at the beginning of the *Metaphysics*.(7) It is instructive that his example of this distinction concerns medical knowledge. The difference adduced is that between knowing, from practical experience alone, what will cure this or that instance of a disease; and knowing the principles which hold for all instances of a given disease. Aristotle characterizes this latter knowledge, or understanding in two ways: first, that it provides a knowledge of principles in the actual therapeutic practice, as noted; but second, that such an understanding makes it possible to explain to another, and thus to teach or transmit such principles by rational means. Thus, at the basis of Aristotle's profound epistemological approach, he adduces two modes of learning: first, inductively: by imitation or by emulation, which he says has its roots in animal learning, in the instinct to imitate, and in the capacity for memory; but second, by the transmission of principles, or of universal forms by rational means. That his example is medical is not accidental. This division between what we might call clinical and didactic aspects of the medical curriculum is thus introduced from medicine into general epistemology, as one of its constitutive forms, or as one of the most basic categorical distinctions between alternative modes of cognitive acquisition.

IV. The Relation of Theory and Practice in
General Epistemology and in Medicine

This brings us to a distinctive epistemological question—or I should say, *the* epistemological question: what is the relation of theory to practice? Perhaps it is worth a digression here to consider the very form and import of this question for epistemology. For I will argue that medicine provides us with an important model of this relation, and one which is both autonomous and distinctive. This model may serve as a critical one, by means of which to probe basic questions in general epistemology.

The question of the relation of theory to practice is often reformulated in epistemology in different terms, and the reformulations themselves are revealing. Let me explore several such reformulations here:

1. The question is sometimes raised in a more general context as the relation between reason and experience, and in particular as the question of how we acquire knowledge of the "external world." Put in this form, the question already presupposes (or establishes) a framework: the separation of the knowing subject from the object of knowledge, and the characterization of the object of knowledge as "external." The *problematique* posed in this way requires for its resolution some way of mediating or connecting the subject with the object. Sense perception or observation by means of the senses is then seen as this mediation, and the classic alternatives in epistemology— empiricism and innatism; phenomenalism and realism; the distinction between self and other—come to be posed as solution-frameworks. Now a solution-framework is not itself a solution to a problem; rather it establishes what will count as a solution, and directs inquiry in a certain way. The options are clear: either (a) all knowledge comes from the "external world," by means of sense-experience or observation, in which the knowing subject simply records this knowledge; or at most, receives it passively and orders it actively "in the mind" (by association, etc.); or (b) *some* knowledge, if not all, is already innate, and is merely elicited by external stimulation, like tones on a keyboard which is already structured in a certain way; or (c) knowledge requires selection and structuring of experiential input, by an active subject intervening in the external world by perception, in which perception is itself taken to be an activity of constituting knowledge, an activity of synthesis.

All three of these classical epistemological models assume a fixed general or essential character of human knowledge, and most often characterize experience in terms of sense perception, taken as a receptive process at the periphery of the subject, or as active only "internally,"—"in the mind" or "in the brain."

2. A second reformulation of the relation of theory to practice emphasizes the theoretical character of the subject's knowledge. Theory is here conceived as an objective body of knowledge, and as a structure of concepts, beliefs, or claimed truths which are regarded as established, or provide the framework within which the knowing subject operates cognitively, and which bestows cognitive significance upon the sensory or perceptual content of experience. Traditionally, such theoretical knowledge is conceived of as a body of universal statements (in the rationalist tradition) or as a systematically ordered body of data, organized by some functional relation, or by some principle of ordering, such as association or correlation (in the empiricist tradition). The feature of such theoretical knowledge is that it can be articulated in some linguistic or symbolic form—and can be therefore *objectified*—and the knowing subject participates in it, together with other knowing subjects; contributes to it; and comes to use it as a socialized or educated, member of a community of shared beliefs and practices. The body of knowledge is therefore a *construction*, and the subject relates to experience by means of it, or through it. It therefore mediates experience. Most typically, such an epistemological model relates such theory to either observation or experiment: observation as either the source from which such theory is constructed, or by means of which it is interpreted, or applied to experience; experiment as the means of testing such theories for cognitive significance, or for truth, or as a means of interpreting such theories in a given and controlled domain of experience. On an inductivist-empiricist view, such theories are simply the abstracted or well-ordered image of observational experience, a reflex in thought or language of experience itself, and of its structures. On an anti-inductivist rationalist view, such theories are creations, constructs, conjectures, imaginative frameworks, or mental entities by means of which we construe and assimilate experi-

ence, or rules by means of which we order our inquiry, or probe the object of knowledge. The issue which has reemerged in contemporary philosophy, particularly in philosophy of science, is the extent to which our observation—our experiential access to the external world—is theory-neutral, or the extent to which such observation is theory-laden.

3. A third model of the knowledge relation is a frankly biological one: it conceives of knowledge as a process, a mode of interaction between an organism and its environment. The shift of emphasis here—compatible with some of the previous models—is from passive contemplation or reception of experience (on the one hand), or merely internal reflex activity by the knowing subject, as "mental activity" (on the other), to an activist model in which the knowing subject acquires knowledge by actual practical activity in the world, and as a life-process of adaptation to an environment, or the adaptation of an environment to life-needs. This model, which underlies naturalistic and evolutionary epistemological theories, construes beliefs, concepts, and theories as themselves instrumentalities of such adaptation, and construes the *value* of cognitive activity, or of knowledge—for example, the *truth*-value of cognitive claims—in terms of utility, or the satisfaction of needs. Such a view is most often, therefore, pragmatic in its interpretation of theory or cognition; and praxical or activist in its account of the knowledge relation. Thus, this model most closely approximates the formulation of the epistemological problem as one concerning *theory and practice*, rather than as one concerning *knowledge and experience* or *theory and observation*, both of which have overtones of passivity in the characterization of the subject's relation to the object of knowledge.

What is lacking in all these formulations of the epistemological problem, in my view, is that they are abstract in the following sense: whereas the first two construe the knowledge-situation as an essential or universal one, they presume that one can construct a general epistemology on this basis, without reference to the historical and social contexts of cognitive activity, or with reference to such contexts only in abstract and unchanging form. The third, or biologically oriented epistemology, while it takes environmental context as the arena within which cognitive activity emerges, and through which it is structured, takes it as a universal species-specific context also, without reference to changing social and historical contexts of such cognitive activity as themselves constitutive or causally efficacious in the formation, development, and change in the very modes of cognitive activity.

Thus far, I have digressed to characterize some alternative formulations of the theory-practice relation in epistemology. Now let me return to the specific questions of the epistemology of medicine by means of this detour, in two ways: first, to suggest how, in the history of epistemology (of epistemological *theory*), the contexts of medical praxis have served as sources of and influences upon such theories; second, conversely, to suggest how epistemological theories, often rooted in nonmedical contexts, have served to influence and affect medical theory and practice. In general, what I am suggesting is a subtle and complex interplay between medicine and epistemology. But I am not suggesting that epistemological theories somehow stand apart from forms or modes of praxis, as philosophical constructions derived from pure reason, and then somehow interact with the applied or specific epistemologies embodied in, or derived from specific modes of praxis. Rather, the model here is one in which philosophical or theoretical epistemology itself comes into being from a variety of praxical contexts, bearing the impression of this multiple genesis; and that these different praxical contexts then are brought to bear on each other, historically, through the mediation of their epistemological-theoretical forms. Philosophy is no virgin. One could say in fact that philosophy survives only by intercourse, and withers and dies without it. Historically, I believe it can be shown that the epistemological models drawn from medical theory and practice influenced not only the models of social theory, or of justice (in Plato and Aristotle) but also theology and physical science (in obvious ways in theories of salvation, or of the "cure" for evils done or suffered, in theories of cleansing and purification, and in demonology in general; in less obvious ways in the institutional forms of the priesthood, and in theories about its mediating role; and in organic analogies of the "body" of the church, or of the "body" of believers). In physical science, one has to look to the premechanistic forms of Aristotelian thought in Hellenistic, and later, in medieval science, imbued as they were with organic conceptions of the physical world; but also, I would suggest, one has to look to the influence of physiology and anatomy on the very development of mechanism itself, that is, as sources of mechanism beyond physics and mathematics proper;(8) and to the large role played by the seventeenth- and eighteenth-century medical materialism in the popularization and reception of Newton's physics as a general model of nature, including biological and human nature. But the converse is also true. The development of the mechanistic model in physics had profound effects on medicine, and the technology and theory which led to the development of hydrostatics and hydrodynamics provided the context of Harvey's discoveries on the circulation of the blood, just as Gilbert's work on magnetism led to an elaborated set of analogous theories and fancies in medicine.

I do not mean simply that physical science provided discoveries which were then used in medicine, although that is certainly and obviously true. Rather, I am suggesting that the epistemological frameworks, the cognitive outlooks provided on the one hand by medicine, on the other, by theology, physical science, politics, and modes of economic practice infected each other, so to speak. The lesson for philosophy is to recast its study of epistemology in the mold of this rich historical interaction of praxical contexts. The lesson for medicine is to see, in so-called *philosophical* epistemology, both the reflection of its own, distinctive medical modes of cognition, and that of other sciences, arts, and social practices.

To be historical, however, is to recognize that the modes, emphases, and structures of medical praxis have themselves changed historically. Thus, as we have noted, the secularization and naturalization of institutional medical praxis, in the Hippocratic school in ancient Greece, provided fundamental models for the characterization of knowledge-acquisition, and moreover, also provided models for social and ethical theory, and for a fundamental characterization of human nature. A striking contrast is provided by the seventeenth- and eighteenth-century theories of knowledge. With the impact of the mechanist view of the universe, with the successes of Newtonian science, with the advent of atomic theories of the structure of nature, and of geometric models of this structure, human nature and human knowledge was itself reconceived on this model. Locke's epistemology, as complex and problematic as it is in its systematic details, nevertheless operates on a physiological model of perception which is essentially mechanistic. Experience is construed, on the model of impact or action by contact, as a causal effect of the action of physical agencies upon a receptive *tabula rasa*. Descartes had freed both physics and physiology from the theological requirements for the immortality of the soul, and from final causes or teleology, by construing the body as a mechanism, as extended matter organized in a certain way. Mental activity, divorced from such extension, provided one realm; but sense experience itself, the interaction of organism and environment, the account of sensory physiology was reserved for a completely mechanistic and materialistic account (up to the point of its "interaction" with consciousness—a problem Descartes could not resolve).

Locke was trained originally as a physician. So too were such notable eighteenth-century theorists as David Hartley, and Julien Offraye de la Mettrie. La Mettrie's works, *Man a Machine* and *The Natural History of the Soul*, derive clearly from his medical studies with Boerhaave, in Leyden, whose medical works he translated into French. He also published medical treatises of his own—one on vertigo, one on venereal disease. Thus, the joint influences of a mechanist-geometrical natural science and of a medical physiological materialism which was also cast in mechanist terms, largely determined the shape, and the particular models of theories of knowledge. The point is that epistemology, in its historical development, does not simply legislate for the sciences or for medicine, on the basis of *a priori* philosophical theory. Rather, epistemological theory itself is largely formed on models derived from these other modes of praxis, specifically in terms of their own historically changing modes or forms.

Thus the relation between theory and practice, as a general epistemological question, needs to be recast in the most concrete and differentiated frameworks provided by specific historical contexts of theory and practice. The relation between medical theory and medical practice is a particularly instructive context in this regard. The extent to which, for example, Aristotelianism or Galenism provided heuristic force in the development of applied medical techniques is clearly a question for which historical research and interpretation can provide answers. So too is the correlate question of the extent to which such problem-and-solution frameworks inhibited or prevented more fruitful medical research, and indeed, more fruitful diagnostic and therapeutic practices. For too long, the contemporary philosophical enterprise has drawn its epistemological models either from the classic formulations of Greek thought, or from the seventeenth-century constructions of a mechanistic mathematical-physical ontology. These are, to be sure, rich historical contexts of fundamental and even revolutionary modes of cognitive praxis, for the Greeks and the seventeenth-century thinkers both reflected and helped to shape major changes in general modes of human praxis in such contexts as social organization and the technologies of production. But medicine provides an ignored and distinctive context for epistemology in the following sense: its praxis is *essentially* one concerning human welfare. It is hopelessly value-bound, centered as it is upon the phenomena of life, death, and human suffering. Its technology and its theory, though they may be construed as achievements of a disinterested scientific understanding, stand in too close a proximity to human weal and woe to permit a distracted divorce from actual medical practice. So too, such a practice is not merely "successful" or "failed" in some abstract epistemological sense. Its consequences for human life are, if not immediate, then not very far removed from immediacy.

The consequence for epistemology of such closer attention to the medical models of the relation of theory to practice is just this recognition of the normative character of our knowledge and of its human consequences. The great achievement of the seventeenth-century scientific revolution may have required, in its time, that divorce of the natural from the human, that universal objectivity which identified human ends as no more than local prejudices in a value-free mechanical cosmos. This, one may argue, was a condition for the liberation of science from the narrow confines of medieval teleology and from parochial views of providence. But the cost of this objectivity has been high, both in practical and social life, and in theoretical epistemology. The balance needs crucially to be set right, in both contexts; and this is indeed at the heart of the crisis in contemporary epistemology. Patchwork resolutions of the divorce between theory and practice result from failure to abandon an anomalous framework, in which human needs and interests are seen as merely external ends for which science (and knowledge in general) provide indifferent, or more or less efficient means. It is my contention that, in taking medicine seriously as a model, we have one way of probing a more intimate relation between knowing and caring. Not to be pious about the prospects here, one should add that a critical consequence of such an examination of the actual relations of theory and practice in medicine may reveal how medicine itself has, in its modes of practice and institutional forms, failed to maintain this very intimacy between knowing and caring, and has itself taken on the features of an objectivism ill-suited to its functions and purposes.

In many cases an examination of medical theory and practice, in their historically changing forms, provides an extraordinarily rich source for an historical epistemology. The interplay between practice and theory, between the normative and the factual, between ongoing techniques and the theoretical imagination seems to me to be close to the surface, and not yet buried under layers of preemptive epistemological prejudice. The "mind's eye" and the "hand's brain" are still transparent in their mutual interactions, in the medical practitioner, however far the division of labor between scientific medicine and clinical practice may have proceeded.

It is time, then, to make some further sense of the title of this paper: "The Mind's Eye and the Hand's Brain." By "the hand's brain," I mean to suggest the information of our cognitive apparatus itself by the modes of practical activity we engage in. Apart from the more exotic aspects of this view (the neurophysiological theories which see both the phylogenetic and ontogenetic development and differentiation of brain-structure or neural-structure as a mapping into the organism of the patterns and modes of its "external" motor activity), the image I seek is that in which the patterns and modes of medical praxis—in all of its ramifications, in all of its "external" forms, as technical skill, as institutional structure, as characteristic mode of interaction with patients, with diseases, with societies —come to be "internalized" or "mapped" into our cognitive structure itself. My claim is that this is not simply a phenomenon which affects medical practitioners, but that medical practice, as something we all engage in, either as agents or patients, shapes our general world-view, our general cognitive structure. I am pointing to, therefore, a social epistemological effect. At the same time, such a shaped structure of understandings, expectations, beliefs, and values comes to affect the very practices we engage in generally. The mind's eye is shaped by the hand's brain, but then, in turn, guides the hand by its conception. Moreover, in the mind's eye, the imagination of possibilities beyond the range of present *hand-arbeit*, or of present limits of skill, technique, or practices presents the hand with an imperative to experiment and probe beyond these limits.

I conceive of the medical imagination as something which goes beyond its obvious capacities for technical therapeutic or diagnostic innovation, and also beyond its capacities for theoretical and scientific innovation and discovery in the understanding of disease. But what lies beyond these is the conception of medicine itself, of its role, its function, its possibilities, and the critical recognition of its limits as a present institution. In short, the critical function of the medical imagination—the mind's eye of medicine—is to reexamine its basic forms of praxis, its fundamental concepts of disease and treatment; to see itself in historical perspective as having undergone radical changes in such fundamental conceptions and forms of praxis; thereby to enlarge its vision of alternative possibilities in its service of healing the sick and preventing disease.

NOTES

1. I am using the term "praxis" here in a very broad sense to include the whole range of distinctively human activity, from what might be regarded more narrowly as technological or instrumental action

(production) to the skills, rituals, and forms of institutional or social organization which characterize the forms of human action and the modes of human interaction. In this sense I am compounding the meanings of two distinct terms in Aristotle's usage: *praxis* and *poiesis*. Aristotle reserves praxis for the typical interaction among human beings which characterizes social life and constitutes the domain of *ethics*; whereas poiesis has to do with the *making of things*, that is, with art, or with the production of artifacts. John Dewey typically follows this Aristotelian distinction in talking about *making* and *doing*, and we might paraphrase this distinction as one between *production* and *action*. The compounding of both senses, however, yields the distinctive notion of praxis developed by Karl Marx, in which the intimate relation between modes of production and modes of social organization and social interaction is proposed. Insofar as I am taking all forms of human practice and action as cognitive, that is, as requiring and employing the distinctive modes of human intelligence and rationality for their fulfillment, to speak, as I do, of "the demands made on cognition by different modes of (medical) praxis" is to speak of changes in the existing modes of cognition which changing praxis demands. I regard *praxis* therefore as a central epistemological concept, as I hope this essay will show.

2. See, for example, J. E. Gerich *et al.*, "Prevention of Human Diabetic Ketoacidosis by Somatostatin—Evidence for an Essential Role of Glucagon," *New England Journal of Medicine* 292:19 (May 8, 1975); 985-89; D. J. Koerker *et al.*, "Somatostatin: Hypothalamic Inhibitor of the Endocrine Pancreas," *Science* 184 (April 26, 1974), 482-84. W. A. Miller *et al.*, "Hyperglucagonemia in Diabetic Ketoacidosis; Its Prevalence and Significance," *American Journal of Medicine* 54, 52-57; and bibliography in Gerich, p. 989.

3. For further discussion, see my essay "Organs, Organisms and Disease" in H. T. Engelhardt, Jr., and S. F. Spicker, eds. *Evaluation and Explanation in the Biomedical Sciences* (Dordrecht and Boston: D. Reidel, 1975), pp. 67-83.

4. Marx Wartofsky, *Conceptual Foundations of Scientific Thought* (New York: Macmillan, 1968), pp. 43ff.

5. Bernard Ortiz de Montellano, "Empirical Aztec Medicine," *Science* 188:4185 (April 18, 1975), 215-20. Professor de Montellano gives an account of how "empirical" (or what I have called "naturalistic") medicine—that is, traditional Aztec herbal therapies—coexist side by side with the more ritualized (or what I have called "theoretical" or "professional") practices of Aztec physicians. In this case, de Montellano writes that treatment "combined religion, magic, and positive medical intervention" (p. 215). But what he describes as a "positive

medical intervention" is precisely the "empirical" component, i.e., the herbal therapies, and *not* the "theoretical" attribution of the disease to "specific deities or to evil sorcerers." The source of de Montellano's view is the context of his study itself: in it he reports on the methodological problems of assessing the therapeutic value of Aztec herbal prescriptions by modern pharmacological and botanical techniques. That is, were the "empirical" (herbal) therapies fitted for or effective in treating the diseases for which they were prescribed? The role which "religion and magic" played, either in the discovery of, or the administration of these therapies, or in the diagnostic procedures of the Aztec physicians is simply written off. But, in effect, it is just this "theoretic" component, conjoined with the "empirical" component, in Aztec medicine, which makes the case interesting. Still, we have no method or technique (other than historical research and reconstruction) to test this hypothesis, and so we deem as "positive medical intervention" only what we can test by positive pharmacological means. De Montellano thus claims that the empirical techniques, though *also* practiced by Aztec physicians, were used as therapies without a "scientific" account of the etiology of the diseases. The theoretically ("religiously," "magically") conceived agency of the disease (god or sorcerer) was not connected with the "empirical" therapy according to de Montellano, so that both existed "side by side." But it is possible that this was not simply a coexistence, but a fruitful interaction. De Montellano imposes contemporary criteria of "scientific" and "nonscientific" components of Aztec medicine, but fails, I think, to recognize that the early animistic account of disease agency is nevertheless a "scientific" (or protoscientific) element in the development of medicine. Parenthetically, the sources of the contemporary historical and pharmacological reconstruction are in the careful account of the Spanish court-physician to Philip II, Francisco Hernandez, who was sent to Mexico from 1574-77, to gather materials on the plants, animals, and minerals of the New World. His unpublished *Codex* was later published in various versions as *Historia Natural de Nueva España* (1651, 1889, 1942). A careful historical reconstruction would also have to consider what a sixteenth-century Spanish court-physician would regard as worth recording, and what he would write off as ignorant or heathen practices.

6. A striking contemporary context for examining the relation of traditional or folk-medicine and professional "Western" scientific medicine is described in Chi-Pang Wen and Charles W. Hays, "Medical Education in China in the Post-Cultural Revolution Era," *New England Journal of Medicine* 292:19 (May 8, 1975), 998-1005. What is relevant

to my own account here is the extent to which there has taken place a radical change in the social and institutional contexts of medical practice, medical education, and forms of health care delivery. At issue is not simply the well-known combination of traditional and "Western" medicine in medical education and practice in China, but also the shift in what constitutes "medical knowledge" and what components are given weight both in medical-school admission procedures, the curriculum, the ongoing medical practices, and health-care delivery. The interaction of traditional or folk medicine with "Western" medicine is not simply a matter of content, or therapies, but an interaction between "folk" and "professional" values, attitudes, goals, and modes of doctor-patient interaction. For example, the admission and recruitment processes for medical education are based on social origin and work experience, prescreening for motivation and ideological mastery (of socialist principles exhibited in practice, that is, in previous community and work relations), as well as on academic preparedness. The latter is taken as least important, to be made up by "academic catch-up" periods and on-the-job training (p. 999). Also, selection is by four mechanisms: self-nomination, recommendation by the student's community; selection by political committee or organization of the community; and through screening exam given by the medical schools. What counts as relevant medical "knowledge" therefore includes a major component of community accountability, motivation to serve, and working-experience on farms, in factories, or in the army, especially in paramedical contexts. Such "knowledge" is what we might regard as background or normative context, rather than cognitive content. But here, it is taken as a major component of the cognitive praxis itself.

Further: the institutional forms of health-care delivery, hospital administration, and the combination of "traditional" and "Western" ("empirical" and "theoretic") medicine all provide a radically different spectrum of medical praxis which makes what will count as relevant medical "knowledge" a different sort of thing from what we are used to in professional Western medicine. Indeed, the impetus and ideology are explicitly deprofessionalizing in a deliberate social policy aimed at changing the very character of medicine. Does this mean that the content achieved by the "theoretical" tradition is lost? Or is there a trade-off of technical progress in medical theory and practice for wider diffusion of primary medical services? Will the advance of medical knowledge be helped or hampered by these changes? More fundamentally, is the patient-practitioner relation changed in a radical way? Is the very *sense*—that is, the structure, phenomenology, mode of human interaction in the medical relation—so changed as to mark an epistemological break with previous conceptions and practices of medicine? These are all *practical* epistemological questions. My own views here are not formed, but this provides a contemporary example of what I would like to take to be the *problematique* which I am posing in my paper.

7. Aristotle, *Metaphysics*, 980^a-982^a.

8. This is clear in the important role of the University of Padua in the fifteenth century. The emphasis on medicine there provided an ambience for the development of that scientifically and empirically oriented Aristotelianism, or late Latin Averroism from which there developed the very critique of Aristotelian science, and the beginnings of sixteenth-century mechanical physics, which in turn culminated in Galileo's work in the early seventeenth century. This medical tradition contributed as much as the other current of mechanism (developed in the mathematical analysis of motion by the fourteenth-century Merton school at Oxford, and by Jean Buridan in Paris, among others) to the rise of the mechanism which dominated seventeenth-century science and philosophy.

7

Ethics and "Social Functioning": The Organic Theory Reconsidered

Stephen Toulmin

I. The Reciprocal Influence Between Biology and Ethics

The historical development of human thought about ethics and its relations to society has been dominated by a restricted repertory of theoretical models or images. One particularly longstanding and striking tradition relies on analogies between society, on the one hand, and an organism, on the other. Thus, the state has been compared to a giant sea-beast, or "leviathan"; different groups and classes of men within society, or the state, have been likened to the different organs of the "social organism"; and, in the extreme case, the whole duty of man, so far as this springs from his position in a larger social body of men, has been traced back to a foundation in the individual's specific "function"—that is, his "function" as one particular "cell," or subunit, within that larger organic being.

In these very broad terms, the organic theory of society is familiar to anyone who has studied the earlier development of social and political philosophy. (Plato and Hobbes are the two most obvious and prominent thinkers to have developed this analogy.) So, there is a tendency nowadays to treat the organic theory as more or less "old hat," and even to suppose that it has

195

by this time become the stock-in-trade more of demagogues than of serious thinkers. The first aim of the present paper is to demonstrate that this is false; on the contrary, updated versions of the organic theory continue to play significant and influential parts in social, political, and ethical thought during the twentieth century—notably, in shaping some of the basic conceptions of twentieth-century sociological theory. Far from being superannuated, the organic theory—in these updated versions—remains a topical, and in some respects a damaging, element in contemporary thought about the structure of society, the organization of human behavior, and the foundations of morality.

Nor have the basic strengths and weaknesses of the organic theory been discussed in anything like a definitive way. Indeed, there are certain fundamental new issues that we are in a position to raise today, which have not hitherto received the attention they deserved. To say this is not to imply that earlier philosophers have been negligent in their analysis of the organic theory. It is, rather, to acknowledge that the concept of an "organism" has itself been subjected to important refinements during the past 100 to 150 years, and that some of these conceptual refinements have reflected back also onto the organic theory of ethics, society, and the state. To put the point succinctly: *all changes in the biological concept of an "organism" also entail corresponding changes in the "organic" theory of society.* If we no longer conceive of organisms—in the literal sense of the term—in the same way that people did 200 or 2,000 years ago, then we are in no position to conceive of "society" as an organism—in an analogical sense—in precisely the way our predecessors did either. The second aim of the present paper, accordingly, is to draw attention to some of the respects in which recent refinements in our understanding of organisms and organic phenomena have immediate consequences for "organic" analogies and theories in ethics and social thought.

In consequence, we shall be concerned here with a relationship between biology, medicine, and human values, which reverses the usual direction. Instead of considering ethics as basic to—as being a source of ideas and ideals, and canons of practice for—medical practice and biological theory, we shall here, conversely, regard medical practice and biological theory primarily as basic to—a source of ideas and ideals, and canons of practice for—ethical, social, and political thought. In point of historical fact, our ways of thinking about the social relationships between individual human beings influenced the development of fundamental patterns of thought in biology, medicine, and natural history; these biomedical ideas subsequently reacted back onto thought about human relations; and there has been a continual interplay between theories of *society* and theories of *organism*. That reciprocal influence between biology and ethics forms our central topic.

Most particularly, I shall be discussing the influence on sociology, psychology, and ethics of the theories about "regulatory mechanisms" and "homeostasis" launched by Claude Bernard just about a century ago.(1) These notions (I shall argue) have played a significant part in the thinking of such men as Emile Durkheim,(2) Talcott Parsons,(3) and Jean Piaget.(4) Parsons has acknowledged quite explicitly his debt to the writings of L. J. Henderson,(5) which introduced Bernard's concepts to the American public; while Durkheim's own direct debt to Bernard himself has not been hard to see.(6) Finally, Piaget's whole analysis of intelligence as a "biological adaptation," and his emphasis on the notion of "equilibration" in the development of cognitive capacities, will justify our adding him to the roll of twentieth-century organic theorists.

As we shall see, the continued influence of physiological and evolutionary analogies and concepts on our theorizing about society and social obligations has contributed significantly to the intellectual power of twentieth-century sociology and related subjects, but it has also had certain deleterious effects. In the first place, it has tended to conceal the assumptions involved in all such organic analogies, and to establish within sociology an excessively "conservative" view about the nature, value, and significance of "social relations." Furthermore, by relying in part on notions that are outdated in physiology itself, the social theorists in question have placed even more severe restrictions on their ethical, political, and sociological speculations. Properly used, "organic" metaphors and similes need do no harm in social theory: too often, however, the social reapplication of such concepts is used to impose a particular set of conservative doctrines, with the help of analogies with certain nineteenth-century physiological doctrines that have, by now, lost their place even within biology.

We should pay particular attention to the interlinked ideas of "function," "adaptedness," and "environment." There is in fact a crucial ambiguity to be noted in the biological uses of words like "adapt," "adaptive," and "adapted." The physiological sense, in which these terms apply to the relations between an *individual* organism and its immediate environment, has very different implications from the evolutionary sense, in which they apply to the relations between entire *populations* of organisms and their larger-scale ecological niche. Specifically, ideas like "homeostasis" and "equilibration" have a genuine application only to physiological, not to evolutionary "adaptation"; and this distinction must be continually borne in mind when we resort to biological analogies in ethical and social contexts. For our purposes, it will prove advantageous to distinguish between two different "organic theories"—one based on physiological, the other on evolutionary models. Or, to speak more exactly: we should distinguish the traditional type of organic theory—which views the synchronic "functioning" of social institutions as analogous to the bodily functioning of physiological systems or organs, and their diachronic "evolution" as analogous to physiological development—from an alternative organic theory, which can be built around analogies with neo-Darwinian "population dynamics"—analogies which are both much looser and much less liable to impose conservative prejudices on social and political thought.

Even now, references to "social evolution" still tend to evoke memories of Herbert Spencer's teleological ideas, rather than of Charles Darwin's population analyses: to this extent, the crucial differences between physiological development and organic speciation—which Spencer himself never fully grasped—have yet to be fully digested by sociologists, anthropologists, and political theorists. Until this is done, appeals to biological modes of thought and description in the discussion of social and ethical issues will remain essentially ambiguous. If we talk of ethical concepts, for instance, as concerned with "social functioning and adaptation," are we to take those terms in a physiological, or in a populational sense? If we talk of institutions as the "organs" of the social structure, which maintain a mutually "adaptive" equilibrium by their "functional" interactions, are we invoking "social homeostasis," or rather some sort of "ecological balance of advantage"? In a word, should we—like "social physiologists"—analyze the makeup of society as a network of interacting but self-maintaining "systems"? Or should we rather—like "social ecologists"—analyze it as comprising always a changing "population" of mutually reactive institutions, whose tendency to self-preservation has no direct connection with any good they may do to the human beings involved? If we take the former interpretation in each case, the biological analogies will by themselves preempt some fundamental ethical questions, and impose on us a particular set of social values whose legitimacy we shall then be unable to challenge. If we take the second, looser interpretation (by contrast) the need to confront those ethical issues head on, and to make explicit choices about them, can be brought back into clear focus.

II. Bernard's Concept of "Homeostasis"

The first necessary step is to consider the refinements that were introduced into our ideas about the physiological functioning of organs and organisms, at the stage when Claude Bernard inaugurated the analysis of physiological "systems" a century ago.(7) This will serve as a preliminary to any consideration of the ethical implications of the organic theory of society, and of the conditions that must be satisfied if we are to reapply the concepts of physiology or evolution theory in any general analysis of "human values."

According to Bernard, the operation of physiological systems involves a strong and very specific connection between the concepts of "function," "adaptive response," and the "environment." At the heart of his view, indeed, there lay a novel distinction between two kinds of environment (*milieu*): what he called the "internal environment" (*milieu intérieur*) and the "external environment" (*milieu extérieur*). If organisms —notably, warm-blooded animals—are so successful in maintaining their stability, functional integrity, and form, that was to be attributed to the efficacy of certain newly discovered "mechanisms" within the organism, which embody what we would now call "feedback loops" and preserve constant physicochemical conditions within the body of the organism, despite wide variations in the external conditions.

For example, there is a striking contrast between the internal body temperature of warmblooded animals, which remains very nearly constant around (say) 37° C throughout their life cycle and the external ambient temperature, which may vary over a range of some 60° C without immediate damage to the organism. This maintenance of a steady internal body temperature greatly helps warmblooded animals to survive, despite quite severe external changes. How is this constancy maintained? The key to understanding this phenomenon (*la chaleur animale*) lay in the manner in which circulating body fluids and the central nervous system together succeed in regulating the physicochemical conditions holding within the organism: specifically, the manner in which they react to external influences which might otherwise tend to modify those physicochemical conditions. Various different corrective mechanisms (opening or closing the pores of the skin) modify the rate at which heat is first generated, then dissipated, both within the organism and between the organism and its immediate surroundings. In this way, changes of temperature in the surroundings initiate changes within the organism, whose overall effect is to cancel out those internal physicochemical changes which would otherwise follow from the direct action of the primary, external changes.

So, physiologists—especially French physiologists, working in the direct tradition of Bernard—who talk about the "adaptive responses" of organisms to changes in their immediate "environment," must be understood in relation to their implicit theoretical context: namely, a homeostatic, feedback model, in which external and internal physicochemical conditions are linked together in a positive, systematic manner. This implicit context imposes on us a particular way of understanding the term "environment" itself. The "external environment" comprises, on this view, the totality of external objects and influences—or alternatively, the totality of external physicochemical conditions—with which each individual organism has to cope in its day-to-day life. Correspondingly, the "internal environment" comprises the totality of internal systems and mechanisms—or, alternatively, the totality of internal physicochemical conditions—whose mutual regulation (or "autoregulation") serves to maintain the normal functioning of the living organism itself.

In this physiological sense, the words "adapt" and "adaptive" relate to the same theoretical context. To the extent that the individual organism reacts to changes in its immediate *external* "environment" with corrective changes in its own *internal* "environment," and so preserves its internal conditions and functioning unchanged, it is said to be "adapting" to those external changes. Correspondingly, the internal physiological feedback mechanisms called into play by that response are spoken of as "adaptive mechanisms," by virtue of their homeostatic or autoregulative mode of operation. Thus, from Bernard's point of view, "normal functioning" and "physiological adaptation" involve the maintenance of a constant "internal environment," in the face of variations in the "external environment," through the operation of specific, self-corrective feedback mechanisms within the organism.

To underline the key point: for Bernard and his successors, it is the *individual organism* that "adapts" to its own immediate "environment" in a "functional" manner, by maintaining or restoring an "equilibrium" between the two. Further, the mechanisms by which this equilibrium is maintained take the form of positive "homeostatic systems," whose proper "functioning" depends upon the continual and impeccable cooperation of all their constituent "elements."

III. The Impact of Darwinism
on Organic Theory

In almost every respect, the physiological uses of these key terms turn out, on examination, to be contrary to the uses which are made of those same terms in the Darwinian and post-Darwinian theory of organic evolution. The point is worth dwelling on for a moment: both for the light it throws on the character of the physiological theories themselves, and for its bearing on any extension of these terms, in a metaphorical or analogical sense, into sociology, ethics, and value theory generally.

To twentieth-century readers, the appearance of such words in any kind of a biological context quite naturally suggests a broad Darwinian inspiration, if not a specifically "evolutionary" content. In fact, however, any such impression would be totally anachronistic. Recall briefly the state of biology in the 1860s and 1870s. French and British biologists were deeply divided across their whole field of study. In France, natural history was dominated by the antievolutionary tradition of Cuvier, but physiology had been well launched on the physicochemical road, through the work of Magendie and his colleagues. In Britain, by contrast, Darwin had put natural history on a new, historicoevolutionary road, while physiology was by comparison languishing in a clinical, nontheoretical posture. As a result, Bernard and Darwin made their respective, highly original contributions to biology quite independently, and it took several decades before they could be integrated into a common account of "general biology."

For instance, Bernard was concerned entirely with the physiological working of individual organisms, not at all with the historical transformation of organic populations or species. His mode of theoretical analysis was essentially systemic, not at all populational. He used to insist that any satisfactory physiological theory must be fully "causal"; and he was opposed to the use of statistical analyses and explanations in physiology. In these respects, he was a worthy successor to Descartes in the mechanistic tradition of French physiological thought. Questions about the statistical distribution of phenotypic characteristics across an entire population of organisms did not apparently strike him as theoretically significant, or even "scientific." From his point of view, a true "science" of physiology must set itself the task of discovering "physiological mechanisms" whose operation was explicable in fully causal, physicochemical terms.

True, the special characteristics of the "internal environment" within organisms gave the resulting physiological phenomena a correspondingly specific "vital" character; but the operation of the biochemical and biophysical causes involved—*qua* "chemical" and "physical"—presumably conformed to the same laws and regularities, whether they took place inside or outside the organism.

In short, the intellectual genealogy of Bernard's views, which set the pattern for much subsequent development in physiology, places them squarely in one particular family tree. They have a quite explicit connection with the ideas of twentieth-century systems theory, with its concepts of "negative feedback," and the rest; so much so, indeed, that Bernard's explanation of "animal heat" represents perhaps the first fully convincing application of the principles of feedback to solve a basic problem in natural science. (By contrast, the earlier use of the same principles in the design of the steam-engine governor was technological, rather than scientific.) Correspondingly, the fundamental methods of the contemporary "synthetic" theory of evolution, such as population dynamics, owe nothing whatever to Bernard, and are in some respects antithetical to his basic methodological principles.

If we find Bernard using such terms as "environment" and "adaptation" in his theoretical discussions, accordingly, we must recognize that this use is non-Darwinian. Strictly speaking, we could better describe it as pre-Darwinian. For the adaptedness of *individual* organisms and organic structures to their surroundings had, for many years before Darwin, been a commonplace in discussions of natural theology. Works of popular apologetics, by British Protestant theologians particularly, placed great weight on the Argument from Design: the "wonderful harmony" between living things and their conditions of life provided much edifying grist for their particular mill. Such best sellers as Archbishop Paley's *Evidences* and the *Bridgewater Treatises*, for instance, used this seemingly providential harmony as a strong confirmation of the Divine Wisdom and Benevolence.

Consider the citations in the Oxford English Dictionary, under "adaptation" and "environment." The word "adaptation" dates from 1610, and Paley is already using it in a theological context in 1790. The word "environment" appears very occasionally from 1603 on, but became generally current only from the time of Carlyle (1827, 1830, 1831). By 1855, four years before the *Origin of Species*, Herbert Spencer is already speaking of a "division of the environment into two halves, soil and air"; while Bain is writing of the structure of the outer ear as being "adapted to collect and concentrate the vibrations." As late as 1874, Henry Sidgwick combines both words in his *Methods of Ethics*: "The organism is continually adapted to its environment"; while, in an article for the *Fortnightly Review* (December 1881), Romanes defined "environment" as "the sum total of the external conditions of life." Only in May 1887 were the ideas of "environment" and "evolution" finally linked, in a citation from the *Athenaeum*, which refers to "the external or environmental explanation of evolution."

In this way, Darwinism slipped into men's minds without at first disturbing the older views of "adaptedness," as a relationship between individual organisms and their immediate surroundings: conceived of either theologically (as a product of Divine Wisdom) or physiologically (as the effect of specific bodily mechanisms). And, at the hands of such men as Spencer and Sidgwick, this older view remained influential within ethics and social theory, long after Darwinian ideas had become well established in biology, at any rate in Britain and the United States.

Darwin's theory of evolution by "variation and natural selection" has, however, the ambiguous honor of undercutting several features of that older view. In the first place, it makes clear that the existence in individual organisms of physiologically "adaptive" mechanisms, such as the vasomotor system, represents only a small part of the overall evolutionary "adaptedness" of the population to which those individuals belong. Second, it compels us to recognize that this overall, populational "adaptedness" is always in fact something less than totally complete, by comparison with the mechanistic operation of the physiologist's "adaptive mechanisms." And finally, as against the "creationist" views of traditional natural philosophy, it suggests very strongly that the individual's evolutionary "adaptedness"—including its capacity to make "adaptive responses," in the narrower physiological sense, to changes in its environment—is the outcome of populational (even, statistical) interactions during the historical development of the species. In all these respects, the new historical interpretation that Darwin brought to the problems of speciation and evolution implied a very different view of diachronic change, on the level of natural history, from that associated on the physiological level with the developmental process of individual ontogeny. The first kind of change was populational, even statistical in nature: the second was presumably mechanistic, and strictly causal.

These further implications of Darwinian evolution-theory, which we might be tempted to bring with us to our reading of Bernard's theories, were in fact quite foreign to it. They formed no part of Bernard's purpose, nor of his conceptual scheme. Bernard was, and remained, a causally-minded physiologist, and he had no more use than most of his scientific compatriots for the historical and statistical feature of Darwin's arguments. He was not interested in some vague, overall "adaptedness" of entire populations to their collective conditions of life, since what intelligible physicochemical mechanism could be advanced to account for so noncausal a notion? He was interested only in direct causal interactions between the physiological systems of individual organisms and quite specific factors in their physicochemical surroundings.

Even in Britain, early attempts to extend "evolutionary" patterns of thought to problems in sociology and other human sciences largely failed to allow for these special features of Darwin's evolutionary ideas. Thus, although Spencer thought of himself as an enthusiastic supporter of Darwin, he never succeeded in grasping the full differences between the populational processes of organic evolution and the mechanistic processes of individual development. As a result, his first attempts at an "evolutionary sociology" interpreted social change in terms of analogies drawn more from embryology and morphogenesis than from "evolution theory" properly so-called. For most of the nineteenth century, indeed, all proposals to develop sociological and anthropological theories on an "evolutionary" basis were understood in that same sense. And today, much of the disrepute that in some quarters still hangs around the idea of an "evolutionary" theory of human affairs derives from the defects of Spencer's first efforts. The fact that Darwinism implied a radical rethinking of the relationship between such notions as "organism" and "environment," "mechanism" and "adaptation," has yet to be considered fully in the discussion of society and human values.

IV. Bernard's Influence on Modern Theorists

At this point, let us return to the contemporary discussion of ethics, psychology, and social theory. Appeals to terms like "structure" and "function," "system" and "adaptation," may lend an air of authenticity and modernity to the arguments of a Durkheim, a Parsons, or a Piaget; yet we should not be in a hurry to take this tone at its face value. Failing hard evidence to the contrary, we shall do better to assume, rather, that their biological models have purely physiological and/or embryological (pre-Darwinian) origins, rather than authentically evolutionary (post-Darwinian) ones. There are in fact independent grounds for believing that this is the case. Durkheim himself was directly influenced by Bernard. Parsons' biological analogies were derived from L. J. Henderson, who in this respect represents little advance on Bernard. Meanwhile, Piaget claims a quite explicit parallel between his own account of cognitive development and C. H. Waddington's account of embryological development. But, since (as we have seen) Bernard's concept of "adaptation" had more in common with that of the traditional natural theologians than it had with the Darwinians, some quite specific assurance is needed that these twentieth-century writers were aware of the resulting distinctions, before we can accept their theories of society as a genuine and radical departure from older forms of the "organic theory."

By itself, indeed, the use of metaphors and analogies derived from Bernard's *Experimental Medicine* can do little new for ethics and the theory of society, beyond adding certain fashionable details of the traditional organic theory. Our novel understanding of the "systemic" relations linking the elements in the "autoregulative" feedback mechanisms of the body suggests that it may be worth undertaking parallel inquiries into the workings of the "social system," and of the individual "subsystems" into which physiologically-minded sociologists analyze society. In other respects, however, a "systems" model simply confirms and reinforces the ideological conservatism of the organic theory, in its familiar Platonic form. Sociologically speaking, the conduct of any individual is then "functional," to the extent that he becomes an effective element in some constituent "subsystem" of society; while the "adaptedness" of any particular institution/mode of conduct/custom is measured by its "functional" role, in contributing to the stability of the entire "social system." So, the implications of the resulting "structural/functional"—or, more properly, "homeostatic"— model of society are strictly conservative, not to say conformist.

This conclusion can be illustrated easily enough from the arguments of Durkheim and Parsons. Durkheim in particular was anxious about the danger of twentieth-century society "falling apart," and desired to reinstate an "organic" view of social relations, as a help in restabilizing the moral and institutional bonds of social life. Parsons, for his part, makes the conservative implications of his analysis quite explicit: he admits the possibility of historical change, but sees the proper functioning of society as leading always to some renewed equilibrium, both within and between the individual "subsystems" of the entire "social system." Piaget not only takes over his biological analogies from the field of embryology, but actually reads into Waddington's embryological theory certain conservative doctrines that are not present in the original. For instance, Piaget takes it for granted that all cognitive development must proceed through a sequence of "equilibria," whereas the terms "equilibrium" and "equilibration" nowhere play any serious part in contemporary embryological or morphogenesitic theory. On the contrary, those terms belong rather in normative physiology, where the "right functioning" of any organ or system is automatically equated with its stable, self-correcting functioning.

That being so, when Piaget speaks of intelligence as a variety of "biological adaptation," it seems likely that the "adaptation" he has in mind is that of Bernard's "adaptive mechanisms," rather than that of Darwin's "populational advantages." The twin operations of "assimilation" and "accommodation" have (on this view) done their task correctly, if they succeed in leading to an "equilibration"—by which, after the perturbation of a novel experience, an "adaptive balance" is reestablished between the individual and his environment. Yet the question should be pressed: if the analogy required is really with embryology and/or evolution-theory, rather than with physiology, what meaning then attaches to the ideas of "equilibration" and "equilibrium"? From an evolutionary point of view, describing some change as "adaptive" implies only that it is *advantageous*, not that it is *conservative* or *recuperative*: considerations of stability or homeostasis play little part in the discussion of evolutionary adaptation. (Nor does contemporary embryological theory provide anything like the same place for static "stages" and the like that we find in Piaget's theories of cognitive development.)

If we extend a "systemic" analysis from physiology into sociology, therefore, we shall find it helpful only to a very limited extent. Beyond quite an early point in human development, the direction and content of changes—both psychological and, in certain respects, somatic also—become matters of human choice and decision, rather than consequences of pure psycho-physiological mechanisms. Specifically, the direction and content of these changes become matters of cultural values and preferences. So, the question arises for us, "What values should we ourselves prefer?" (This is the point at which social theory merges with ethics.) What help does the physiological model give us in making those choices? Rather than giving us any such guidance, a homeostatic model simply imposes tacit, conservative assumptions. Or—more exactly—it leaves us with the impression that we have only two options: either, a *conservative* option, of accepting "the social system" in its entirety, and seeking merely to preserve or restore it, or a *revolutionary* option, of rejecting it in its entirety and seeking something quite new. Either we accept the one hundred percent "adaptedness" of the existing state of affairs, or we set ourselves outside "the social system" entirely. There is apparently no middle way.

In particular, the homeostatic/physiological model of society gives us no criteria for recognizing *desirable* changes, either in society itself or in the behavior of a developing child. It gives us no criteria for judging the comparative evolutionary "adaptiveness" of different social institutions and modes of conduct, in the face of cumulative, unforeseeable historical changes. For the social physiologist, as for the physiologist proper, institutions and/or behavior can either be "adaptive" or not: this is a yes or no matter, not a question of degree. But for the neo-Darwinist in biology, for a future evolutionary sociologist, different social changes and policies will hold out the promise of being more or less "advantageous," and so more or less "adapted." This adaptedness will be essentially a comparative, more-or-less matter, not a categorical, yes-or-no one. Like conservative theories in other contexts, a physiologically inspired sociology thus gives us no intellectual basis for deciding questions of "rational reform." If anything, it suggests that those questions are "dysfunctional," and so illegitimate.

V. Physiology as the Embodiment
   ## of External Value-Judgments

Significantly enough, Bernard's fundamental pattern of physiological analysis can no longer be accepted as self-justifying, even for the purposes of physiology. On the contrary, it is by now apparent that such a pattern can be given an empirical application only on certain special conditions, and that even in those cases it gives us an idealized picture of a more complex physiological reality. Furthermore, as we shall see, the shortcomings of a "systems" analysis within physiology are very similar to those that make physiological analogies so misleading in social and ethical theory. As a result, Bernard's account of homeostasis, which was so influential on Durkheim and Parsons, needs to be qualified and refined both in its direct physiological application and, even more, in its analogical application to psychology, sociology, and ethics.

To begin with physiology: here we need to look at the refinements that are called for in physiological theory, as a result of a hundred years' work on the theory of evolution. When Bernard inaugurated the tradition of analyzing bodily processes and functions in terms of "physiological systems"— e.g., the central nervous system, the respiratory system, the lymphatic system—each of these was seen as having a clearly defined "structure," and the resulting theory had no serious connections with organic evolution. Until well after Bernard's death, in fact, French biology remained impervious to Darwinism: in this, as in so many other ways, the Straits of Dover were as much of a barrier as the entire Pacific Ocean. Only during the twentieth century, indeed, have his physiological ideas been subjected to an evolutionary critique. So, at this point, we must notice the consequences of such a critique for the basic concepts of physiology.

To put the chief points concisely: first, despite all its analytical sophistication and empirical detail, Bernard's view of the structure/function relationship was almost as static and simplistic as that of Plato's *Timaeus*. The existence of any particular physiological system was taken as a basic datum. To the extent that it served a manifest function in the life of the organism, that fact by itself presumably gave the system "value" for the organism. The typical healthy state of such a system thus represented a *norm*; while departures from that "normal" condition were presumably pathological, and therefore "dysfunctional." This theoretical distinction between "normal functioning" and "dysfunction" was of course helpful when it came to discussing the relations between physiological theory and clinical medicine: for most clinical purposes, the equation of the "typical" and the "healthy" was accurate enough. (In any case, the "typical" was never understood as merely the "average," though the distinction between the "most frequent" condition of any system and its "most desirable" condition was in practice drawn intuitively, rather than by appeal to explicitly theoretical criteria.)

In the light of a Darwinian understanding, we can see the simplifications embodied in this view. In both structure and function, the characteristics of a physiological system can vary substantially without destroying the organism's evolutionary "adaptation"–to say nothing of its "viability." The demand that we should be able to specify with great exactitude the "typical and therefore healthy" condition of a physiological system thus involves *idealizing* the organism's life-situation, beyond the actual evolutionary requirements of any real-life ecological niche.

From this more recent point of view, accordingly, the typical stage of any physiological system represents, not a *norm*, but a *mean*. The only absolute physiological imperative is to avoid becoming "nonviable." All other demands depend on prior judgments about the comparative *desirability* of different modes of life, within any specific ecological/evolutionary context. (Strictly speaking, even the conditions of viability or nonviability themselves depend substantially on ecological considerations.) So, the *evolutionary* question:

> Are these specific physiological features "adaptive" for a *species or population* of organisms, given their current "environment" (ecological niche)?

differs in meaning from–and is more sophisticated than–the *physiological* question:

> Does this organ or system enable the *individual* organism to "adapt" to changes of this-or-that kind in its immediate "environment" (external conditions)?

Furthermore, the physiological question can by now be properly dealt with, only in the light of our answer to the evolutionary one. The physiologically "adaptive" character of any system can–from an evolutionary point of view–be specified *only* to whatever degree of accuracy the demands of evolutionary/ecological "adaptedness" require. Imagine a vasomotor system which responded to fluctuations in the ambient temperature every one-thousandth of a second, instead of with a time delay of seconds or even minutes. The mechanisms required to achieve such instantaneous "adaptive" physiological response would be so elaborate and energy-consuming that they would end by being "evolutionarily maladaptive."

To put the crucial point in a single sentence: Any *normative* specification of the "structure" and/or "function" of a system, on the physiological level, takes for granted a prior judgment of *comparative desirability*, on the evolutionary/ecological level. Rather than physiology serving as an ultimate source of values for ethics, therefore, physiology itself embodies—and depends on—*external* judgments of value.

This point bears directly on the central topic of this paper. The qualifications introduced into our understanding of "homeostatic systems" by an evolutionary critique has a double importance, when it comes to considering the implications of "systems analysis" for psychology, sociology, and ethics. If we accept the physiological analogies suggested by Bernard and Henderson uncritically, we may be inclined to operate with clear-cut and rigid ideas about "autoregulative" patterns of organization in cognitive development, and stable, self-correcting "systems" within social groups and societies. Yet doing this puts great weight on precisely those features of physiology that are most vulnerable to an evolutionary critique. If the structure of a physiological system can vary over a substantial range, without affecting its evolutionary "adaptedness," there will no longer be any *single* compulsory "equilibrium state" for that system. Rather, we shall now need to open up questions about the ranges of variation and innovation compatible with "adaptive performance"—questions about the "acceptable limits" of performance—compatible with a given set of ecological conditions. And, once these questions have been opened up within physiology, they apply *a fortiori* when we use physiological ideas as a model for social and political thinking.

If physiology is no longer the source of its own norms, then, it can hardly be used analogically as the source of social or ethical norms. Even if we could always recognize "autoregulative" cognitive patterns or stable "social systems" for purposes of theoretical analysis, we could not afford to treat these systems as any more cut-and-dried than the physiological systems which serve as their theoretical inspiration. If the possible modes of functioning of a given physiological system can vary substantially, within the "acceptable limits" of viability and/or adapted behavior, so too must the possible modes of functioning of any cognitive capacity, institution, or social system. And the question, "Just what limits to this range are indeed acceptable?" is an independent question, to which we must give an answer drawn from outside the resources of the physiological analogy itself.

The familiar, conservative picture—of self-correcting "social systems" and "compulsory mental structures," which "adapt" in a quasi-physiological manner to (maintain their *stability* in the face of) changes in the conditions of life—can thus no longer claim any support from contemporary biology. Does this mean that we should renounce all biological inspiration in our social, ethical, and political theorizing, as being *intrinsically* misleading? Not necessarily so: the charms of biology are so strong that we shall probably never be able to dispense with "organic theories" entirely. Rather, we shall do better to make sure that our biological analogies are as well-founded and refined as they can be, and that we are clear in our minds about the concealed presuppositions involved in their use. So we should be constructing an alternative picture of social institutions and human behavior patterns, not as static elements in rigid "homeostatic systems," but as free to vary and/or change in ways that "adapt" (in a quasi-evolutionary sense) so as to take effective advantage of novel opportunities and conditions.

In this quasi-evolutionary sense, of course, the comparative "adaptedness" of alternative cognitive operations or social arrangements is quite distinct from the quasi-physiological "adapting" of the traditional "social system" or "mental structure." Specifically, *changes* in social or cognitive structure will no longer be confined to "autoregulation," or the elimination of "dysfunctional variations." On the contrary, they must now be judged with an eye to the question, how far they in fact "take effective advantage" of novel conditions and opportunities. And that is a question which cannot be answered *indirectly*, on the basis of any physiological analogy, but only *directly*, in terms of the specific psychological and/or sociological subject matter under discussion. Before doing anything else; accordingly, we must face the independent problem of deciding what are the "acceptable limits of functioning," within the novel situation created by changed conditions and/or opportunities, and so what kinds of "effectiveness" are either desirable or desired in that situation.

VI. The Organic Theory in Terms of
Contemporary Biology

To sum up: once Bernard's brilliant and powerful physiological analysis of "homeostatic" or "systemic" functioning is subjected to an evolutionary critique, its *empirical* applicability and validity turn out to depend on preferences, or judgments of value, external to physiology itself. As a result, the "homeostatic" pattern of analysis ceases to provide the kind of apodictic model for sociology and psychology that made it so appealing to Durkheim and his successors. To go further: it turns out also that the conservative implications of Durkheim's sociology rested for their justification on precisely those features of Bernard's physiology that have since lost authority, even within physiology. In particular, Durkheim's difficulty in dealing with questions about "rational reform"—as contrasted with the reestablishment of "social stability"—evaporates in the face of a quasi-evolutionary critique.

The crucial question now becomes, "Just how are we to recognize which possible social changes are *better or worse adapted* to the demands of any specific situation?" In this way, a quasi-evolutionary account of social or psychological change lands us with all the basic "reformist" problems—notably, the criteria of social or cognitive "progress"—back on our laps. To a strict supporter of the traditional organic theory, change in social institutions can be of only two types—*disruptive* or *restorative*. Once we modify the organic theory to allow for the implications of Darwinism, that limitation is removed. Our central question now becomes, "What *ranges* of social or cognitive function are more or less acceptable or desirable, and so what changes in functioning enable an individual or society to "adapt" in a more or less effective and/or satisfactory manner to changes in the external conditions of life?"

Just how much extra freedom of movement this qualification allows us will become clear, if we remark on one further thing. The "acceptable or desirable range" of social and/or behavioral functioning is—arguably—much broader than the "acceptable or desirable range" of physiological functioning. For instance, the acceptable-or-desirable limits of "breathing" (or "respiratory functioning") are determined by natural physiological factors much more narrowly than, say, the limits of acceptable-or-desirable ruling and/or legislating, teaching and/or music-making, are determined by ineluctable psychic and social factors. While an evolutionary critique of physiology introduces some new flexibility into our physiology, the corresponding critique of systemic or structural theories in the human sciences is thus positively liberating. Subordinating physiology to ecology confronts us with fresh questions about viability and the like, but the corresponding questions in the human sciences present us with ethical and political choices of a much broader and more substantial kind.

Attempts such as Durkheim's to represent ethical and social norms as based on the demands of moral or social "health," therefore, drew their plausibility from views about "organic functioning" that have themselves been largely superseded during the twentieth century. Further, the conservative prejudices built into any "physiological" account of society, behavior, and ethical norms are far more rigid and arbitrary than the corresponding assumptions in physiology proper. For the simplifications involved in accepting Bernard's original vision of "physiological systems" was, and still remains, a legitimate one for most of the purposes of clinical medicine: the ecological refinements discussed in this paper are of much more significance for biological theory than they are for medical practice. Not so in ethics and social theory: there, the central questions of rational reform had been discussed at great length by liberal thinkers for centuries, before Durkheim did his best to close them off. And the chief conclusion of this present paper simply is: *organic analogies based on contemporary biology, properly understood, can free us from the limitations that Durkheim did his best to place on ethical and social thought.* Even from a quasi-biological standpoint, questions about the most desirable and effective directions of social reform remain matters of legitimate and crucial theoretical—as well as practical—concern for politics, sociology, and ethics.

If we are prepared to go along with the organic theory to this extent, all sorts of further, consequential questions remain. For example, just how can terms like "functional" and "well-adapted," "ecology," and "environment" be extended to social and psychological activities without damaging intellectual con-sequences? This is evidently a question that takes us beyond the limits of both physiological analysis and existing "systems theory." It is also a question that takes us beyond the self-imposed limits of the present paper. One final note: if we touch finally on the *converse* relationship—by which ethics and the theory of value provide ideas, ideals, and canons of practice to biology and medicine—we shall recognize how an intrinsically conservative sociology can in turn react damagingly on our understanding of experimental medicine itself.

Once we accept Durkheim's "physiological" restrictions on our understanding of social functioning, we may find ourselves drawn willy-nilly in a very modern, but very inhumane, direction. We may be tempted, that is, to view social noncon-formity and political dissent as manifestations of social or psychological "ill health." Whereas the practical damage that can follow in somatic medicine from Bernard's theoretical simplifications are comparatively minor, in the social and behavioral sphere by contrast there is a standing danger that diagnoses of psychopathology can be used as instruments of moral suasion and/or political oppression. It may be unjust to blame Durkheim's arguments about "social pathology" for the political misuse of psychiatry in the contemporary world. Still, the long-standing alliance between organic theory and totalitar-ian practice is no accident, and we should remain on guard. Where, for the classical Greeks, a tyrant became open to suspicion once he started spending too long with his architect, we ourselves should be particularly on our guard against autocrats who set up alliances with their psychiatrists!

NOTES

1. Claude Bernard, *Leçons sur la Chaleur Animale* (Paris: J. B. Bailliere, 1876).
2. Emile Durkheim, *Les Règles de la Methode Sociologique* (Paris: F. Alcan, 1895).
3. Talcott Parsons, *The Structure of Social Action* (New York and London: McGraw-Hill Book Company, 1937).
4. Jean Piaget, *Biologie et Connaissance* (Paris: Gallimard, 1966).

5. Talcott Parsons, "On Building Social Systems Theory: A Personal History," *Daedalus* 99:4 (1971), 828, 830-831.

6. An excellent new book which not only documents but analyzes the relations between Durkheim and Bernard in detail with special reference to *The Rules of Sociological Method* is Paul Q. Hirst, *Durkheim, Bernard and Epistemology* (London and Boston: Routledge and Kegan Paul, 1975). See also Guy Aimard, *Durkheim et la Science Économique* (Paris, 1962), esp. pp. 277 n. 2, and 286-287. Aimard makes good use of Canguilhem's *Essai sur quelques problémes posés par la distinction du normal et du pathologique* (Strasbourg, France, 1943).

7. For a useful discussion of Bernard's ideas about the vasomotor system, which was the prototypical case of a "homeostatic system" as applied to physiology, see G. J. Goodfield, *The Growth of Scientific Physiology* (London, 1960).

Commentary

Medical Praxis and Manifest Images of Man

Patrick A. Heelan

I WANT TO APPLY a useful distinction between two types of knowing which at first sight present alternative, competing pictures of the world and raise some fundamental questions of epistemology and ontology. The two pictures are called— to borrow a phrase from Wilfred Sellars—"manifest" and "scientific images" of the world.(1)

In a manifest image, things, events, and processes are given in terms of personal factors—perceptions, goals, meanings, significances—in a world that contains and is oriented toward and is intelligible only in relation to persons and personal and social values.

In a scientific image, things, events, and processes are given in terms that exclude personal factors: a scientific image contains only nonpersonal items and is intelligible exclusively through relating these to one another through interactions, similarities, and symmetries of an impersonal kind. Whatever the value of retaining the term "science" in its old and more general sense of systematic well-grounded theoretical knowledge, I am, for the purposes of this paper, restricting the term to refer exclusively to the type of experimentally based knowledge using mathematical models that has characterized the natural sciences since the seventeenth century.

Each type of image is comprehensive, and imperialistic in its demands to assimilate and place all that can be known.

Let me illustrate this distinction: a chair is a typical item in a manifest image, intelligible only in relation to a society of persons and a certain lifestyle. A chair, however, can be subjected to an exhaustive scientific description that accounts comprehensively for the fact that it serves its manifest purpose, without itself needing however (or being able) to use or define or explain the notion of human purpose. Similarly, electrons are typical items of a scientific image—they are also classified as "theoretical entities." Electrons, however, can manifest themselves as objects for human use through applied science or technology; thus, every child can easily understand what a beam of electrons is by understanding how the television screen is activated. In some sense, theoretical entities like electrons "seek" a place in the world of man, that is, as items of a manifest image, or more correctly expressed, man seeks to make them manifest in his life-world.

Because of the comprehensive and imperialistic claims of both manifest and scientific images, and the seemingly contradictory character of the predications made in them, it was deemed certain by many philosophers that one and only one set of images was to be identified with the "really" real. Since objects belong to or can come to belong to both types of images, the distinction then is set up not between two classes of things, events, and processes, but between two ways of describing all things, events, and processes. Those who adopt the ontology of manifest images attribute to scientific images the force merely of conceptual models or instruments useful for the purpose of manipulations within manifest images; those who, like Sellars, take their ontology from scientific images, regard manifest images merely as phenomenal and subjective or as merely symbolic of the noumenal and scientific world.

My own view is that the two images do not yield contradictory accounts, since the accounts are contextual and the contexts of the two images differ: manifest images describe objects with respect to their value for a society of persons, the context of what Wartofsky calls "praxis," if I read him correctly; scientific images, on the other hand, describe objects with respect to the interactions, similarities, and symmetries that occur within a world of nonpersonal entities, the context of a nonpersonal "praxis." Both reveal the same ontology but as implicated in two quite different contexts and therefore as endowed with two quite different descriptions. I have tried elsewhere to articulate the differences between these two contexts and to show how entities characteristic of scientific images come to be appropriated as new entities within enlarged and transformed manifest images through what I call the "hermeneutic shift" in the subject-object cut, such as that which occurs when persons learn to embody themselves in, or to extend their embodiment so as to encompass, *standard* instrumentation or *standardized* technology.(2) This hermeneutic shift is that which makes it possible for us to observe theoretical entities and so provides an explanation of the theory-laden character of scientific observations.

To turn to the main papers on which I am asked to comment, Dr. Engelhardt has attempted to describe and define the notion of disease. Two kinds of terms enter into his account and any account like it: terms that belong to manifest images, like "pain," "deformity," "inability to function in one's usual way," and other terms that belong to scientific images like "haemoglobin count," "blood sugar," "biochemical systems and their operations." The state of the patient can be comprehensively described within either a manifest image or a scientific image. Certain elements must be present in the manifest image if the state is to be called "diseased"—it must result in pain, or disability or deformity, or the imminence or inevitability of one or other, for "disease" is a person-oriented term. Similarly, since therapy is a medical intervention that aims at removing disease, it is a person-oriented action in the life-world of manifest images.

To every state of the organism as described within manifest images, there is a correlative state or a collection of states belonging to scientific images, expressing the biochemical and biophysical states of the organism without reference to the principal categories of manifest images. Likewise, to any state of the organism as described in scientific images, there is a correlative set of states in manifest images: the relationship is one-to-many and many-to-one and will be subject to certain populational regularities that depend on the cultural, historical character of manifest images and on the ecological and evolutionary character of biological organisms in scientific images of biological organisms.

There are then two taxonomies for states of the human organism: manifest and scientific. Each has its system of classifications and divisions. It is a logical point that any classification of disease that confuses these two taxonomies is methodologically unsound. A point made by Dr. Pellegrino is that the traditional taxonomy of disease, at least in certain areas, does in fact confuse the two.(3) "Disease," "health," "well-being," "life," and "survival," as well as all terms relating to medical praxis or therapy, belong to manifest images and incorporate scientific terms or scientific images only in a transformed sense—in the sense in which a standardized selection of these are appropriated in a person-oriented way to define or clarify what it is to be a person—healthy or sick—in the society of that time and culture with that medical praxis. A hermeneutic shift is involved in this transformation. Only after this shift are we in the presence of the fundamental constituting mode of general human knowledge spoken of by Professor Wartofsky. Wartofsky, however, has failed to specify what it is that is constituted (namely, the person), why it is general and fundamental (the person is the most general and fundamental reality in the manifest image), and how the constituting takes place (through a hermeneutic shift which changes the embodiment of persons by appropriating elements of a scientific image and making them part of a new manifest image).

The two taxonomies—manifest and scientific—have their analogues in the evolution of physical science. The conceptual frameworks are different, separate and incommensurable. I disagree with Wartofsky when he says that "tool production, social organization, artisanal skills"—defined only in manifest images—is the genesis of science." Whatever the genesis of science, it was not in logical continuity with tool production, social organization, and artisanal skills: it was a break away from them. Historically, this break consisted in the pursuit of a metaphysical clue that nature was ruled by numbers, points, and lines, and by the invention of an experimental praxis with which to test and develop this metaphysical clue.

The real genesis of science is experimental praxis, the praxis of scientific images, about which Wartofsky has surprisingly nothing to say in his paper. Experimental praxis is precisely the strategy of manipulating nature in order to find a coherent set of nonperson-oriented categories formally modeled in a mathematical system with which to describe it—categories therefore that prescind from tool-use and artisanship and social function. Science then in the first instance was a detour from the straight route of artisan and social praxis. Only in the second instance did it come to rejoin that tradition through technological application. To say that the genesis of science is in practical skills is then to confuse the praxis of experimentation with the praxis of personal and social life, with the praxis of manifest images of life-worlds.

The two taxonomies have their analogues in the biological sciences. Negative feedback, biochemical or biophysical systems are members of a scientific image; ecological systems are analogously members of a manifest image. The relationship between them is not one-to-one, but one-to-many and many-to-one. The dynamic of systematic evolutionary change, as Toulmin pointed out, is populational and, according to my argument, lies within the analogue of manifest images, that is, within ecological systems. It is then the ecological system and its movement that correctly provides the analogue for the changing value-structures of manifest images. Claude Bernard's homeostatic systems, being negative feedback biochemical and biophysical systems, are incorrect analogues for a basic evolutionary ethic, since their analogue is that of scientific images, namely, of events, things, and processes that get their intelligibility exclusively in relation to nonpersonal items.

This analogy breaks down once one is confronted with an ethical situation affecting an individual which then is to be assessed circumstantially—at a certain time and place—according to a value-structure that is virtually fixed and static for the

duration of the situation. This description happens to corre-
spond to the vast majority of clinical situations in which a
physician intervenes in the life of an individual patient. The aim
of the intervention is usually to bring about recovery, that is,
return to an original normative equilibrium of functioning. For
such cases, the ethical model is indeed that of Bernard's
homeostatic systems; disability is followed by negative feedback, medical intervention, and the restoration of equilibrium.
There is then assumed to be a value, at least in the short run, in
maintaining with the aid of medical intervention a state of
health or well-being univocally, nonhistorically, and "homeo-
statically" described.

Professor Toulmin's study of the biological analogy in ethics
forcefully points up the possibility of revolutionary historical
movement of the entire value-structure we use, as against those
who would see the principles of ethics as being exclusively
equilibrating and conservative.

Dr. Cassell's paper raised the question: how does one use the
scientific images within medicine—that is, biophysical and
biochemical systems, as well as impersonal artifacts such as
institutional facilities, impersonal procedures such as surgery,
chemotherapy, etc.—to provide person-oriented medical praxis
that has the kind of integrity capable of being in Wartofsky's
phrase, "a constituting mode of general knowledge" and "a
primary or fundamental mode of cognitive praxis." I am
assuming that both Cassell and Wartofsky are not content
merely with a utilitarian "nontransforming" view of medicine as
comprising merely a set of techniques useful to cure disease or
allay pain. They are in search of a "constituting mode of general
knowledge" expressing fundamental views about persons, values, life, and death. What we are talking about is a type of
medical praxis that transforms the elements of the many
scientific images that are provided by biology and medicine and
by the impersonal techniques and institutional facilities of the
medical profession, into a new and integral manifest image in
which will be found a *new* concept of the person, of well-being,
of life, survival as a personal entity, and death. The concept of
person is a historical cultural concept; therefore, the new
concept emerging with the new praxis will be both in continuity

with the past and, it would appear, radically new. I have tried elsewhere to explain the lattice logic of such a development: the new is a lattice synthesis of the old manifest images and the new scientific images.(4) I have made the point earlier that the characteristic epistemological move is a hermeneutic shift of the subject-object cut with a consequent change in what counts as the body experienced by the person as his own.

NOTES

1. Wilfred Sellars, *Science, Perception and Reality* (New York: Humanities Press, 1963).
2. P. Heelan, "Hermeneutics of Experimental Science in the Context of the Life-World," *Philosophia Mathematica* 9 (1972), 101-44; and "Nature and its Transformations," *Theological Studies* 33 (1972), 486-502.
3. E. D. Pellegrino, R. M. Biltz, J. M. Letteri, and J. A. Hight, Jr., "Numerical Taxonomy of Uremic Bone Disease in Man," *Clinical Research* 23 (1975), 446 A.
4. P. Heelan, "Logic of Framework Transpositions," *International Philosophical Quarterly* 11 (1971), 314-34.

Values in Medicine

Lester S. King

SINCE THE TITLE OF THIS ESSAY uses terms of great complexity, I will, for the sake of clarity, offer certain definitions. By "medicine" I mean the professional activities of physicians and the information accumulated therefrom. Obviously, physicians engage in a great many different activities. Some devote themselves to research, others to teaching, others to so-called "primary patient care," others to "secondary" care, still others to public health, others to administration in one or another capacity. Each of these categories could in turn be subdivided further and still other categories added, yet they all aggregate into the term "professional activities" of physicians. The historian is able to describe the way these activities have, in the course of time, increased in number and expanded in scope. We speak of this as "the growth of medicine."

The term "value" is more difficult. As a philosophic concept it has formed the subject of dispute for millenia—all the more reason, therefore, why I should clarify the precise sense in which I use the word.

In this essay value is a property that inheres in objects of desire. For example, we want food, clothes, books, automobiles—these are things, material objects of desire, and to obtain them we make effort and sacrifice. We also have desires that do not refer to anything material. We may hunger for knowledge, or seek various pleasures, or perhaps the approbation of our colleagues, or perhaps the inner peace that often has been sought in religion. All these, as objects of desire, *have* value. We may equally well say that they *are* values.

Values can be placed in a rank order, a sort of hierarchy, wherein an object of desire that is lower on the scale will be given up in order to obtain one that is higher. Each individual has a personal rank order, and we call this hierarchical arrangement a personal set of values. Sometimes the word "priorities" is used, and individuals may be called upon to "reorder their priorities," that is, reexamine the scale or hierarchy of values. Furthermore, values—entities or objects of desire and esteem—are held by groups as well as by individuals.

To study values in medicine we must make certain arbitrary divisions into categories. Perhaps we might better say that we must examine a complex whole from different points of view. I suggest three different categories or points of view: (1) the physician as scientist; (2) the physician as practitioner; and (3) the physician as part of society. This division places the physician first in relation to nature; second, in relation to his patients; and third, in relation to society. And in each of these categories we must examine the characteristic values involved—in turn, the theoretical, practical, and social values of medicine.

To make any subdivisions more precise, philosophers often used the special word *qua*. We may, therefore, speak of "the physician *qua* scientist," or "the physician *qua* practitioner," or "the physician *qua* social unit." This indicates a sharp isolation of context. A person *qua* this or that gets placed into a specific and limited category with distinct boundaries—a sort of contextual straitjacket whereby he is removed from the world at large and forced into a narrow, limited setting. Within this setting certain functions and activities are deemed relevant and all others irrelevant. However, the same person *qua* something else then finds himself in a different context, with equally sharp borders, equally sharp circumscription.

If we regard a person first as *qua* this and then as *qua* that, we have a useful maneuver for sharpening the attention and facilitating discourse. It is comparable to a stage setting where we focus a spotlight on one portion of the stage and try to keep all the rest in darkness. Then we may shift the light to a different portion. In this way the audience can attend to one very limited area without distraction from adjacent areas. But we must not confuse a spotlight technique—the rhetorical *qua*—with a description of reality. The area under illumination is not really separated from the adjacent areas of darkness. The division is artificial, for convenience only, and does not indicate distinct categories of being. The failure to appreciate this can lead to difficulties, ranging from creating a straw man whose principal function is to be destroyed to subtler but even more serious confusions.

I. The Physician *qua* Scientist

The scientist is concerned with the study of what has been loosely called the "laws of nature." He searches for correlations and regularities among natural phenomena—for the so-called "universals." He seeks to organize these into systematic form and to construct theories of greater or less generality. We can appreciate the difficulty in defining with precision the term "theory" if we regard the recent volume of almost 650 pages, *The Structure of Scientific Theories*.(1)

I appreciate the drawbacks of any simplistic definition, but for our purposes I offer this definition: medical science is the aggregate of professional activities, engaged in by those who are recognized as medical scientists. This definition, although it may arouse sharp dissent, is thoroughly defensible.

Medical theories get organized into what we may call "systems," a term of vast historical significance. A system of medicine is a coherent body of doctrine, resting on a small number of first principles, deriving ultimately from experience. A system, when adequately articulated, has both explanatory and predictive power.

We become particularly aware of theories and articulated systems when there is a conflict between them. For example, in modern medicine we have such problems as: should we use anticoagulants in cardiac infarction? or, should we keep to a low-fat diet in arteriosclerosis? The proponents of the different views are offering different systems, quite comparable to the opposition of systems in the seventeenth or eighteenth century. In any conflict, we may ask what are the criteria that help us to reach a decision that one theory or system is better than another. Philosophers have developed certain well-recognized criteria, such as simplicity, comprehensiveness, predictive power, ability to harmonize with new data, and the like. I will call these the "logical values" of medical theory, although other designations are equally acceptable.

From the standpoint of the physician *qua* scientist, we can achieve considerable insight by examining certain historical systems and the conflicts between them. Indeed, examination of historical examples is particularly helpful for getting us away from the parochialism of the present.

Let us examine some conflicting systems. One of the most dramatic struggles in all intellectual history took place between physicians of the late seventeenth century, between those who supported the traditional Galenic or, as I prefer to say, the neo-Galenic philosophy and those who supported the so-called mechanical philosophy. The neo-Galenists, who relied heavily on Aristotle, took as their first principles the *archai* of Aristotle—privation, form, and matter—as conditions under which nature can be made intelligible. "Privation" soon vanished from consideration, and form and matter remained the first principles of explanation. In the field of medicine numerous subsidiary concepts were necessary, such as the elements, the temperaments, the humors, and the like, as well as certain of the Aristotelian categories, such as substance, quality, quantity, and the like. The details of neo-Galenism as a system, and the specifically medical applications to health and disease, I have expounded elsewhere(2) and I will not repeat them here.

Form provided specificity to a given object, and also accounted for its dynamic and functional aspects, not only of what the thing *is*, but what it *becomes*. Goal and purpose were important. Form exerted its activity through qualities, which would be either *manifest* or *occult*. Manifest qualities concerned the hot and cold, the moist and dry, and their derivatives; while the occult qualities, such as the capacity of the lodestone to attract iron, was by definition not manifest. Instead, this property rested in the "whole substance." Neo-Galenism represented a system that emphasized process and change, described the world in terms of qualities, and these had primary metaphysical status while quantity held a subordinate position. Causal activity depended on an immaterial power or force that existed in the form and had to do with goal or purpose.

In addition to its "scientific" values, neo-Galenism harmonized with the prevailing religious doctrines, with views about God, soul, mind, and spirit, and with the prevailing doctrines in politics, education, and social organization. To neglect this harmony can lead to serious historical confusion, which will be apparent later.

The neo-Galenic system aroused much opposition, and the successful rivals embodied different aspects of the mechanical philosophy. Atoms, the void, and motion could serve as the basic principles; quantitative aspects—size, shape, position, and pattern—held prime metaphysical status while qualities retreated into a subordinate position.

Particularly under the influence of Robert Boyle, the notion that atoms have different sizes and shapes seemed to "solve" the phenomena in a satisfactory fashion. To be sure, the ideas of goal and purpose, which inhered in the concept of the discarded "form," fell by the wayside; but only a relatively few thinkers considered their loss significant.

New empirical studies greatly enlarged the data base of medical science. When the phenomena became too numerous and complex, the explanatory capacity of neo-Galenism failed. The proponents made valiant attempts to increase the explanatory range of the basic terms through subdividing and multiplying the manifest qualities, but all these proved to be only temporary expedients. The category of occult causes became too all-inclusive and served chiefly as a scrapbag into which were dumped more and more phenomena. Molière, with his *virtus dormativa*, satirized the inadequacies. Neo-Galenism, as a theory, fell a victim to complexity, and proved to have a value much inferior to that of the various types of mechanical philosophy.

The mechanical philosophy, however, could not remain in a purely logical or methodological isolation. It had its own difficulties, one of which was a potential conflict with current religious views. The mechanists had to avoid the accusation of materialism and atheism. One way of meeting this difficulty was simply to shunt the whole problem of related values out of the realm of medicine—in other words, to contract the universe of discourse and consider the theories in isolation from all other aspects of experience, to place the scientific theories in a contextual straitjacket. This solution led to the notion of science as "value-free," a concept that merely reflects an arbitrary separation of values. The notion of a value-free science is simply a sort of tool to help in choosing between opposing systems. It discards all aspects of experience that do not bear on the purely logical values of the scientist. It limits the universe of discourse in order to make a neater set of principles. In this regard the medical doctrines of the seventeenth and eighteenth centuries furnish a vast area for studying the character of logical systems, the canons of explanation, and the grounds for decision. No discussion of today's values can afford to ignore the past.

I suggest the propositions that the scientist tries to establish theoretical knowledge of nature, that this knowledge aims at maximum generality, and that knowledge of nature—it might be called "scientific truth"—is good in itself. As such it represents the highest object of desire, the highest value, of the scientist and, with appropriate limitation of subject matter, of the physician *qua* medical scientist.

But the concept of "truth" might be regarded only as an envelope, whose contents are not entirely clear. Five thousand years of reflection teach us that truth appears different to different persons. Rival formulations and opposing theories all claim to be "true" and to represent "knowledge." To judge between rival formulations we have developed well-known criteria, such as simplicity and neatness, comprehensiveness, capacity to absorb new empirical data and harmonize with new subsidiary theories, capacity to make predictions, and the like. All these are intrinsic parts of the philosophy of science. We might call these criteria "aesthetic," but I prefer the designation "logical."

If truth is good, and if there is dispute involving rival claims to truth, then these criteria provide the means for decision. Within the universe of discourse—scientific truth—these criteria indicate the rank order, distinguishing the better from the less good. The physician *qua* scientist will choose a theory or concept or system that has a greater simplicity or comprehensiveness, in preference to one which has less. Since these criteria are the measure of values, we can, by changing our viewpoint, represent them as values to be sought, *within the specific universe of discourse.*

The physician *qua* scientist seeks truth. In his search he is adhering to a limited set of values. To speak of science as "value-free" is, of course, absurd. Such an expression merely segregates social and interpersonal and religious values from those of a logical or logico-aesthetic character. The latter values relate to the search for scientific truth, the former do not. Such is the merit of the word *qua*.

II. The Physician *qua* Practitioner

Now let us change our orientation and consider the practice of medicine, rather than its theory. In regard to theory, for example, knowledge may be good for its own sake, with its own set of values. But when we ask: do theories affect the cure of sick persons? the historian readily realizes that some do and others do not. When we talk of practical application of theory to medicine, we must change our universe of discourse and invoke a quite different set of conditions. We must consider the physician *qua* practitioner. Then we find, in the realm of medical practice, that there is a set of goals or values quite different from those that apply to theory. In medical practice the physician is concerned primarily with caring for sick persons and with restoring them to health; or, if they are already well, in keeping them in that state. If the most elegant theory does not have concrete effect in getting the patient well, then its elegance, although possessing high logical or aesthetic value, has no great consequence in medical practice.

As a practitioner the physician enters into a special relationship with a patient as a person, a relationship that involves marked circumscription of context. The physician and the patient form a relatively isolated system, in which the physician as healer tries to cure the patient. All else is irrelevant.

Consider the case of a convicted murderer who, the day before his scheduled execution, attempts suicide by slashing his wrists. The prison physician sews up the wound and gives necessary blood transfusions, thus saving the patient's life. Why? So that he can be handed over to the executioner the next day. The physician has entered into a strict doctor-patient relationship, with its own special values. That the patient will be executed the next day is irrelevant to the doctor's professional conduct. His duty is to his patient, regardless of the latter's moral or legal or intellectual status. Similarly, think of the various melodramatic stories in which a surgeon finds himself operating on, say, his wife's lover. *Qua* husband, he may want to kill the person on the operating table, a wish that is consonant with one particular set of values. But *qua* physician he has a different set of values, which demand the care of the patient as the highest good. Soap operas can make much of this situation, but there is still a valid point, that the professional relationship between doctor and patient has a specific set of values. In this special context, what we may call social values disappear.

If we leave melodramatics aside and return to a more sober discussion, we realize that whatever helps the physician cure the patient is good, and the goodness is proportional to the degree that the help is effective. Helpfulness in healing the patient is the measure of practical value. And physicians who have had any practical experience realize that for a great deal of medical theory, the practical relevance is negligible.

A simplistic formulation, of course, is always beset with pitfalls, of which I am fully aware. For example, we speak glibly of restoring the patient to health after we have cured him of the disease. But what *is* the disease from which he suffered; and what *is* the health to which we try to restore him? Are these terms merely opposites or is there something additional involved? Some of these facets I discussed more than twenty years ago,(3) and the problems are still entirely moot, as Tristram Engelhardt analyzes so penetratingly.(4) Then, if the patient does get well, how do we know just what cured him? To what do we give the credit? If we pursue this, we find ourselves heading toward epistemology. Thus readily does almost any aspect of medicine lead us into a whole philosophy of medicine, a subject only just beginning to be adequately explored. But in this paper I must avoid the latent hazards and keep to a relatively simplistic path.

The important distinction between the values of theory and those of practice are summed up in the old saying, "Better a live patient without a diagnosis than a dead patient whose disease is fully explained." If we limit ourselves to the area of medical theory, then a successful explanation is the highest value, regardless of whether the patient recovers or does not. On the other hand, if we consider only the area of practice, then the highest value is the recovery of the patient, regardless of how it came about. Most persons do not care for any sharp dichotomy, but feel that the two areas should somehow fuse. Such persons are declaring that sharp circumscription is not possible.

Let me elaborate the distinction between theory and practice with a few historical examples. Medical practice has always distinguished the rationalist from the empiric. The former knows the theory, he knows the causes of things, and he can explain *why* things happen. The empiric, on the other hand (the word "empiric" is, of course, quite distinct from the word "empiricist"), is relatively ignorant of causes. He has learned by experience that certain sequences *do* occur but he does not know *why*. Nor does he care. He is content if he can cure the patient. Here is the distinction between the learned physician and the humble practitioner, a distinction that has persisted from earliest recorded medicine to the present.

We then face the question: does theory, *in point of fact*, help the practice of medicine, and if so, to what degree? The present-day emphasis on research and the avalanche of "wonder drugs" and "breakthroughs" have perhaps clouded the historical perspective. We should recognize the vast hiatus between discoveries of great theoretical importance and their actual benefit in practice. Robert Boyle, for example, emphasized that the great discoveries of the seventeenth century did not permit man to "cure disease much better than before."(5) But he believed that "in process of time" various new discoveries will "highly conduce to the improvement of the therapeutic part of physick."(6) Boyle had great faith in the ultimate practical value of pure science, but he seemed quite aware that theory and practice, although perhaps ultimately connected, would pursue rather separate ways. His viewpoint indicates a separation of overall theory from the specific demands of practice.

Baglivi, at the end of the seventeenth century, made this distinction even sharper, and created a virtual divorce between theory and practice. Having become involved in the dispute between the ancients and the moderns, he emphasized the merits of the ancients who relied on careful and continued observation. He condemned the type of practice that determined therapy not from precise observation but from logical dictates of theory. He declared, in trenchant terms, that "he who . . . promiscuously forms his notions of practice from the rules of theory, will never be a happy practitioner."(7) Differently phrased, treatment must have an empirical rather than merely a theoretical basis.

We see this to a striking degree when enthusiasts try to apply so-called "Western medicine" to peoples of different cultures. Western medicine—and when I use this term, please apply at all times the qualifying words "so-called"—rests on a mass of theory translated into various practical activities and specifically directed behavior. When applied to other races these practical activities may run counter to deeply ingrained cultural patterns, to traditional views of the healing arts, and to economic values. In such instances the Western-trained physician, especially the inexperienced doctor, may cleave to the procedures dictated by theory, but may find his advice totally ignored. Such a doctor is neglecting the primary values of medical practice, namely, getting the patient well, regardless of theoretical dictates. He may have to temper his own theoretical beliefs with those of the native culture, and rely on procedures that his own theory does not justify.

This does not mean that our Western-trained doctor must adopt the theories of a culture he considers backward. It does mean, however, that he must be ready to subordinate the intellectual demands of his own theories to the demands of getting the patient well.

Obvious retorts come to mind, for example, that *in time* Western medicine will prove its superiority; or that the "backward" medical practices of other cultures may find theoretical justification in Western theories as, for example, through a placebo effect. These objections may be valid. But they depend on faith in the future, not on present cogency; and they do not affect the main point, that the values of medical practice are distinct from the values in medical theory.

III. The Physician *qua* Social Unit

So far we have considered the values of medicine in two rather distinct contexts. The first, which deals with theory, I might call "the doctor in contemplation." He is dealing with relatively abstract, descriptive, and explanatory concepts; and in this sense medicine may be considered an intellectual system. The second context deals with the therapeutic relationship. This I would call "the doctor in a one-to-one relationship," wherein the physician is concerned with a particular patient. In this relationship theory is good, but subordinate to experience.

In my third category the doctor enters into a relationship with "society." *Qua* member of society he is part of an indefinitely large group. In the third subdivision, which I might call a "one-to-many relationship," the physician is no longer the solitary thinker or researcher, no longer the healer whose responsibility is to his patient, but a member of a larger group to which he contributes and from which he derives certain advantages. This subdivision of our topic leads us into the enormous area sometimes called "social medicine." For example, a doctor is in symbiosis with society—he is largely supported by society, enjoys a favored and monopolistic position, and in turn must contribute to the medical welfare of the entire group. Society looks to the special expertise of the physician in helping solve problems that deal with health—epidemics, securing pure water, or wholesome milk, or suitable disposal of garbage, or other measures of public health.

But "society" is an abstraction, drawn from a great many different groups, each of which may have different interests and contradictory desires. There is no single set of values governing the relation of doctor to society-as-a-whole, but each subgroup —and they are innumerable and overlapping—may have its own values. These values include varying physical, emotional, intellectual, economic, political, social, and religious desires.

In this welter of overlapping and competing groups, the welfare of one may involve the ill-fare of another. For example, in times of epidemics community leaders call on physicians to recommend suitable measures of control. Various proposed measures such as quarantine can seriously incommode some persons who may reject the regulation. We have a struggle between particular subgroups whose own desires and values can conflict with those of other and possibly larger groups.

The same problem applies to all areas of so-called public health measures: the establishment, for example, of laws for pure food, for proper garbage disposal, for control of harmful drugs, for truth-in-advertising, and the like. In the whole field of public health each competing group tries to advance its own desires—its own values—at the expense of other groups. For example, the attempts to set up standards for pure milk meant economic disaster for many of the existing dairies that flourished only because they could adulterate the product in various ways. Economic advantage for one group ran counter to health benefits for other groups. Or, in the struggle centering around compulsory vaccination, the health benefits of large groups contended against complex and multiple value systems that included philosophical convictions and ethnic prejudices, as well as political advantages. What are the grounds for comparing these distinct values?

There are innumerable other possible examples. Let me merely mention such issues as abortion, contraception, or organ transplantation. These varied subjects for conflict exist only because medical theories have made such stupendous advances. But these "breakthroughs" in medical theory concern not merely the physician, but also various other groups within society as a whole, groups that in their struggles exhibit quite diverse value systems, based on religious, economic, biological, or humanitarian values.

It is the task of the historian, in tracing the origin and resolution of conflict, to describe the various groups and also to identify their values. But how, in the face of such multiplicity, can we place these in some sort of rank order? Or, differently phrased, how can we evaluate their values?

IV. Resolving Conflicts between Value Systems

At the beginning of this paper I stressed that medicine must be conceived as a unity in which different aspects can be conveniently and approximately identified. I indicated three divisions: theoretical, practical, and social. I would now introduce a new dimension that I call "ethical values" in medicine. These, however, are not correlative with the other three, in the sense of a separate and coordinate division. Instead, ethical values apply to the whole area of medicine, an area that I insist is unitary and can be broken up only at a significant cost. So-called ethical values of medicine have to do with resolving conflicts between the other values.

Every physician belongs simultaneously to many different groups. He is scientist, clinician, spouse, father, taxpayer, member of the school board, of the golf club, of the Catholic church, of a conservation society, and so on. Each of these groups has its own goals and standards of value that we may call its value system. I define ethics as the norm by which conflicts between value systems are resolved. In regard to medicine I point out that there is no single set of values that applies to the entire area. Social medicine wherein, for example, religious, economic, professional, and interpersonal values come into collision is thus a prime field for ethical judgments.

Let us narrow down the field and discuss a few concrete situations. Let us take the doctor-patient relationship. A surgeon treats a patient with abdominal pain and making a diagnosis of acute appendicitis, decides to operate. But when the abdomen is opened he finds and removes a normal appendix. In most hospitals a case such as this, where normal tissue is sent to the pathologist, comes before the Tissue Committee, which has the task of evaluating the situation. For purposes of discussion I suggest three different excuses that the physician might offer.

> 1. He might say, "My diagnosis was wrong. I thought I was dealing with acute appendicitis—the signs and laboratory findings all pointed to that, and yet I was mistaken. It was an honest error in judgment."

In this instance we might say that there was an error in intellectual discrimination. The physician, after analyzing the evidence, reached a reasoned conclusion—but a wrong answer. He had used all due care, but medicine is not a mathematically exact science. It is probabilistic only. In this instance only professional values are involved and there is no scope for what we may call ethical judgments.

> 2. The doctor might say, "The diagnosis was uncertain and I was not sure what to do—the risks from surgery are not great. The patient might have had appendicitis which might have gone on to rupture. In such a case the risk would have been greater than immediate surgery. And so I operated just to be on the safe side."

In the first instance, only professional judgment was involved, but in this second case professional judgment may have been tempered by extraneous considerations. Was it *really* in the best interests of the patient to be operated on at that time? What factors would have been involved in waiting? The choice is difficult, and it may involve more than surgical judgment alone.

> 3. A third possibility might be, where the doctor says (to himself), "I was not at all sure about the diagnosis, but the patient does not need his appendix and I need the $500. So I operated."

Here there is obvious conflict of interest between strict professional values and those of a more selfish character, conflict between the claims of the patient and the claims of, say, the doctor's growing family and his need to provide for them. Here is an area where value systems conflict, and where ethical judgments are appropriate.

Another example suitable for discussion is the topic of abortion, where there may be innumerable conflicts between different value systems: What *is* the welfare of the patient? what are the rights of society? the validity of law? the relationship between majorities and minorities? the relationship between religious doctrine and social situations? in the conflicting welter, what are the obligations of the physician? how does the doctor-patient relationship fit into the larger web of relationships? Here, obviously, we have a conflict of value systems—precisely the area where ethics applies. Ethics is the discipline that helps resolve conflicts among different value systems.

Now it is my contention that we rarely if ever have real situations where only a single value system is concerned. The closest we can come, perhaps, is in actual surgery, in a situation that involves only the welfare of the patient and the professional judgment of the surgeon. Here the surgeon's universe is contracted to a few cubic inches of living tissue; and, in this situation, he may run into some emergency that demands instant decision, instant action. What he does may have far-reaching consequences, but the decision cannot wait for weighing of consequences. Such a situation involves only a single set of values. The further we get away from such a melodramatic situation, the more the likelihood that conflicts of value systems may arise.

Similarly with the so-called search for truth, wherein we consider the physician-as-scientist. I had used the phrase "doctor-in-contemplation," but we might also phrase it as "doctor-in-isolation," quite remote from the real world. For the most part the medical scientist can devote himself to his test tubes and his guinea pigs, without having too many distractions from other value systems. But the search for abstract truth, for pure theoretical values, always mingles with a host of other considerations, even though *for the most part* they are not blatantly operative. But we need only think of the conflict between research and expediency in Sinclair Lewis' novel *Arrowsmith* to see how the search for truth may be overwhelmed by other considerations. In my viewpoint ethics is the discipline that must resolve the conflicts among value systems.

V. Conclusion

At the beginning of this essay I indicated that medicine was a unitary field but that if we wanted to study values in medicine we must break down that field into manageable units. I offered three divisions for purposes of convenience. Such a separation promotes analysis and offers heuristic advantages, but it also falsifies the whole by giving us only a partial view. Such a partial view, adopted for convenience, causes infinite trouble if we try to endow it with some sort of quasi-absolute status. If we do so, we are merely erecting a straw man whose chief function is to get knocked down by clever argument.

It is my position that all men are at all times total individuals, inseparably related to each other and to the environment. Separations are necessary for practical purposes, such as discussion and communication, or lawmaking, or treating appendicitis, or playing tennis, but the separations are only approximate and "for the most part." And if we look, we can always find connections that have not been severed and that can easily lead us into conflicts. It all depends on how hard we look.

As soon as we speak of the individual as *qua* this, or *qua* that, we have falsified our total universe of discourse. What I call separate value systems have no existence unless we fragment the total individual into "*qua*-this" or "*qua*-that." Then, since *qua*-this can conflict with *qua*-that, the values can obviously conflict. However, if we deal with total individuals in total environments, we reduce fragmentation, reduce the degree of separation (we cannot abolish it entirely) and reduce the number of value systems.

I suggest that ethics is the value system of total individuals. To speak of the values of medicine is to speak of fragmented individuals in a fragmented environment. And the values inherent in any such artificial separation have only a partial validity. Let us at least recognize the limits of our efforts and their necessary incompleteness.

NOTES

This study was supported, in part, by a Public Health Service Research Grant LM 01804-02.

1. Frederick Suppe, ed., *The Structure of Scientific Theories* (Urbana, Ill.: The University of Illinois Press, 1974).
2. Lester S. King, "The Transformation of Galenism," in *Medicine in Seventeenth Century England*, Allen G. Debus, ed. (Berkeley: University of California Press, 1974), pp. 7-31.
3. Lester S. King, "What Is Disease?" *Philosophy of Science* 21 (1954), 193-203.
4. H. Tristram Engelhardt, Jr., and S. F. Spicker, eds., *Evaluation and Explanation in the Biomedical Sciences* (Dordrecht-Holland: D. Reidel, 1975), pp. 125-141.
5. Robert Boyle, "Of the Usefulness of Natural Philosophy," *The Works of the Honorable Robert Boyle*, 6 vols., Thomas Birch ed., (London, W. Johnson *et al.*, 1972 [reprinted, Hildesheim, George Ohms, 1966]), II, 163.
6. *Ibid.*, pp. 163, 164.
7. George Baglivi, *The Practice of Physick*, 2nd ed. (London: Midwinter *et al.*, 1723), p. 117.

Commentary

Historical Notes on
Value Systems in Medicine

Guenter B. Risse

IN HIS QUEST for studying values in medicine, Dr. King has chosen various spheres of activity in which professional healers function, albeit simultaneously. Historically, each of these roles could be analyzed in great detail, but such a task would result in a new textbook on the history of medicine.

In order to examine King's categories in some detail, I have selected one rather short period with which I am fairly familiar: German medicine between 1790 and 1820. Judgments made about this era, vaguely known as "romantic medicine,"(1) have unfortunately been based solely on the analysis of one set of criteria—scientific progress—thereby leading to a rather negative assessment of the entire period.(2)

A careful examination of the medical literature during those three decades reveals the extraordinary interest of physicians in coherent theories or explanatory systems.(3) The old and rather entrenched humoral pathology had already been displaced gradually by authors such as Jerome D. Gaub (1705-80) and William Cullen (1710-90), who emphasized the central role of the nervous system in pathogenesis. These new ideas were based on some experimental conclusions achieved by Albrecht von Haller (1708-77), who distinguished two distinct vital properties: irritability and sensibility. To confuse matters even further,

Luigi Galvani's (1737-98) so-called animal electricity and Franz A. Mesmer's (1734-1815) magnetism were provoking new thoughts on the normal and pathological functions of the human body.

With the onslaught of these and other new discoveries in chemistry, the traditional medical systems of the eighteenth century began to crumble. Unable to accommodate the new data within their theoretical frameworks, they became suddenly devoid of the hitherto explanatory and predictive capacity so greatly valued by physicians.

In the face of such theoretical confusion, certain physicians, especially those belonging to the French clinical school, opposed the establishment of new systems.(4) The German healers, however, persisted in their search for simpler and more comprehensive theories, and by 1795 they had adopted the system elaborated by the Scottish physician John Brown (1735-88).(5) Brown founded his medical system on a basic vital quality—"excitability"—whose fluctuations and imbalances were responsible for disease.(6) His theories had a certain aesthetic appeal and seemed, to some extent at least, to be based on Haller's experimental conclusions.

The subsequent incorporation of the Brownian scheme into a vastly more comprehensive philosophy of nature by the idealist philosopher Friedrich W. J. von Schelling (1775-1854) further stimulated physicians to seek ultimate explanations regarding life, health, and disease. Assuming that speculation was a superior road for the acquisition of new knowledge, such prominent figures as Andreas Röschlaub (1768-1835), Ignaz P. Troxler (1780-1866), Conrad J. Kilian (1771-1811) and Dietrich G. Kieser (1779-1862) established new medical theories based on *Naturphilosophie*.(7)

Thus, German physicians *qua* scientists as a group assigned—using King's terminology—great value to the quest for knowledge of the natural world. It should also be remembered that the ability of healers to explain and even predict illness strengthened their specialized role and position in society, setting them apart from laymen and paraprofessionals attempting the same. The depth and intricacy of such explanations, as well as the mastery of certain doctrines decisively influenced professionalization in medicine. Physicians were portrayed as intellectuals and philosophers, and the logical or aesthetic nature of these theoretical explanations was highly esteemed. The highest compliment was to be identified as a "thinking" or "philosophical" physician instead of merely a technician, that is, a person with special insight into the mysteries of nature. Thoroughly imbued with classical and philosophical studies which sustained a rather broad concept of *Wissenschaft*, these "romantic" physicians considered the task of penetrating the complexities of human biology one of their noblest efforts.

While the scientific quality of these endeavors—"scientific" according to modern standards—has been severely criticized, the physician *qua* practitioner has been largely neglected in the assessment of so-called "romantic" medicine. A glance at the contemporary medical practice reveals an almost total divorce between theory and practice reminiscent of Baglivi's time.(8) When confronted with individual patients, these "philosophical" physicians laid aside their theoretical speculations and resorted to the traditional standby measures based on discarded humoralism: bleeding, vomiting, and purging. Their goal was the recovery of their patients, and to achieve it, they went to great lengths, using diet, balneology, botanicals and metals, often to the detriment of those in their care. Even one of the most prominent leaders of German "philosophical" medicine, Andreas Röschlaub, declared that the basis for his intellectual battles was the achievement of a better therapy for his patients.(9) The employment of Mesmer's "animal magnetism" and Brown's "stimulants," such as opium, camphor, and alcohol, were only partial and circumscribed instances in which some of the new theoretical formulations were directly applied.(10)

The lack of extensive clinical facilities in the small and scattered German urban centers, the scarcity of medical journals, and the paucity of meetings severely impeded the acquisition and exchange of clinical experience. Therapeutics therefore remained a hodgepodge of isolated empirical successes and contradictory claims, a situation which prompted and facilitated the rise of such therapeutical sectarianism as homeopathy and hydropathy.

The German physician *qua* member of society came into contact with other spheres of interest, quite different from those already discussed. A product of Central European cameralism and political absolutism, Germany witnessed a flourishing of the concept of *medical police*, a set of governmental regulations established for the cure and prevention of diseases in the general population.(11) The trend-setting work of Johann Peter Frank (1745-1821), *System einer vollständigen medicinischen Polizey*, was soon emulated. A barrage of books, articles, specialized journals, and courses descended upon the medical profession; and many German states and cities began enacting medical ordinances and health codes. Questions of housing, clothing, food supply, first aid, prevention of epidemics, and other matters were considered.

A personal friend and disciple of Kant's, Johann B. Erhard (1766-1827) illustrated the awareness of intersecting and often conflicting roles when he defined in 1802 a *salus privata*, consisting of empirical medical therapy partially based on theoretical knowledge from the natural sciences, and a *salus publica*, which included interests and principles from political science, cameralism, economics, military knowledge, and medical police.(12) The physician was ideally the selfless servant of the state who lost his moral standing if he only cured for an honorarium.

Finally, an awareness of the conflicting interests in medicine and their possible resolution appear rather prominently in books and articles of the period. Stressing the "complications of duties" and their "collision" in individual clinical situations, Goethe's physician Christoph W. Hufeland (1762-1836) wrote on topics involving contraception, abortion, euthanasia, and human experimentation.(13) And in 1805 the prominent clinician Christian G. Gruner (1744-1815) began a monthly section entitled *Annalen der Heilkunst* in one of the more popular German medical periodicals.(14) In cooperation with other authors, Gruner penned articles of interest to practicing physicians, among them some reflecting ethical questions, such as truth-telling,(15) respect for the religious values of physicians and patients,(16) and others.

To summarize, King pointed out a number of interrelated spheres of activity in medicine, each with somewhat different ends and potentials for conflict. Historians concentrating on any one of these categories will find them useful for their reconstructions of medical activities and assessment of implied and explicit goals. This is especially true as medical historiography evolves from a purely descriptive to a more interpretative level. More important, perhaps, these categories could allow a better analysis of the ends which healers have pursued, and the means whereby such ends were ordered into value systems.

NOTES

1. G. Rosen, "Romantic Medicine: A Problem in Historical Periodization," *Bulletin of the History of Medicine* 25 (1951), 149-58.
2. See, for example, Fielding H. Garrison, *An Introduction to the History of Medicine*, 4th ed. (Philadelphia: Saunders, 1929), pp. 428-29; and Julius Pagel, *Einführung in die Geschichte der Medicin* (Berlin: Karger, 1898), pp. 335-40.
3. Useful in this regard is the *Journal der Erfindungen, Theorien und Widersprüche in der Natur-und Arzneiwissenschaft*, the *Salzburger Medicinisch-chirurgische Zeitung,* and the *Allgemeine Medizinische Annalen.*
4. J. B. Montfalcon, "Système," in *Dictionaire des Sciences Médicales* 54 (Paris: Panckouche, 1821), 164-75.
5. G. Risse, "Scottish Medicine on the Continent: John Brown's Medical System in Germany 1796-1806," *Proceedings of the XXIII Congress of the History of Medicine* I (London: Wellcome, 1974), 682-87.
6. G. Risse, "The Brownian System of Medicine: Its Theoretical and Practical Implications," *Clio Medica* 5 (1970), 45-51.
7. Andreas Röschlaub, *Untersuchungen über Pathogenie oder Einleitung in die medicinische Theorie,* (Frankfurt a.M.: Andreae, 1798-1800); Ignaz P. V. Troxler, *Grundriss der Theorie der Medicin* (Wien: Camesina, 1805); Conrad J. Kilian, *Entwurf eines Systems der gesammten Medizin,* (Jena: Frommann, 1802); Dietrich G. Kieser, *System der Medicin,* (Halle: Schwetschke, 1817-1819).
8. This fact was first stressed by E. Hirschfeld in his article "Romantische Medizin," *Kyklos* 3 (1930), 38-40. Isolated works on specific authors confirm the dichotomy: W. Brednow, *Dietrich Georg Kieser, sein Leben und Werk* (Wiesbaden: Steiner, 1970); Max Neuburger, *Johann Christian Reil* (Stuttgart: Enke, 1913).
9. "Dr. Andr. Röschlaub an Herrn Dr. C. W. Hufeland," in *Journal der Heilkunde* 32 (1811), 9-21.
10. A brief discussion can be found in Erwin H. Ackerknecht, *Therapeutics* (New York: Hafner, 1973), especially pp. 94-97.

11. G. Rosen, "The Fate of the Concept of Medical Police 1780-1890," *Centaurus* 5 (1957), 97-113.
12. Johann B. Erhard, *Theorie der Gesetze, die sich auf das körperliche Wohlsein der Bürger beziehen, und der Benutzung der Heilkunde zum Dienst der Gesetzgebung* (Tübingen: Cotta, 1800).
13. Christoph W. Hufeland, "Von dem Rechte des Arztes über Leben und Tod," in *Neue Auswahl kleiner medizinischer Schriften* (Berlin: Veit, 1834), pp. 244-94.
14. "Bemerkungen über die fernere Tendenz und Bestimmung dieser Zeitschrift, mit Rücksicht auf den dermaligen Standpunkt der wissenschaftlichen Medizin," *Allgemeine Medizinische Annalen des Jahrs 1804* (January), pp. 5-17.
15. "Über die Wahrhaftigkeit des Arztes," in *Allgemeine Medizinische Annalen des Jahrs 1810* (March), pp. 273-78.
16. "Über Religiosität der Ärzte," in *Allgemeine Medizinische Annalen des Jahrs 1810* (June), pp. 557-64. A summary of the most important social issues can be found in E. Heischkel-Artelt, "Die Welt des praktischen Arztes," *Der Arzt und der Kranke in der Gesellschaft des 19 Jahrhunderts* (Stuttgart: Enke, 1967), pp. 1-16.

9

Toward a Theory of Medical Fallibility

Samuel Gorovitz and Alasdair MacIntyre

NO SPECIES OF FALLIBILITY is more important or less understood than fallibility in medical practice. The physician's propensity for damaging error is widely denied, perhaps because it is so intensely feared. Patients who suffer at the hands of their physicians often seek compensation by invoking the procedures of malpractice claims, and physicians view such claims as perhaps the only outcomes more earnestly to be avoided than even the damaging errors from which they presumably arise. Malpractice insurance rates soar, physicians strike, legislatures intervene, and, in the end, health care suffers from the absence of a clear understanding of what medical error is, how it arises, to what extent it is avoidable, when it is culpable, and what relationship it should bear to compensation for harm. It is to this cluster of questions that we direct our efforts.

We seek to provide the basic outlines of a theory of medical fallibility. Such a theory, to be accepted as adequate, must account for certain basic data. Those data include the facts that medical error not only occurs but seems unavoidable; that some medical error seems innocent even when severely damaging, whereas other medical error seems culpable; that the harm that results from medical error seems sometimes but not always to warrant compensation; that the error that causes harm seems sometimes but not always to warrant sanctions; and, finally, that the relationships among culpability, harm, compensation, and sanctions are obscure. To succeed, our theory must increase our understanding of why medical error occurs and must help us distinguish between culpable and innocent error—it must diminish the obscurity surrounding the relationships among harm, culpability, compensation, and sanctions. Finally, and most importantly, it must thereby provide a basis for a more rational societal response to the reality of error in clinical practice.

Medicine as a practice is more opaque than we normally take it to be. We approach it too easily with already well-formed categories devised for other purposes such as those reflected in the sociology of the professions, the philosophy of the natural sciences, and the law. By so doing we overlook a unique blending of epistemological and social factors in the practice of medicine. For example, lawyers apparently assume that legislators and the courts are competent to determine when medical error is culpable and, correspondingly, when harmed patients are entitled to compensation, merely by applying the general principles with which our legal system handles torts. The reaction of the medical profession has normally been to claim prerogatives of professional jurisdiction in response. Relevant as the attitudes of both the legal and medical professions have been, both parties seem to assume that we already have an adequate understanding of the types of error to which physicians are liable.

Our theory of medical fallibility will challenge this assumption. In order to do this, however, we have to turn away from the conventional discussions which center immediately upon the notion of medical responsibility, usually with some help from sociological studies of professional responsibility, and examine instead certain more fundamental notions which derive not from medicine understood as a profession, but from medicine understood as a science.

I. Scientific Norms and the Sources of Error

Natural scientists tend not to have an entirely clear view of the normative character of their own activity, of the values that guide, constrain, and inform their activities. But there is a good deal of evidence for their finding plausible a distinction between *internal* and *external* norms. Internal norms are those which derive from the essential character of scientific activity as a cognitive pursuit. External norms are those which govern motives either for participating in or for making use of the results of scientific activity. Internal norms are concerned with such factors as verifiability, truth, and reason; external norms are concerned with such factors as curiosity, ambition, and social utility.

The recognized norms which are internal to scientific practice are fourfold. One norm prescribes attention to central rather than to peripheral problems of the science in question. A second prescribes the standards of scientific craftmanship—in the design of experiments, for example, or in the criteria of confirmation that determine when a claim is well enough supported to be accepted into the body of scientific knowledge. A third, belonging to the mathematical element in natural sciences, prescribes elegance and simplicity as the aesthetic hallmarks of distinguished theorizing. And finally, dominating all, the fourth norm prescribes the search for truth, that is, the search for a theory which will mark a gain in respect of truth relative to currently accepted theory.

These norms all presuppose that at any given moment a scientist's standards are necessarily set by the present state of his discipline. For that state he or she clearly cannot be held accountable; and there will be limits to the extent to which even the greatest thinker can revolutionize a science. Indeed, should everything be known about a given area of science, all *scientific* activity in that area would cease, even though work might continue on the practical applications of that knowledge. Therefore, where there is scientific activity, there is partial ignorance—the ignorance that exists as a precondition for scientific progress. And since ignorance is a precondition of progress, where there is the possibility of progress there is the possibility of error. This ignorance of what is not yet known is the permanent state of all science and a source of error even when all the internal norms of science have been fully respected.

Among external norms of natural science are those which are relevant to personal motives for entering upon a scientific career or for doing science. One of these prescribes a certain kind of honesty: assiduous care in acknowledging debts to others and in acknowledging priority of publication. Such a norm is not internal to the practices of natural science in the way that the norms governing experimental design or theory construction are. Natural science could remain essentially what it is now, even if the norms about priority of publication were somewhat different. Natural science might, for example, if it had had a different cultural history, have adopted the ideals of anonymity and impersonality which informed medieval architecture; who precisely built what is for that architecture relatively unimportant, vastly unimportant compared with who precisely built what in modern architecture or who discovered what in modern science. Modern science is thus a competitive race, although one could have an internally impeccable science without the competition.

Some of the other external norms of natural science have a good deal to do with this accidentally competitive aspect of its activities: that which warns young scientists against making premature claims or that which enjoins a certain kind of respect for the processes of election to a Fellowship of the Royal Society or to a Nobel Prize. But others concern the reasons which a particular scientist may have for doing this rather than that sort of science: such reasons as that inquiry in some particular area is likely to lead to socially useful discoveries. What some external norms prescribe may sometimes be at variance with what internal norms are held to prescribe. When, for good ecological reasons, Barry Commoner persuaded a distinguished colleague in chemistry to turn his attention to problems concerning the nitrates in agricultural soils, the other chemists in his department were disturbed because the problems involved are not central to chemical inquiry as presently understood. But the very nature of the disagreement exhibits the acknowledgement of the two sets of norms as distinguishable.

Note that it is *not* our contention that this classification of norms is good or bad, clear or confused, complete or incomplete, for any particular purpose; it *is* our contention that these norms, classified in this way, are as a matter of fact implicit in current scientific practice and that practicing natural scientists will readily recognize them as distinguishable influences or pressures on their own behavior. What matters for our subsequent argument is that this understanding of the norms of natural science involves acceptance of one particular way of classifying scientific errors. For on this view all scientific error will arise *either* from the limitations of the present state of natural science—i.e., from ignorance—or from the willfulness or negligence of the natural scientist—i.e., from ineptitude. This classification is treated as exhaustive. Willfulness and negligence will arise when those motives which are to be restrained by the external norms of natural science—ambition, impatience, competitiveness, a great anxiety to do good in the world—are allowed to override the internal norms. One function then of at least some external norms is to prevent extrascientific matters from invading and corrupting scientific activity; they could be other than they are in some respects, but some such set of norms would always be necessary.

To the extent to which our account so far is successful—that is, in being a recognizable version of what scientists characteristically would acknowledge about their practice—it is likely to seem familiar and even trivial. But it is the unsurprising character of the account that itself invites surprise when we go on to claim that this view of the sources of error in science presupposes a mistaken view of natural science. What will the relevance of this argument be to medical science? This view of ignorance and ineptitude as the only sources of error has been transmitted from the pure to the applied sciences, and hence, more specifically, from medical science to medical practice viewed as the application of what is learned by medical science. In order to understand this connection we will next examine the way in which the distinction between pure and applied sciences is customarily understood.

II. Pure vs. Applied Sciences

Applied sciences are commonly held to differ from pure sciences in two main respects. First, they are defined with essential reference to some practical aim, such as the building of bridges, the expansion of agricultural production, or the promotion of the health of men or of animals. Second, they are defined in terms of some subject-matter which is identified in prescientific terms. Pure sciences by contrast are only accidentally related to practical aims, and they continually redefine their own subject matter. What physics is about is for physicists to say. Further, there is a useful distinction to be drawn between an applied science and a technology. An applied science is, like a pure science, a body of theoretically organized knowledge, even if the principle of organization points toward a practical goal. A technology is a series of devices for realizing certain ends. Engineers, agriculturalists, and medical scientists are unlikely to be entirely innocent of technology, but not every one of them need be a technologist.

Just as the pure scientist can err from one of only two types of cause, so it is also with the applied scientist, on the view we are describing. If the physician prescribes a drug which turns out to have drastically unfortunate side effects on his patient, then *either* the limits of pharmaceutical and physiological knowledge are to blame *or* the physician was negligent, that is, he failed to act in accordance with the best knowledge available. On the assumption that the physician did not bring about the side effects willfully, then one of these two causes must have been operative. Where a surgeon is concerned, lack of technological skill may also be a factor. But failures from lack of technological skill are themselves classified in terms of the view of the sources of error which we have identified. Either they spring from the general level of the art; the technology in question just has not advanced far enough—in which case lack of technological, say of surgical, skill compares to scientific ignorance—or else the particular technologist, on the assumption that he is not willful, has been negligent either in acquiring or exercising the requisite available skill. Hence technologies, as ordinarily understood, do not provide a counterexample to the account of error which we have imputed to the natural scientist's characteristic understanding of his own activity. The complexity of that last phrase is not accidental. For what we are suggesting is not that natural science requires this account, but only a particular dominant interpretation of natural science. What that interpretation is, why it is dominant, and what the alternative to it is are the questions to which we turn next.

III. Reinterpreting Natural Science

Natural science did not in the seventeenth century discard quite as much of Aristotelianism as its philosophical protagonists supposed. What it retained included an inability to give a plausible account of our knowledge of particulars, of individuals—an inability for which Aristotelianism is notorious. For natural science, on a modern physicist's view just as much as on Plato's or Aristotle's, the objects of knowledge are universals, that is, the properties of objects classified by *kinds*, and the generalizations that link those properties. The scientist looks for law-like relationships between properties; particulars occur in this account only as the bearers of properties, and the implied concept of a particular is of a contingent collection of properties. To explain the behavior of a particular is nothing else than to subsume its particular properties under the relevant law-like generalization; to predict is to use the same stock of law-like generalizations about the relevant properties. Notice that on this view, predictive failure in science can have only two sources: factual ignorance as to the relevant laws or as to just which properties are present in a situation, or inferential error, such as when conclusions are drawn carelessly from the laws and descriptions of properties. Thus, where we are not ignorant, any inadequacy in our predictive powers must be attributed to the predictor, to his willfulness or his negligence.

What is it about *particulars* that escapes notice on this view? To answer this question, we must first say what we mean by "a particular." It will not do, for our present purposes, to give a syntactic definition in terms of the specification of some class of expressions, such as denoting expressions of a particular kind. The class of particulars with which we are concerned includes neither the square root of minus two nor the horizon.

It does include such varied items as salt marshes, planetary systems, planets, dolphins, snowflakes, hurricanes, cities, crowds, and people. A particular occupies a region of space, persists through time, has boundaries, has an environment, has peripheral and more central areas, and characteristically can split into two or more parts. Notice that in this use of "particular" certain collectivities are particulars—states, herds, forests, crowds, and cities, for example. Every particular continues to exist and has the characteristics that it has only in virtue of the operation of some set of physical and chemical mechanisms. Some particulars—ice cubes and molecules are notable examples—are such that nearly everything that we might want to know about them can be explained simply by citing the relevant mechanisms. Further, the generalizations that describe their behavior are generalizations that we accept as impeccably reliable. Thus, roasted ice cubes melt, and we can predict with complete assurance that any particular ice cube that we roast will in fact melt. This is in large measure because there is little diversity—at least, of any sort that interests us—among ice cubes. Each example of the type is, roughly speaking, quite like any other. The basic mistake made by that interpretation of science which considers that all genuine scientific knowledge is of universals is to suppose that all particulars are of this kind. But this is clearly false. Many particulars—salt marshes, hurricanes, and the higher primates, for example—cannot be understood solely as the sum-total of the, physical and chemical mechanisms that operate on them. What effects such mechanisms have are affected by the unique history of that specific particular with all its contingent circumstances, contingent, that is, and even accidental, relative to the operation of the mechanisms. One cannot expect therefore in the case of such particulars to be able to move from a theoretical knowledge of the relevant laws to a prediction of the particular's behavior. The history of the law-governed mechanisms and of the particular which is their bearer is, so to speak, an intervening variable which may always to some degree elude us.

It may be objected that this is a familiar point made in a misleading way. To predict any outcome, the scientist must possess not only accurate formulations of the relevant laws, but also knowledge of the initial and boundary conditions. Are we not merely saying that in the case of some types of particular we do not possess adequate knowledge of these conditions? This way of putting matters is however itself highly misleading. For the whole vocabulary of laws, initial conditions, and boundary conditions has application to situations where either we have a controlled and limited environment or else we have a natural environment resembling a controlled environment to a high degree, wherein the transition from one state to another by the operation of a specific mechanism is detached from its historical antecedents as well as from the interventions of environmental circumstance. There are indeed types of particulars whose past and future can be mapped entirely in these terms, such as the roasted ice cube, but there are also types of particulars with respect to which this is not so.

Hurricanes and salt marshes, for instance, interact continuously with a variety of uncontrollable environmental factors. No hurricane is quite like any other hurricane, no salt marsh quite like any other salt marsh. Certainly everything that occurs to and in a hurricane or a salt marsh is law-governed, but because we never know what historically specific interactions may impact on such historically specific particulars—for example, because of melting icebergs, flocks of migrating birds, changes in the temperature of deep sea waters, and so on—we never know in advance which the relevant law-like generalizations will be—even if we know them all—and which the relevant boundary conditions are. Indeed, in order to have such knowledge, we would need to know in detail what the behavior would be of each potential influence on the particular subject of our inquiry. To understand perfectly the behavior of a given hurricane, we would need to have perfect understanding of the polar icecap and the gulf stream. But these, too, are particulars interacting with their larger environments, which include among other things the very hurricane we wish to understand. We thus *cannot* have perfect knowledge of our hurricane, short of having a complete understanding of all the laws that describe natural processes, and a complete state description of the world. In short, perfect knowledge of that one particular hurricane is unavailable except under conditions of omniscience. Thus it is not so much ignorance either of the initial conditions or of the relevant laws, or even of both conjoined, that is in question; rather it is ignorance of the contingencies of the environmental context, a context that differs from that of experiment more radically than has normally been allowed. Hence, in the context of actual practice, no amount of theoretical meteorological knowledge will enable us to do more than score a certain degree, although perhaps a high degree, of predictive success with hurricanes.

This difference between types of particular—ice cubes on the one hand and hurricanes on the other—in respect of our predictive powers, is matched by a difference between the types of generalization by means of which we may reasonably aspire to describe their behavior. For that type of particular wherein the particular's history is crucial, wherein a theoretical knowledge of the mechanisms will by itself never be adequate for explanatory or predictive purposes, wherein the actual environment does not adequately match the conditions of the ideal environment presupposed by the theory (as it sometimes does), the generalizations by means of which we effectively grasp their behavior will not be genuine universal law-like generalizations, but rather generalizations prefaced by "Characteristically and for the most part. . . ." Of such generalizations it is true that when we are in possession of the best possible formulation, we may still encounter counterexamples and yet not be supplied thereby with any good reason, even any *prima facie* reason, for discarding or revising our formulation.

Consider the example of smallpox vaccination. One in 1200 will experience side effects as a reaction to the vaccination; for one in a million the effects will be fatal. Although there must *be* reasons why some individuals succumb—factors that distinguish them from the majority who are unharmed by the vaccination—we do not know what those factors are. We thus cannot accept as a *universal* generalization the claim that vaccinated individuals, even of a certain sort, will not thereby be harmed. But we can accept with confidence the claim that characteristically and for the most part, vaccinated individuals will suffer no adverse consequences. *That* generalization is not refuted by the illness or death of the occasional individual. What, then, are we to say of an individual about to be vaccinated? Of course, the effect of the vaccination on him will be determined by natural laws, his condition, and perhaps the way he interacts with his environment subsequent to vaccination. But we do not and cannot know all the relevant laws and conditions; thus our knowledge of this individual is limited and our predictive ability is constrained. We can have reasonable, empirically based expectations, accepted with a high degree of confidence. But no more is available to us than that. Yet more would be needed to eliminate entirely the possibility of causing harm by giving the vaccine.

One observation should be appended to the argument so far. When we have spoken of law-like generalizations we have intended this to refer to genuine law-like probabilistic generalizations as well as to nonprobabilistic ones. For our purposes there are no relevant differences between these. From this it does not of course follow that, as in the case of smallpox vaccinations, we may not on occasion be able *de facto* to assign a number to the proportion of individuals in a population who escape our formulation. But such a statement of a *de facto* proportion must never be confused with the kind of law found in, for example, statistical mechanics.

What is true of hurricanes and salt marshes is thus also true of animals and people. This is an empirical claim. That is, it is a question of fact about a given class of particulars whether the empirical, inductively founded generalizations with which we describe their behavior for explanatory and predictive purposes in our practical transactions with them can be simply deduced from the law-like generalizations of the relevant part of theoretical science. Where this is not so, practical experience becomes relevant in a manner quite different from that in which practical experience is important in a laboratory. What is important to the theoretical or experimental scientist is experience in research, not experience of the distinctive features of the particular crystals or molecules or other entities which provide a subject-matter for the research. That is, the scientist does have an interest in those particular entities, but it is an interest in what they have in common that typifies the activities of research. Thus, principles of crystal formation or solubility are inferred from the observable characteristics of diverse particular crystals, but the *differences* among such crystals are not to the point; it is their *similarities* that support generalization. In contrast, what is important to the meteorologist, navigator, or veterinary surgeon is an understanding of particular, individual hurricanes, cloud formations, or cows, and thus what is distinctive about them as particulars is what is of crucial importance. How such particulars differ from one another in their diversity thus becomes as important as the characteristics they commonly share. Experience of a single entity over time is necessary for an understanding of that entity as a particular in all its distinctiveness, for its individual characteristics will not typically be inferable simply from what is known about the general—that is, commonly shared—characteristics of the *type* of entity of which it is an instance.

Our thesis is then that the Aristotelian inheritance of natural science, as a result of which natural science is defined so that it is concerned exclusively with the knowledge of universals, blinds us to the existence of particulars as proper objects of knowledge. In the process, it blinds us to the role of a type of generalization that is different in crucial respects from those law-like generalizations that are usually treated as the characteristic genre of the natural scientist. This thesis could be developed in either a stronger or a weaker version. Its stronger version would involve a challenge to that whole picture of natural science which makes theoretical physics the most fundamental of disciplines and then ranks chemistry and biology before the applied sciences. For in this stronger version the thesis would insist that nature consists of nothing but more or less complex particulars, that theoretical physics is the most abstract kind of knowledge, and that it therefore always has to be based on our knowledge of particulars gained by means of sciences of the concrete. The most fundamental sciences on this view would be the disciplines concerned with our practical transactions with particulars: medicine, veterinary medicine, engineering, military and political sciences, and so on.

But this stronger version of the thesis is unnecessary for our present purposes. Even on the weaker version of our thesis—

namely, that the dominant interpretation of natural science must be revised to allow a place for our knowledge of particulars alongside our knowledge of generalizations—it is clear that those sciences which do deal with particulars require a view of error quite different from that which is derived from the dominant interpretation. To this topic we shall therefore return. But first, we will examine one more feature of our revised view of natural science.

IV. A Science of Particulars

The internal and external norms recognized by natural scientists do not always point in the same direction. Those doctors who performed experiments on living prisoners in Auschwitz did not violate any of the internal norms concerning truth-seeking and problem-solving. Indeed, at least some of them might have been quite exceptionally devoted to these norms, and for this reason they flouted the external norms which for most of us place ethical constraints upon experimental practices. This example will serve to bring out a sense in which science is often thought of as nonmoral or as morally neutral. The scientist discovers what he or she can. It is his or her duty to pursue empirical truth, but *qua* scientist he or she has no further concern with the social effect of the discoveries or the ethical status of the process of inquiry that led to them. *Qua* citizen, *qua* parent, *qua* teacher, he or she must have moral concerns. But this will always be a matter of norms external to science.

Underlying this view there is once again the position that the statements of fact made by scientists *qua* scientists are value-free. They are, after all, statements of fact. The familiar thesis that statments of fact cannot entail statements of value is often used to underpin this view of science. We shall not be concerned here with this general thesis. What we do want to assert is that once it is realized that science is properly concerned with particulars as well as with universals, then it must also be recognized that a concern for certain values other than those belonging to truth-seeking and problem-solving is internal to science. For at least some of the types of particulars which are objects of scientific inquiry have to be understood as wholes which either maintain themselves in the world or fail to do so. They prosper and flourish or they fail and decline. We need to employ in speaking of them some concept very like Spinoza's *conatus in suo esse perseverandi.*

Thus not only does it make sense to speak of the good of such particulars, we cannot even study them without some reference to that good—without indeed an ability to understand the particular from the perspective of its own *conatus*, its own striving toward its own good. It may seem somewhat odd to speak of the good of a hurricane or a salt marsh; it is surely not odd to speak of a salt marsh as flourishing or a hurricane as failing. But the concepts of the good of a tree, of a dolphin, or of a gorilla are crucial to inquiry into trees, dolphins, and gorillas. Unless one understands what it is for a tree, dolphin, or gorilla to flourish, one simply fails to understand them. This is why for many purposes one cannot study animals such as gorillas with profit outside of their natural habitat or by methods other than those which approximate to participant-observation. But a condition of success for such inquiry is a treatment of the tree, dolphin, or gorilla with a kind of regard which is in fact ruled out by a purely experimental relationship, on the traditional view of that relationship as being governed only by the traditionally acknowledged internal norms of scientific research.

Hundreds of years of understanding nature as the mere instantiation of universals, where particulars are nothing more than specimens for study in the quest for general truths, have contributed strongly to the ecological violence which we have done to nature. That is, not merely the forms of our economy or of our technology, but also—perhaps surprisingly—those of our science have contributed to our estrangement from nature and from other species. To say this is in no way to decry experiment, the search for laws, or the construction of fundamental theory. It is to say that the norms which are internal to the project of understanding nature and the individuals within it turn out to be broader and more complex than has been generally acknowledged. The S.S. doctors were indeed violating a relationship to men and to nature which is an essential part of the project of understanding men and nature; they thus failed as scientists and not only as men and citizens. Being a scientist then is a morally complex matter. It is often thought that the moral problems of medicine spring primarily from its professional and not from its scientific character. *Qua* scientist the physician has no particular moral commitment except to truth and the like; *qua* physician he of course has those moral problems that arise from his professional relationship to his patients. This is the view that we are rejecting (although we fully recognize that the professional relationship does engender its own set of moral problems). The importance of rejecting it will become clear when we consider the moral dimensions of the problem of medical error. To the reformulation of that problem we now therefore return.

V. Necessary Fallibility

Precisely because our understanding and expectations of particulars cannot be fully spelled out merely in terms of law-like generalizations and initial conditions, the best possible judgment may always turn out to be erroneous—and erroneous not merely because our science has not yet progressed far enough, nor because the scientist has been either willful or negligent, but because of the necessary fallibility of our knowledge of particulars. For it is characteristic of empirical, inductively founded "characteristically and for the most part" generalizations, as we have already noticed, that they may be the best possible instruments of prediction about particulars, and yet lead on occasion to unavoidable predictive failure as the evolving environment interacts with the particular with which we are concerned. What types of particulars must be understood, at least in part, in terms of this type of generalization is an empirical question; for that very reason it is also an empirical question to what degree of error we are liable in a given area. The nature of the gap between theoretically perfect predictive power and our actual predictive powers at their best is itself a notable subject for empirical inquiry, and the answers will certainly turn out to be very different in different areas. The necessary fallibility of the meteorologist may turn out to be of a very different degree than the necessary fallibility of the veterinary surgeon.

The recognition of this element of necessary fallibility immediately disposes of that twofold classification of the sources of error which we have seen both to inform natural scientists' understanding of their own practices and to be rooted in the epistemology that underlies that understanding. Error may indeed arise from the present state of scientific ignorance or from willfulness or negligence. But it may also arise precisely from this third factor which we have called necessary fallibility in respect to particulars. If this revision of our view of the sources of error were to be accepted, two very important consequences would have to be faced which fly in the face of contemporary medical attitudes and practices.

The first of these concerns the research programs of medicine. It is not common clinical practice to keep full and systematic records of medical and surgical error. Physicians and surgeons often flinch from even identifying error in clinical practice, let alone recording it, presumably because they themselves hold the very theory of error which we are engaged in criticizing—that is, that error arises either from their or their colleagues' ignorance or ineptitude. But without detailed records of erroneous diagnoses and prognoses, of unpredicted side effects, of failures of effect of treatment, and the like, we cannot provide the empirical basis necessary for any adequate theory of the limitations upon the predictive powers of physicians. Of course, there is nothing peculiar to physicians and surgeons about this lack of documentation of error. Political scientists, economists, and sociologists, for example, also do not usually keep systematic records of their own false predictions, and almost never advert to them in public utterance. Indeed, the only profession we know which fully and publicly documents predictive successes and failures is that of horse-racing correspondents in Great Britain. These journalists systematically predict the outcome of flat racing and steeple-chasing. Their failures as well as their success are fully documented in *The Sporting Times*; it is possible to make a precise quantitative assessment of the limits of the predictive powers of the best predictors. Thus, although genuine law-like generalizations may not be available as a result of the best possible study that might be made of the behavior of hurricanes, horses, and *homo sapiens*, they may well be made about the predictive powers of those who study such phenomena.

The other consequence of our thesis is practical: it concerns the physician's liability for error and the patient's attitude toward the physician. At present, the typical patient is systematically encouraged to believe that *his* physician will not make a mistake, even though what the physician does may not achieve the desired medical objectives, and even though it cannot be denied that *some* physicians do make mistakes. The encouragement of this inflated belief in the competence of the physician is of course reinforced by the practice of not keeping systematic and accessible records of medical error. Yet everyone knows that this is a false confidence. It is, one suspects, only recently that the statistical chances rose above 50 percent that a randomly chosen patient with a randomly chosen disease who encountered a randomly chosen physician would benefit from the encounter. And the current high incidence of iatrogenic illness constitutes a medical problem of enormous proportion, well recognized within government agencies and segments of the medical profession, but only dimly suspected by the public at large. There is still a relatively high probability that a patient will suffer from medical error.

It is here that the moral dimension of a science concerned with particulars becomes important. Patients and the public have to learn to recognize, accept, and respond reasonably to the necessary fallibility of the individual physician. The physician-patient relationship has to be redefined as one in which mistakes necessarily will be made, sometimes culpably, sometimes because of the state of development of the particular medical sciences at issue, and sometimes, inevitably, because of the inherent limitations in the predictive powers of an enterprise that is concerned essentially with the flourishing of particulars, of individuals. The patient and the public therefore must also understand that medical science *is* committed to the patient's prospering and flourishing, and that the treatment of the patient is itself a part of that science and not a mere application of it. The patient thus must learn to see himself as available for clinical study by methods which aim at his good, but which may do him harm. Indeed, the familiar distinction, comfortable to the public but suspect to clinical researchers, between therapeutic medicine and medical research, seems utterly to break down. Since the effect of a given therapeutic intervention on a given patient is always to some extent uncertain no matter how much is known about the general characteristics of interventions of that type, every therapeutic intervention is an experiment in regard to the well-being of that individual patient.

All experiments necessarily involve the possibility of failure in the sense that the expected or hypothesized outcome may not occur, whereas other outcomes, unintended and not usually specifiable entirely in advance, may occur. Thus the possibility of failure, and even of damaging failure, is linked conceptually—and not merely contingently—to the notion of experimentation, and therefore to the practice of clinical medicine.

It should seem obvious at this point that it is an error to link the notion of injury directly to the notion of culpability. A physician may not merely fail to cure, but may damage a patient, without violating the canons of impeccable practice. A common response to such outcomes is an attitude of humility in regard to the state of development of medical knowledge, but we suggest that what is more appropriate is humility in regard to the richness and diversity of individuals regardless of the state of medical science. If we are right, one consequence is that the hypothetical clinical practitioner who is fully informed of all the general principles that apply to medical practice—not merely to an extent reflecting the present state of medical knowledge, but even to the unachievable extent that represents the aspirations of medical research as an ongoing program of inquiry—even such an Olympian physician would be far from infallible. Indeed, he would stand humbled by the mysteries of individual diversity, and would know that an inquiry into the distinctiveness of each individual patient is an essential ingredient in his practice. Inquire as he might, there would always remain the prospect of his harming the patient whose well-being is in his trust, for even that inquiry itself, that effort to understand the distinctiveness of the patient, could be damaging in unexpected ways. And if such is the plight of our hypothetical physician, actual physicians of course are also limited by an irredeemably inadequate understanding of the individuals in their care.

Again, we may seem open to the charge that we have simply emphasized the obvious. Of course, good clinical practice involves respect for the importance of individual distinctiveness: witness the widespread acknowledgment of the importance of the individual medical history as a part of competent clinical practice. But, again, we believe that the appearance of obviousness is illusory. For what we have shown is not simply that a regard for the particular, for the individual, is essential to good medical practice. Rather, we have provided a theoretical account of why it is that knowledge about the individual patient is not merely essential, but is always and necessarily potentially inadequate to the extent that damaging error may result from conscientious, well-motivated clinical intervention by even the best-informed physicians.

It follows that injury is no proof of culpability. If physicians were to act as if they recognized this point, they might become far less reluctant to acknowledge, systematize, and learn from injury. But that would require a widespread willingness on the part of patients also to acknowledge the point, and thereby to lower their expectations about what physicians can accomplish and to refrain from assuming, even in the disappointment or despair that attends iatrogenic injury, that the physician is culpable.

The distinction between this view of the patient's role and attitude toward physicians and that which is current is obvious. The first reaction of physicians to the invitation to dispense with the masks of infallibility is likely to be a humane alarm at the insecurity that a frank acceptance of medical fallibility might engender in the patient. But we wonder whether the present situation, in which the expectations of patients are so very often disappointed during medical treatment, is not a greater source of insecurity. It is certainly one key source of malpractice suits. Indeed, a consequence of our view ought to be a rewriting of the laws on malpractice and compensation for iatrogenic injury in such a way as to acknowledge the inevitability of medical error and to make the burden of proof on those who allege malpractice quite different than it is now. This last practical consequence may not itself make our thesis more credible to physicians, but it certainly ought to make it more interesting.

VI. Malpractice and Compensation Policy

We have said that the concepts of culpable medical error and of entitlement to compensation for injury have historically been more closely linked than is appropriate. John Boyden, in his study of medical injuries in hospital patient records, undertaken for the Commission on Medical Malpractice for the Department of Health, Education, and Welfare, proposes consideration of medical injury insurance that would compensate patients who suffer iatrogenic injuries, independently of whether or not such injury was the result of blameworthy medical treatment. The Boyden study thus accepts the distinction between injurious action on the one hand and culpable malpractice on the other, although it addresses no attention to the task of characterizing either category. The question of what constitutes culpable malpractice, like the question of what constitutes injurious medical activity, is of fundamental importance in the determination of a specific policy governing the relationships among culpability, sanctions, and compensation. We will not here attempt to answer this question, but we do want to shed some light on what sort of question we take it to be.

Whether or not a given instance of medical action is an instance of malpractice is a question not of whether the action had undesirable consequences, but rather whether the action was justifiable as performed. To be sure, the question of justifiability may involve a consideration of what the expected consequences are, and this consideration may involve reflection on the past consequences of similar medical interventions under similar circumstances. But none of that depends on the actual consequences of the intervention in question. The specification of the canons of good medical practice thus will depend heavily on an accurate understanding of what has worked in the past, and of the degree to which autonomy of judgment in clinical circumstances tends to be conducive to a good medical result. Once those canons are specified, however, whether or not they have been honored becomes a simple matter of fact, to the determination of which the subsequent well-being of the patient is not material.

A profession concerned to minimize malpractice should then specify as well as possible the canons of good practice, it should require as an inherent part of good practice the maintenance of accurate medical records including records of error and injury, and it should adopt some effective mechanisms to identify culpable error. There should be procedures of due process, and sanctions for the performance of culpable error. But no injury to a patient should be required as part of the proof of any malpractice claim. If a violation of good medical practice is of a *kind* that is likely to cause injury that proper treatment would avoid, the absence of *actual* resulting injury is simply not material to the claim that malpractice has occurred.

In this respect, malpractice, we are claiming, is properly viewed as a formal violation of rules, procedures, and canons of practice—what philosophers among themselves would describe as a deontological offense. It is, of course, possible that there be a broad spectrum of degrees of seriousness of such offenses, and correspondingly of appropriate sanctions, ranging from the most gentle—calling the error privately to the attention of the offending physician—to the most extreme, at least within the profession—revocation of license to practice.

On this conception, the primary burden for discovering malpractice, bringing charges, supporting claims, and imposing sanctions falls not to the individual injured patient, but to those who are concerned with the integrity of the medical profession, including perhaps most prominently the practitioners of medicine themselves. Injury at the hands of physicians is quite another matter. Having argued that the question of physician culpability is independent of the presence of injury to the patient, in the sense that there can be malpractice without injury and injury without malpractice, we need to reassess the relationship of injury to entitlement to compensation. That is, we need to reconsider the formulation of a policy for societal response to iatrogenic injury.

No specific policy follows from our theory of medical fallibility, nor will we argue for any specific policy. Rather, we will focus attention on the question of what sorts of policy make sense in the light of that theory, and thereby will argue that a revision of current policy is in order. To do so, we will describe two alternative policies for which one could argue with the support of our theory—one in what might be called a liberal social-welfare tradition; the other in the spirit of what might be called a more conservative individualistic viewpoint.

The liberal argument might go like this: the costs of medical care are borne broadly by all those who support it, including its specific beneficiaries. Where there is no specific beneficiary, a medical cost is absorbed into medical overhead. For example, some drugs purchased by hospitals are spilled, contaminated, made obsolete, or otherwise rendered useless. The costs of their original acquisition are passed on in various ways as a part of the overhead of operating a hospital. Obviously, such costs cannot be passed along to direct beneficiaries, since, by hypothesis, they are not used to the benefit of anyone.

Iatrogenic injuries incur costs—most obviously those resulting from the additional medical care that is required in the treatment of the injuries, but also including the secondary costs associated with disability in all its forms. One could, of course, argue that these costs ought to be borne by the individual patient since they are incurred in the treatment of particular patients, and hence specific beneficiaries of the expenditures can be identified. An alternative view of the matter is to view the costs resulting from iatrogenic injury as akin to those medical costs which cannot be associated with specific beneficiaries, and hence are absorbed into the general overhead of medical care.

Iatrogenic injury, as we have argued, is to some extent inevitable. Whether or not one will fall victim to it is largely a matter of chance. It seems less than just to have the full burden of its costs compound the plight of those victimized by such injury. Consider again the example of the smallpox vaccine. In fact, vaccination against smallpox is no longer used in the United States precisely because it has been so effective that the risk of falling victim to side effects of the vaccine is greater than the risk of getting the disease now that it has been largely eradicated. But this does not diminish the present usefulness of the example. If we were to plan a public program of vaccination of a sufficiently large population, we would have good statistical grounds for believing that some few would fall ill or succumb as a result of the vaccination. Let us ask what the best way might be of responding to such an instance of illness. We are aware that culpable error is possible; one might be given spoiled vaccine, or an incorrect dosage, or in some other way be mistreated. But even if no identifiably culpable errors take place, someone will likely succumb.

Of course, we could simply reflect the present situation regarding malpractice claims; that is, we could undertake the program with the view that whoever falls victim to the vaccine will be entitled to compensation if and only if the victim can prove that the illness resulted from malpractice. If no such claim can be supported, then whether or not the victim is treated may depend in part on the extent to which the victim has private means or adequate health care insurance.

But we might well prefer to anticipate the iatrogenic illness and to respond to it differently. The program of vaccination will incur costs which must be determined in advance. One can estimate how many people will be victims of the program and how much it will cost to attend properly to them. One can then allow for covering such costs in the planning of the program, so that the statistically expected victim of the vaccine can be cared for as part of the total vaccination program, simply because that victim's illness and the medical expenses associated with it flow directly from the program as a consequence that could be anticipated, even though the specific individual could not be identified beforehand.

It is easy to imagine every one of the potential subjects of the vaccination agreeing to such a provision for compensation; it is similarly easy to imagine objection to the prospect of being injured without compensation. It seems more just, when one knows that someone will be victimized by a program, to construe the costs of caring for the victim as part of the cost of that program than to let the financial burdens of such care fall randomly.

With respect to this example of smallpox vaccination, it seems clear that it is preferable to build into the program of medical treatment an anticipation of the costs of iatrogenic injury. This example should be considered as a model or metaphor for medical care generally. Thus, since injurious medical error is unavoidable and medical care will have its victims no matter how conscientiously it is provided, the need for compensation even in the absence of culpability can be anticipated in advance, and can be construed as an expected part of the total operating costs of a system of health care delivery. The basis for entitlement to compensation thus would become the fact of injury; culpability would not be the issue.

None of this is to claim that questions of malpractice and of entitlement to compensation are wholly unrelated. For punitive damages, one would have to show that one was victimized by battery or negligence. Perhaps one might have to show culpability even for compensation beyond the direct costs of medical care. And, indeed, those who are responsible for providing compensation on the basis of injury, such as the writers of insurance policies, would be interested in making claims against individual practitioners and collecting damages from them where culpability can be shown. But the striking difference between such a structuring of the system of compensation and the present system is that the burden of proof to show culpability would no longer rest with the victim of medical injury; for the victim, compensation would depend only on the fact of injury. The burden of proof for showing culpability would fall instead on those whose responsibility it is to maintain the integrity of the profession and on those who, because of their involvement as insurers against medical injury, seek recompense for claims in cases where the claims result from culpable error.

But there is a conservative response to the sort of argument we have just presented. It might go like this: those structures and institutions that provide social services, ranging from urban governments to medical insurance organizations, are simultaneously under ever-increasing pressure to increase services and under ever more stringent economic strictures. Further, as a matter of empirical fact, such organizations suffer from an inherent tendency to become less efficient and effective as they grow in size and scope, trying to respond to an expanding range of human needs and wants. The consequence is that it is an error to expect our limping, faltering social institutions to be able to undertake such an enormous burden as that of underwriting the costs of compensation for iatrogenic injury. Even without that added economic burden, our health care system is flirting with fiscal collapse. The problem of responding to iatrogenic injury should not, therefore, be addressed on the model of the smallpox program, where there is a high degree of predictability and control. Rather, we should recall again the model of the hurricane as an unpredictable and uncontrollable source of natural disaster. On this model, iatrogenic injury, in those cases where it arises in the absence of culpability, is precisely a species of natural disaster, the costs of which must be borne as the costs of disaster are borne generally. That is, whereas some disaster relief is provided by private insurance and some, in cases of particularly large-scale disasters, is provided by government intervention, there is no sense in which a doctrine of *res ipsa loquitur* applies; the fact of victimization by a disaster does not itself provide a basis for entitlement to relief or compensation. Individuals are prudent to insure against disaster, and governments and charitable agencies appropriately provide relief within the limits of what they can afford. But falling outside the scope of either sort of relief are some cases that are simply disasters—a lamentable, but ultimately unavoidable, part of life. Even when the injury is clearly shown to be the result of physician error, no entitlement to compensation is shown in the absence of demonstrable negligence or battery, for physician error, as we have shown, in one of its forms is most properly viewed simply as a kind of natural disaster.

The choice between policy responses of these two sorts will depend on a large number of complex considerations. What is notable, we think, is that both kinds of policy, one of which enlarges the scope of entitlement to compensation and one of which reduces it, are alike in that they exhibit no direct conceptual linkage from physician-caused injury, through liability, to entitlement to compensation; nor is there a conceptual linkage from malpractice to culpably caused injury. In both these respects, the hypothetical policies we have considered differ from prevailing policy, which seems instead to be based on an outworn understanding of medical error.

We make no attempt here to resolve this question of policy. Rather, it has been our objective to clarify the nature of medical error as a preliminary to such policy determination. Actual policy specification will depend on judgments about the cost and efficiency of various ways of supporting health care, about the extent to which medical error is of the culpable sort, and about many other factors. We raise the policy question because we believe it requires reconsideration. We affirm the outline of a theory of medical fallibility in the belief that any acceptable policy must rest on a clear understanding of the nature and origins of the error to which it is designed to respond.

VII. Conclusion

It is time to take stock. There is a substantial and growing literature on the question of insurance against medical injury under a variety of programs. Over the last decade, the notion of compensation for injury to subjects in biomedical research has received considerable attention, and more recently, the notion of injury as a basis for entitlement to compensation has been extended to iatrogenic injury in therapeutic contexts as well. Thus, policy reform proposals, while they have not been adopted, are at least familiar. What then is novel or valuable about what we have said?

The reasons we have offered in support of our conclusion that revision is necessary in our societal response to medical error include a new ingredient—that is, a theoretical exposition of why it is inherent in the nature of medical practice that error is unavoidable not merely because of the present limitations of human knowledge or even the limits of human intellect, but, rather, because of the fundamental epistemological features of a science of particulars. That medical practice involves error not only assuredly, but necessarily, is a fact that should undergird a revised point of view about response to such error, and thus should strengthen the case for policy reforms.

We labor from no delusion that we have proposed a specific policy for response to medical fallibility or even a complete theory of it. Certain kinds of iatrogenic injuries do not result from errors at all—for example, predictable side effects of drugs which are utilized in full awareness of their side effects because, all things considered, the decision to accept the side effects constitutes the best available response to the presenting symptoms. A complete policy regarding iatrogenic injury would have to include specification of just which sorts of injury constitute a basis for entitlement to compensation, and which constitute a part of the discomfort and physiological disruption that attends medical treatment. Many other questions, as well, would need to be addressed before a specific policy could be affirmed. Nonetheless, we hope to have shown that while a philosophical analysis of issues in medicine cannot by itself resolve questions of policy, the attempt to fashion an enlightened policy toward medical fallibility must rely in part on considerations drawn from the philosophy of medicine—an inquiry which we see as necessary to a more thorough understanding of medicine as a science and as a practical art.

And finally, we hope to have made a point about medical education. We often hear it said that exposure to the liberal arts is advisable for medical students, not for its practical utility, but because of the intrinsic rewards of liberal inquiry. We stand firm on the reality of such rewards, but they are by no means the only reasons for humanistic studies in health care training. On the contrary, our inquiry into the nature of medical fallibility illustrates the way in which even on utilitarian grounds the interests of the medical profession would be well served by a more philosophically informed view of its own activities.

Index